RANDOM-PROCESS SIMULATION AND MEASUREMENTS

RANDOM-PROCESS
SIMULATION
AND MEASUREMENTS

GRANINO A. KORN, Ph.D.

Professor of Electrical Engineering, University of Arizona

McGRAW-HILL BOOK COMPANY

New York   Toronto   London   Sydney

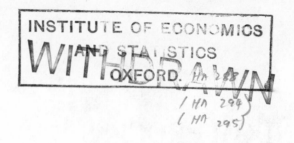
RANDOM-PROCESS SIMULATION AND MEASUREMENTS

This book is for Terry

PREFACE

In recent years, the application of statistical methods to new engineering problems has resulted in decisive advances, especially in the fields of control-system design, communication, and detection. Reduced to simple terms, the reason for these successes is that measured statistics, such as averages or mean-square values, can often be accurately predicted even when individual measurements are wholly unpredictable; and that such statistics, luckily, often have engineering significance. As the price of such progress, our design analysis must now relate distribution parameters instead of simple variables; and the instrumentation engineer must account for the effects of statistical fluctuations as well as of ordinary measurement errors. In the solution of practical problems, even the most elegant analytical methods tend to result in formidable integral expressions, and many practical problems yield to analysis only after impossibly crude simplifications. In such situations, one resorts to the use of electronic computers, either to implement analytical formulas or for direct simulation of random phenomena.

This volume describes modern techniques utilizing analog, digital, and hybrid-analog-digital computers for random-process studies. It attempts a unified treatment of much material otherwise scattered over many publications and research reports, and adds previously unpublished material based on the writer's own research and lectures. Instrumentation and procedures are described as well as the underlying theory, and it is hoped that this book will be useful to a wide variety of engineers and scientists working in the areas of control, guidance, communication, detection, and instrument design.

A minimal background in random-signal theory—like that established in a modern course in control-system theory—is assumed; essential terms are defined, and standard texts are referred to where necessary. For added convenience, Chapters 1 and 2 respectively present concise reviews of random-process mathematics and of analog/hybrid computation to establish a useful vocabulary and symbolism.

Chapters 3 and 4 discuss computer methods for random-process study. Chapter 3 describes *analog-computer implementation of statistical input-output relations for linear systems*, including time-variable linear systems obtained through perturbation of nonlinear state or trajectory equations. A new and simplified derivation of modified-adjoint-system setups is presented; since the modified-adjoint system yields system mean-square error in a single computer run, the practical importance of this technique has been greatly enhanced by the modern iterative analog computer, which permits direct iterative parameter optimization.

Chapter 4 introduces *direct simulation of random phenomena by hybrid-computer Monte-Carlo techniques.* Direct repeated simulation of a system with random inputs is frequently the only possible method for conducting realistic random-process studies. Again, the advent of the modern iterative differential analyzer has made Monte-Carlo simulation so very fast, practical, and convenient that this powerful computer technique deserves much greater popularity and should in no sense be regarded as a last-resort procedure. The study of a *simple ballistic trajectory subject to random perturbations* and a *matched-filter detection problem* are used as illustrations. The chapter ends with several sections describing the *design of practical random-noise generators*, including the new *hybrid-analog-digital pseudo-random-noise generators* being developed by the writer's group at the University of Arizona. These new noise generators, inexpensively constructed from standard digital-circuit modules, are accurate and convenient and permit significant variance-reducing techniques in suitable applications.

Chapter 5 describes *devices and techniques for practical measurement of time and sample averages, correlation functions, and probability distributions*, including *joint distributions of two random variables.* Such measurements constitute an especially fruitful area of application for new combinations of analog and digital circuits; such devices are useful for Monte-Carlo-type simulation as well as for field measurements and processing of recorded data. The *effects of statistical fluctuations* are studied in each case. The definition and measurement of *confidence intervals* is discussed with a view to terminating statistical observations when a preset confidence level or interval is obtained (sequential estimation); this technique is further discussed in Chapter 8.

Chapter 6 deals with the theory and practice of *statistical measurements with quantized data*. A review of the quantization theory of Widrow and Watts, still unknown to many instrumentation designers, leads to remarkable and highly practical results; thus, accurate digital computation of statistical averages and correlation functions rarely requires more than 4-bit analog-to-digital converters, and one-bit correlation with the simplest of analog-digital circuits is made possible by the use of dither signals. Chapter 7 reviews *analog and digital methods for power-spectrum estimation* and modern analog-hybrid computing techniques for *Fourier analysis, frequency-response plotting,* and *impulse-response measurements.*

Chapter 8 attempts to demonstrate the power and sophistication of the hybrid-computer Monte-Carlo technique in terms of some practical examples and applications. A description of a fast analog/hybrid computer specifically designed for fast random-process simulation is followed by an account of special techniques for *hybrid-computer simulation of communication and detection systems* together with their natural environment of *noise, clutter,* and *electronic countermeasures.* Applications of the hybrid-computer Monte-Carlo method are further illustrated by *regression and prediction studies,* various applications to *operations research,* and *Monte-Carlo solution of partial differential equations.* The chapter further discusses *parameter estimation by random parameter perturbations* and includes a discussion of suggested future developments, in particular the use of *variance-reducing sampling techniques* and *sequential measurements.*

The treatment is rounded out with a large number of illustrations, selected statistical tables, a bibliography of over 300 items (arranged by subjects), an author index to make the bibliography more accessible, and a general index.

The writer is grateful to the University of Arizona for its encouragement of his hybrid-computer research, and to the National Science Foundation, the Air Force Office of Scientific Research, and the National Aeronautics and Space Administration for their support of the APE and ASTRAC II hybrid-computer projects. The writer would also like to thank the many students whose term papers and thesis work contributed to his research, and especially the present and former assistants and research associates in the University's Analog/Hybrid Computer Laboratory:

T. Brubaker	R. Maybach
B. Conant	B. Mitchell
H. Eckes	E. O'Grady
R. Hampton	J. Wait
H. Handler	R. Whigham

The writer is indebted to the editor and publishers of *Simulation* for permitting him to use material from his articles in that journal in this book, and to the following individuals and organizations for helping him with reports, illustrations, and research results:

Dr. G A. Bekey	University of Southern California
Dr. J. S. Bendat	Measurement Analysis Corporation, Santa Monica, California
Mr. K. C. Cummings	General Electric Co., Syracuse, N.Y.
Dr. P. Eykhoff	Technical University, Eindhoven, Netherlands

Dr. W. Giloi	Technical University, Berlin, Germany
Mr. B. G. Hall	F. L. Moseley Co., Pasadena, Calif.
Dr. W. J. Karplus	University of California, Los Angeles
Dr. V. C. Rideout	University of Wisconsin
Dr. B. Th. Veltman	Technical University, Delft, Netherlands
Dr. B. Widrow	Stanford University

The writer is also indebted to the literary executor of the late Sir Ronald A. Fisher, F.R.S., Cambridge, to Dr. Frank Yates, F.R.S., Rothamsted, and to Messrs. Oliver & Boyd Ltd., Edinburgh, for permission to reprint Tables III and IV from their book *Statistical Tables for Biological, Agricultural and Medical Research*.

Last but not least, the writer is grateful to his wife and frequent co-author for many stimulating discussions and for her general patience.

Granino A. Korn

CONTENTS

RANDOM-PROCESS SIMULATION
AND MEASUREMENTS

CHAPTER **1**

MATHEMATICAL DESCRIPTION
OF RANDOM PROCESSES

INTRODUCTION

1-1. Statistical Methods. It is often possible to predict suitable functions (*statistics*) of a set (*sample*) of measurement results with useful accuracy, while the results of individual measurements are essentially unpredictable ("random" in the original sense of the word). Fluctuations in the values of statistics computed from different samples frequently tend to decrease with the sample size (physical laws of large numbers). The best-known statistics are *statistical relative frequencies* and *statistical averages*, whose essential properties have been abstracted to define *probabilities* and *expected values* (*ensemble averages*) in the mathematical model of *probability theory*. The model quantities, unlike real measurements, are easily manipulated and interrelated mathematically to yield, e.g., predicted values of filter-output statistics when filter-input statistics are given. Sections 1-2 to 1-7 summarize the most important definitions and relations required for computer random-process studies. More elaborate accounts of the theory will be found in standard textbooks.[1-11]

1-2. Random Processes. A real *random process* is generated by random selection of a real *sample function* $x(t)$ from a population or *ensemble* of such functions (Fig. 1-1). The joint realization of any finite set of sample values $x_1 = x(t_1)$, $x_2 = x(t_2)$, . . . , $x_n = x(t_n)$ must be a random event permitting definition of a joint probability distribution (*nth-order probability distribution* of the random process for the sampling times $t_1, t_2, \ldots, t_n$). For a *continuous* random process, we can, in particular, define the

1

first- and second-order probability densities

$$p_1(X_1,t_1) = \frac{\partial}{\partial X_1} \text{Prob } [x(t_1) \leq X_1] \tag{1-1}$$

$$p_2(X_1,t_1;X_2,t_2) = \frac{\partial^2}{\partial X_1 \, \partial X_2} \text{Prob } [x(t_1) \leq X_1, \, x(t_2) \leq X_2] \tag{1-2}$$

A random process is *stationary* if and only if all its probability distributions remain unchanged when t_k is replaced by $t_k + a$ (shift of time origin). A

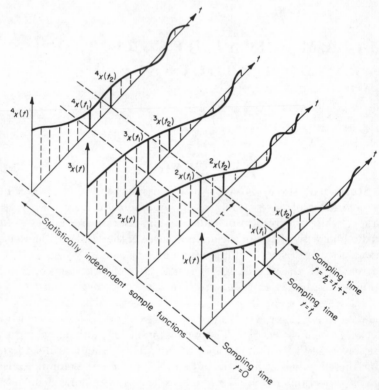

FIG. 1-1. A sample of four sample functions $^k x(t)$ from a continuous random process represented by $x(t)$.

random process is *Gaussian* if and only if all its probability distributions are *normal distributions* described by joint probability densities of the form

$$p_n(x_1,x_2, \ldots ,x_n) = \sqrt{\frac{\det [\Lambda_{ik}]}{(2\pi)^n}} \exp \left[-\frac{1}{2} \sum_{i=1}^{n} \sum_{k=1}^{n} \Lambda_{ik}(x_i - \xi_i)(x_k - \xi_k) \right]$$

$$\tag{1-3}$$

with given $\xi_i = \xi_i(t_i)$ and given $\Lambda_{ik} = \Lambda_{ik}(t_i,t_k)$ such that the exponent is nonpositive.

Two random processes described by $x(t)$, $y(t)$ can have *joint* probability distributions of sets of sample values $x(t_i)$, $y(t_k)$ (*two-dimensional random process*). The two random processes may be *jointly stationary* and/or *jointly Gaussian*.

1-3. Ensemble Averages. Correlation Functions. The *ensemble average* $E\{f\}$ of a given function $f[x(t_1),x(t_2), \ldots ,x(t_n)]$ of n sample values (statistic) is its mathematical expectation over their joint distribution:

$$E\{f\} = \int_{-\infty}^{\infty} dx_1 \int_{-\infty}^{\infty} dx_2 \cdots \int_{-\infty}^{\infty} fp_n(x_1,t_1;x_2,t_2; \ldots ;x_n,t_n)\, dx_n$$
$$= \varphi(t_1,t_2, \ldots ,t_n) \tag{1-4}$$

where we assume existence in the sense of absolute convergence.[7] Note that $E\{f\}$ is *not* a random variable, but a function of t_1, t_2, $\ldots$, t_n. Suitable limiting processes [1,3] also permit definition of ensemble averages of *integrals* like $\int_a^b x(t)\, dt$.

Important ensemble averages are $E\{x(t_1)\} = \xi(t_1)$, $E\{x^2(t_1)\}$ (*mean square*), and

$$E\{[x(t_1) - \xi(t_1)]^2\} = E\{x^2(t_1)\} - \xi^2(t_1) = \text{Var } \{x(t_1)\} = \sigma_x^2(t_1)$$
$$\text{(ENSEMBLE VARIANCE)} \tag{1-5}$$
$$E\{x(t_1)x(t_2)\} = R_{xx}(t_1,t_2) = R_{xx}(t_2,t_1)$$
$$\text{(ENSEMBLE AUTOCORRELATION FUNCTION)} \tag{1-6}$$

We similarly define ensemble averages over joint distributions of $x(t)$ and $y(t)$, such as

$$E\{x(t_1)y(t_2)\} = R_{xy}(t_1,t_2) = R_{yx}(t_2,t_1)$$
$$\text{(ENSEMBLE CROSS-CORRELATION FUNCTION)} \tag{1-7}$$
$$E\{[x(t_1) - y(t_2)]^2\} = R_{xx}(t_1,t_1) + R_{yy}(t_2,t_2) - 2R_{xy}(t_1,t_2)$$
$$= \epsilon_{xy}^2(t_1,t_2)$$
$$\text{(ENSEMBLE MEAN-SQUARE DELAY ERROR)} \tag{1-8}$$

Probabilities, too, can be expressed as ensemble averages. In particular,

$$\text{Prob } [x(t_1) \leq X_1] = E\{f[x(t_1)]\} \quad \text{with } f(x) = \begin{cases} 1 & (x \leq X_1) \\ 0 & (x > X_1) \end{cases} \tag{1-9}$$

For *stationary* random processes, $E\{x(t_1)\} = \xi$, $E\{x^2(t_1)\}$, and $E\{f[x(t_1)]\}$ are constant; and correlation functions and delay error reduce to functions $R_{xx}(\tau)$, $R_{xy}(\tau)$, $\epsilon_{xy}^2(\tau)$ of the *delay* $\tau = t_2 - t_1$ separating the sampling times t_1, t_2.

Each ensemble average is a parameter or function describing certain properties of a random-process ensemble. Values and relations of ensemble averages can usually be interpreted as idealized (model) counterparts of analogous values and relations of statistics obtained from very large random samples. By contrast, finite-sample statistics are random variables, whose measured values will fluctuate even as they exhibit statistical regularity. In many applications, simple ensemble averages and correlation functions are all that can be known about a given random-process model.

STATISTICS AS RANDOM VARIABLES

1-4. Time Averages and Measurements. *Time averages* like

$$
\left.
\begin{aligned}
\langle x(t_1) \rangle &= \lim_{T \to \infty} \frac{1}{T} \int_{-T/2}^{T/2} x(t_1 + \lambda)\, d\lambda \qquad [\text{TIME AVERAGE OF } x(t_1)] \\
\langle x(t_1)x(t_2) \rangle &= \lim_{T \to \infty} \frac{1}{T} \int_{-T/2}^{T/2} x(t_1 + \lambda)x(t_2 + \lambda)\, d\lambda \\
&\qquad\qquad\qquad\qquad (\text{TIME AUTOCORRELATION FUNCTION}) \\
\langle x(t_1)y(t_2) \rangle &= \lim_{T \to \infty} \frac{1}{T} \int_{-T/2}^{T/2} x(t_1 + \lambda)y(t_2 + \lambda)\, d\lambda \\
&\qquad\qquad\qquad\qquad (\text{TIME CROSS-CORRELATION FUNCTION})
\end{aligned}
\right\}
\quad (1\text{-}10)
$$

and

$$
\begin{aligned}
\langle f \rangle &= \langle f[x(t_1), x(t_2), \ldots, x(t_n)] \rangle \\
&= \lim_{T \to \infty} \frac{1}{T} \int_{-T/2}^{T/2} f[x(t_1 + \lambda), x(t_2 + \lambda), \ldots, x(t_n + \lambda)]\, d\lambda \\
&= \lim_{T \to \infty} \frac{1}{T} \int_{-T/2}^{T/2} f(\lambda)\, d\lambda \qquad\qquad\qquad\qquad (1\text{-}11)
\end{aligned}
$$

are *random variables* for each argument value t_1 or each set of argument values $t_1, t_2, \ldots$. Such time averages are idealized statistics of mainly theoretical interest; for the special class of *ergodic* stationary random processes, each time average (11) equals the corresponding ensemble average (4) with probability one.

Unlike the idealized time average (11), the *finite-time averages*

$$
[f]_n = \frac{1}{n} \sum_{k=1}^{n} f(t_1 + k\,\Delta t,\ t_2 + k\,\Delta t,\ \ldots,\ t_n + k\,\Delta t) = \frac{1}{n} \sum_{k=1}^{n} f(k\,\Delta t)
$$
$$
(1\text{-}12)
$$

$$
\langle f \rangle_T = \frac{1}{T} \int_0^T f(t_1 + \lambda,\ t_2 + \lambda,\ \ldots,\ t_n + \lambda)\, d\lambda = \frac{1}{T} \int_0^T f(\lambda)\, d\lambda \quad (1\text{-}13)
$$

can be obtained, respectively, through sampled-data and continuous averaging of finite real data (Chap. 5). $[f]_n$ and $\langle f \rangle_T$ are random variables whose distributions are determined by the given random process. If $x(t)$ represents a *stationary* (but not necessarily ergodic) random process, our definition (4) implies

$$E\{[f]_n\} = E\{\langle f \rangle_T\} = E\{f\} \tag{1-14}$$

The finite-time averages $[f]_n$ and $\langle f \rangle_T$ are, then, *unbiased estimates* of the unknown expected value $E\{f\}$ and will be useful for estimating $E\{f\}$ if their random fluctuations about their expected value (14) are reasonably small. More specifically, the mean-square error associated with estimation of $E\{f\}$ by a measured value of $[f]_n$ is

$$\text{Var } \{[f]_n\} = \frac{1}{n^2} \sum_{i=1}^{n} \sum_{k=1}^{n} \text{Cov } \{f(i\,\Delta t), f(k\,\Delta t)\}$$

$$= \frac{1}{n} \text{Var } \{f\} + \frac{2}{n} \sum_{k=1}^{n-1} \left(1 - \frac{k}{n}\right) \text{Cov } \{f(0), f(k\,\Delta t)\} \tag{1-15}$$

If we introduce $k\,\Delta t = \lambda$ and let $\Delta t \to 0$, $n = T/\Delta t \to \infty$, then the sampled-data average (12) converges to the continuous average $\langle y \rangle_T$ if the latter exists. A similar limiting process applied to Eq. (15) yields

$$\text{Var } \{\langle y \rangle_T\} = \frac{2}{T} \int_0^T \left(1 - \frac{\lambda}{T}\right) \text{Cov } \{f(0), f(\lambda)\} \, d\lambda \tag{1-16}$$

Depending on the nature of the *autocovariance function*

$$\text{Cov } \{f(0), f(\lambda)\} = E\{[f(0) - E\{f\}][f(\lambda) - E\{f\}]\}$$
$$= E\{f(0)f(\lambda)\} - [E\{f\}]^2 = R_{ff}(\lambda) - R_{ff}(0) = K_{ff}(\lambda) \tag{1-17}$$

the mean-square error (15) or (16) may or may not decrease to an acceptably small value with increasing sample size n or integration time T. This question will be taken up in Secs. 5-1 to 5-3, which will also discuss more general types of averaging techniques (averaging filters).

1-5. Sample Averages. Different sample functions generated by the same random process will be denoted by $^1x(t)$, $^2x(t)$, . . . (Fig. 1-1) and are regarded as statistically independent; i.e., every finite set of samples $^ix(t_1)$, $^ix(t_2)$, . . . is statistically independent of every set of samples from a different sample function $^kx(t)$. If we can realize a set of sample functions $^1x(t)$, $^2x(t)$, . . . , $^nx(t)$ in independent repeated experiments, then the sample values $^1x(t_1)$, $^2x(t_1)$, . . . , $^nx(t_1)$ constitute a classical *random sample of size* n; i.e., the $^kx(t_1)$ are statistically independent random variables with identical probability distributions. Similarly, $^1x(t_1)$, $^2x(t_1)$; $^2x(t_1)$, $^2x(t_2)$; . . . ; $^nx(t_1)$, $^nx(t_2)$ or $^1x(t_1)$, $^1y(t_2)$; $^2x(t_1)$, $^2y(t_2)$; . . . ; $^nx(t_1)$, $^ny(t_2)$ constitute bivariate random samples.

Sample averages, like

$$\overline{x(t_1)} = \frac{1}{n}[^1x(t_1) + {}^2x(t_1) + \cdots + {}^nx(t_1)] \tag{1-18}$$

$$\overline{f[x(t_1),x(t_2), \ldots]} = \frac{1}{n}\sum_{k=1}^{n}{}^kf$$

$$= \frac{1}{n}\sum_{k=1}^{n} f[^kx(t_1),{}^kx(t_2), \ldots] \tag{1-19}$$

$$\overline{x(t_1)y(t_2)} = \frac{1}{n}\sum_{k=1}^{n} {}^kx(t_1)\,{}^ky(t_2) \tag{1-20}$$

are, then, random-sample statistics in the sense of classical statistical theory. *Unlike the finite-time averages* (12) *and* (13), *sample averages must be obtained from repeated experiments. It is, however, usually much easier to derive variances and probability distributions for sample averages than it is for time averages.* In particular,

$$\text{Var } \{\overline{x(t_1)}\} = \frac{1}{n}\text{Var } \{x(t_1)\} \qquad \text{Var}\{\bar{f}\} = \frac{1}{n}\text{Var } \{\bar{f}\}$$

$$\text{Var } \{\overline{x(t_1)y(t_2)}\} = \frac{1}{n}\text{Var } \{x(t_1)y(t_2)\} \tag{1-21}$$

should be compared with Eqs. (16) and (17). The use of sample averages permits us to use much existing statistical theory for random-process studies.

LINEAR OPERATIONS AND SPECTRAL DENSITIES

1-6. Linear Operations on Random Processes. (a) Let $x(t)$, $y(t)$ represent real random processes, and let $z(t) = \alpha x(t) + \beta y(t)$ with real constants α, β. From the definitions of Sec. 1-3, the correlation functions $R_{xz}(t_1,t_2)$, $R_{zx}(t_1,t_2)$, $R_{zz}(t_1,t_2)$ or $R_{xz}(\tau)$, $R_{zx}(\tau)$, $R_{zz}(\tau)$ are given by

$$R_{xz} = \alpha R_{xx} + \beta R_{xy} \qquad R_{zx} = \alpha R_{xx} + \beta R_{yx}$$

$$R_{zz} = \alpha^2 R_{xx} + \beta^2 R_{yy} + \alpha\beta(R_{xy} + R_{yx}) \tag{1-22}$$

(b) For a real linear (not necessarily time-invariant) system (filter, servo, modulator, etc.) with input $x(t)$ and output $y(t)$,

$$y(t) = \int_{-\infty}^{\infty} w(t,\lambda)x(\lambda)\,d\lambda = \int_{-\infty}^{\infty} h(t,\zeta)x(t - \zeta)\,d\zeta \tag{1-23}$$

where the *weighting function* $w(t,\lambda)$ is the response at the time t to a unit-impulse input $\delta(t - \lambda)$ applied at the time $t = \lambda$ (see also Sec. 2-10d). $h(t,\zeta) \equiv w(t, t - \zeta)$ is the response to a unit impulse applied ζ sec ago.

It follows that

$$R_{xy}(t_1,t_2) = \int_{-\infty}^{\infty} w(t_2,\lambda)R_{xx}(t_1,\lambda)\, d\lambda = R_{yx}(t_2,t_1) \left.\right\}$$

$$R_{yy}(t_1,t_2) = \int_{-\infty}^{\infty} w(t_2,\mu)R_{yx}(t_1,\mu)\, d\mu$$

(GENERALIZED WIENER-LEE RELATIONS)   (1-24)

For *white-noise input*, with $R_{xx}(t_1,t_2) \equiv \delta(t_2 - t_1)$ (Sec. 1-12), we have, in particular,

$$E\{y^2(T)\} = R_{yy}(T,T) = \int_{-\infty}^{\infty} w^2(T,\mu)\, d\mu = \int_{-\infty}^{\infty} h^2(T,\varsigma)\, d\varsigma \quad (1\text{-}25)$$

Note also that *addition of Gaussian random processes and linear operations on Gaussian processes again yield Gaussian processes.*

(**c**) For *stationary* $x(t)$ and a *time-invariant* linear operator represented by

$$h(t,\varsigma) \equiv h(\varsigma) \equiv \int_{-\infty}^{\infty} H(j\omega)e^{j\omega\varsigma}\, \frac{d\omega}{2\pi}$$

$y(t)$ is also stationary. In this case,

$$y(t) = \int_{-\infty}^{\infty} h(t - \lambda)x(\lambda)\, d\lambda = \int_{-\infty}^{\infty} h(\varsigma)x(t - \varsigma)\, d\varsigma \quad (1\text{-}26)$$

$$R_{xy}(\tau) = \int_{-\infty}^{\infty} h(\tau - \lambda)R_{xx}(\lambda)\, d\lambda = R_{yx}(-\tau) \left.\right\}$$

$$R_{yy}(\tau) = \int_{-\infty}^{\infty} h(\tau - \mu)R_{yx}(\mu)\, d\mu$$

(WIENER-LEE RELATIONS)   (1-27)

or
$$R_{yy}(\tau) = \int_{-\infty}^{\infty} \varphi_{hh}(\lambda)R_{xx}(\tau - \lambda)\, d\lambda \quad (1\text{-}28)$$

where $\varphi_{hh}(\lambda)$ is the "correlation function of the filter,"

$$\varphi_{hh}(\lambda) = \int_{-\infty}^{\infty} h(\varsigma)h(\varsigma + \lambda)\, d\varsigma = \int_{-\infty}^{\infty} |H(j\omega)|^2 e^{j\omega\lambda}\, \frac{d\omega}{2\pi} \quad (1\text{-}29)$$

For white-noise input, with $R_{xx}(\tau) \equiv \delta(\tau)$, we have

$$R_{yy}(\tau) \equiv \varphi_{hh}(\tau) \quad (1\text{-}30)$$

1-7. Spectral Densities. The convolution integrals (27) are expressed in terms of convenient transform products

$$\Phi_{xy}(\omega) = H(j\omega)\Phi_{xx}(\omega) \qquad \Phi_{yy}(\omega) = |H(j\omega)|^2\Phi_{xx}(\omega) \quad (1\text{-}31)$$

if we introduce the (two-sided) *ensemble power spectral densities* $\Phi_{xx}(\omega)$, $\Phi_{yy}(\omega)$, and the *ensemble cross-spectral density* $\Phi_{xy}(\omega)$ by the *Wiener-Khinchine relations*

$$\Phi_{xx}(\omega) = \int_{-\infty}^{\infty} R_{xx}(\tau)e^{-j\omega\tau}\, d\tau = 2\int_{0}^{\infty} R_{xx}(\tau)\cos\omega\tau\, d\tau = \Phi_{xx}{}^{*}(\omega) \left.\right\}$$

$$\Phi_{xy}(\omega) = \int_{-\infty}^{\infty} R_{xy}(\tau)e^{-j\omega\tau}\, d\tau = \Phi_{yx}{}^{*}(\omega)$$

(1-32)

If x and y are voltages, the spectral densities used here are expressed in volt^2/cps. Fourier inversion of Eq. (32) yields, for $\tau = 0$,

$$\left.\begin{aligned} E\{x^2\} &= R_{xx}(0) = \int_{-\infty}^{\infty} \Phi_{xx}(\omega)\, \frac{d\omega}{2\pi} = \int_{0}^{\infty} 2\Phi_{xx}(\omega)\, \frac{d\omega}{2\pi} \\ E\{x(t)y(t)\} &= R_{xy}(0) = \int_{-\infty}^{\infty} \Phi_{xy}(\omega)\, \frac{d\omega}{2\pi} = \int_{0}^{\infty} 2\ \text{Re}\ \Phi_{xy}(\omega)\, \frac{d\omega}{2\pi} \end{aligned}\right\} \quad (1\text{-}33)$$

which describes a "spectral decomposition," vindicating the term "spectral density." If $x(t)$, $y(t)$ represent *ergodic* random processes, then the ensemble spectral densities are identical, with probability one, to analogous transforms of time correlation functions (Sec. 1-3).

EXAMPLES OF RANDOM PROCESSES

1-8. Introduction. Sections 1-9 to 1-13 describe a number of "elementary" random processes which serve as useful examples in discussions and as models of simple random phenomena. More elaborate models can be obtained through superposition, multiplication, etc., of simpler random-process models. Derivations and more elaborate discussions will be found in appropriate texts or reference books.[1-8]

1-9. D-c Process and Random Sine-wave Processes.[7] (a) If $x(t)$ is identically equal to a random constant with given probability distribution (Fig. 1-2a), we have a stationary but *not* ergodic random process, with

$$\left.\begin{aligned} E\{x(t)\} &= E\{x\} & \langle x(t)\rangle &= x \\ R_{xx}(\tau) &= E\{x^2\} & \langle x(t)x(t+\tau)\rangle &= x^2 \end{aligned}\right\} \quad (1\text{-}34)$$

(b) We next consider the random-phase sine wave

$$x(t) = a \sin(\omega t + \alpha) \qquad (1\text{-}35)$$

(Fig. 1-2b), where a is a given constant, and where α is uniformly distributed between 0 and 2π. The process is stationary and ergodic, with

$$\left.\begin{aligned} p_1[x(t)] &= \frac{1}{\pi\,\sqrt{a^2 - x^2}} & (|x| \le a) \\ E\{x(t)\} &= 0 \qquad R_{xx}(\tau) = \frac{a^2}{2}\cos\omega\tau \end{aligned}\right\} \quad (1\text{-}36)$$

(c) If the amplitude a of our random-phase sine wave is not a constant, but is itself a random variable independent of α (as in amplitude modulation), the process is stationary but not in general ergodic. We have

$$\left.\begin{aligned} p_1[x(t)] &= \frac{1}{\pi}\int_{-\infty}^{\infty} \frac{p_a(a)\,da}{\sqrt{a^2 - x^2}} \\ E\{x(t)\} &= 0 \qquad R_{xx}(\tau) = \tfrac{1}{2}E\{a^2\}\cos\omega\tau \end{aligned}\right\} \quad (1\text{-}37)$$

If, in particular, the amplitude a has a *Rayleigh distribution* defined by

$$p_a(a) = \begin{cases} ae^{-a^2/2} & (a \geq 0) \\ 0 & (a < 0) \end{cases} \qquad (1\text{-}38)$$

then the random process is Gaussian (Sec. 1-2).[3]

(d) If α is not uniformly distributed between 0 and 2π, then the process is no longer stationary.

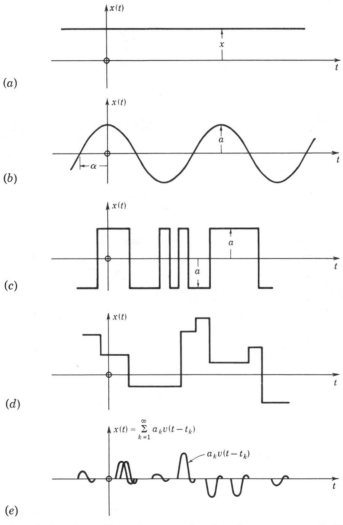

FIG. 1-2. Sample functions $x(t)$ for five examples of random processes. In Fig. 1-2e, $x(t)$ is the *sum* of the individual pulses $a_k v(t - t_k)$ shown. (*From G. A. Korn and T. M. Korn, Mathematical Handbook for Scientists and Engineers, McGraw-Hill, New York, 1961.*)

1-10. Random-phase Periodic Processes. The random-phase sine wave of Sec. 1-9b is a special case of the general random-phase periodic process represented by

$$x(t) = c_0 + \sum_{k=1}^{\infty} [a_k \cos k(\omega t + \alpha) + b_k \sin k(\omega t + \alpha)] \quad (1\text{-}39)$$

where α is uniformly distributed between 0 and 2π. The process is stationary and ergodic, with

$$E\{x(t)\} = c_0 \qquad R_{xx}(\tau) = c_0{}^2 + \frac{1}{2} \sum_{k=1}^{\infty} (a_k{}^2 + b_k{}^2) \cos k\omega\tau \quad (1\text{-}40)$$

1-11. Poisson Process and Random Telegraph Wave.[3,5,7] **(a)** A *Poisson process* is a "counting process" represented by the number $K(t)$ of state changes (radioactive decay, chance equipment failures) occurring in the time interval $(0,t)$; more specifically, the number K of state changes in any time interval of length T has a *Poisson distribution* defined by

$$\text{Prob}\,[K \text{ events in } T \text{ sec}] = \frac{(\alpha T)^K}{K!}\, e^{-\alpha T} \qquad (K = 0,1,2, \ldots) \quad (1\text{-}41)$$

and the numbers of state changes in nonoverlapping time intervals are statistically independent. $\alpha = E\{K\}/T = \text{Var}\,\{K\}/T$ will be called the *mean count rate*.

(b) A (symmetrical) *random telegraph wave* $x(t)$ is a "binary" random function equal to either a or $-a$, with sign changes generated by the state changes of a Poisson process of mean count rate α (Fig. 1-2c). The process is stationary and ergodic if started at $t = -\infty$, and

$$E\{x(t)\} = 0 \qquad R_{xx}(\tau) = a^2 e^{-2\alpha|\tau|} \qquad \Phi_{xx}(\omega) = \frac{4\alpha a^2}{\omega^2 + (2\alpha)^2} \quad (1\text{-}42)$$

1-12. Some Noise Models. White Noise. (a) A Simple Thermal-electron-current Model (Fig. 1-2d).[7] $x(t)$ changes value at each state change of a Poisson process with mean count rate α; between state changes, $x(t)$ is constant and takes continuously distributed random values x with given mean ξ and variance σ^2. The process is stationary and ergodic if started at $t = -\infty$, and

$$\left.\begin{array}{c} E\{x(t)\} = \xi \qquad R_{xx}(\tau) = \xi^2 + \sigma^2 e^{-\alpha|\tau|} \\[2mm] \Phi_{xx}(\omega) = 2\pi\xi^2\delta(\omega) + \dfrac{2\alpha\sigma^2}{\omega^2 + \alpha^2} \end{array}\right\} \quad (1\text{-}43)$$

(b) Impulse Noise (Fig. 1-2e).[3,7] $x(t)$ is the sum of many similarly shaped transient pulses

$$x(t) = \sum_{k=1}^{\infty} a_k v(t - t_k) \quad (1\text{-}44)$$

whose shape is given by $v = v(t)$, with

$$\int_{-\infty}^{\infty} v(t)e^{-j\omega t}\,dt = V(j\omega) \tag{1-45}$$

while the pulse amplitude a_k is a random variable with finite variance, and the times t_k are statistically independent random incidence times of a Poisson process with mean count rate α (e.g., electrons boiled off a vacuum-tube cathode, shot noise). The process is stationary and ergodic if started at $t = -\infty$; it approximates a Gaussian random process (Sec. 1-2) if many pulses overlap. We have

$$\left.\begin{aligned}
E\{x(t)\} &= \xi = \alpha E\{a_k\} \int_{-\infty}^{\infty} v(t)\,dt \\
E\{x^2(t)\} &= \xi^2 + \alpha E\{a_k{}^2\} \int_{-\infty}^{\infty} v^2(t)\,dt \\
R_{xx}(\tau) &= \xi^2 + \alpha E\{a_k{}^2\} \int_{-\infty}^{\infty} v(t)v(t+\tau)\,dt \\
\Phi_{xx}(\omega) &= 2\pi\xi^2\delta(\omega) + \alpha E\{a_k{}^2\}|V(j\omega)|^2
\end{aligned}\right\} \tag{1-46}$$

In the special case where a_k is a fixed constant, the formulas (46) are known as *Campbell's theorem*.

(c) **White Noise and Filtered Noise.** Stationary *white noise* has a constant power spectral density,* i.e.,

$$\Phi_{xx}(\omega) = \Phi_0 \qquad R_{xx}(\tau) = \Phi_0\delta(\tau) \tag{1-47}$$

White-noise samples $x(t_1)$, $x(t_1 + \Delta t)$ are uncorrelated for every $\Delta t \neq 0$. Such a process is not physically realizable, since Eq. (47) implies $E\{x^2\} = \infty$. In practice, white noise is approximated by various types of wideband noise having approximately constant spectral density over a frequency band of interest ("band-limited white noise").

For any stationary input $x(t)$ whose power spectrum is flat over the pass-band of a time-invariant linear system or filter with transfer function $H(s)$, the filter-output spectral density $\Phi_{yy}(\omega)$ is $|H(j\omega)|^2\Phi_0$ (Sec. 1-6). If the input to any linear system is Gaussian, the same is true for the output. The output of every time-invariant linear system with ergodic input is ergodic.

EXAMPLES (see also Secs. 3-3 and 5-2): 1. *Ideal Low-pass Filter*

$$\left.\begin{aligned}
H(j\omega) &= \begin{cases} 1 & (|\omega| < 2\pi B) \\ 0 & (|\omega| > 2\pi B) \end{cases} \\
\Phi_{yy}(\omega) = \begin{cases} \Phi_0 & (|\omega| < 2\pi B) \\ 0 & (|\omega| > 2\pi B) \end{cases} \quad & R_{yy}(\tau) = 2\Phi_0 B\,\frac{\sin 2\pi B\tau}{2\pi B\tau}
\end{aligned}\right\} \tag{1-48}$$

* Note that, in accordance with our definition (1-32) of the spectral density, $\Phi_{xx}(\omega) = \Phi_0$ means $\Phi_{xx}(\omega) = \Phi_0$ volt^2/cps between $\omega = -\infty$ and $\omega = \infty$, or

$$2\Phi_{xx}(\omega) = 2\Phi_0 \text{ volt}^2/\text{cps}$$

between $\omega = 0$ and $\omega = \infty$ in Eq. (1-33).

2. *Simple RC Filter*

$$H(j\omega) = \frac{1}{j\omega RC + 1}$$
$$\Phi_{yy}(\omega) = \frac{\Phi_0}{(\omega RC)^2 + 1} \qquad R_{yy}(\tau) = \frac{\Phi_0}{2RC} e^{-|\tau|/RC} \tag{1-49}$$

3. *Ideal Bandpass Filter*

$$H(j\omega) = \begin{cases} 1 & (|\omega - \omega_0| < \pi B) \\ 0 & (|\omega - \omega_0| > \pi B) \end{cases}$$
$$\Phi_{yy}(\omega) = \begin{cases} \Phi_0 & (|\omega - \omega_0| < \pi B) \\ 0 & (|\omega - \omega_0| > \pi B) \end{cases} \qquad R_{yy}(\tau) = 2\Phi_0 B \frac{\sin \pi B\tau}{\pi B\tau} \cos \omega_0\tau \tag{1-50}$$

1-13. Random Processes Generated by Periodic Sampling.

Certain measuring devices (sample-hold circuits, analog-to-digital converters)

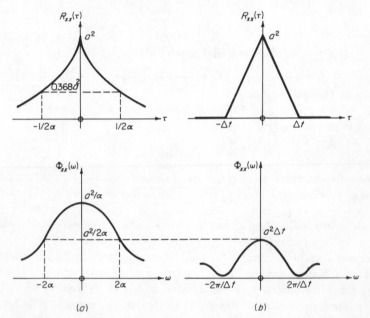

FIG. 1-3. Autocorrelation function and power spectrum for a random telegraph wave (*a*) and a coin-tossing sample-hold process (*b*) having equal mean count rates $\alpha = 1/2\Delta t$, both with zero mean and mean square a^2.

sample a stationary and ergodic random variable $q(t)$ periodically and then hold their output $x(t)$ for a constant sampling interval Δt. The resulting random process is stationary and ergodic if the timing of our periodic sampling impulses is random and uniformly distributed between 0 and Δt. A sample function $x(t)$ will look like Fig. 1-2, *except that state changes must be separated by integral multiples of* Δt. If q is a binary random variable capable of assuming only the values a and $-a$ with probabilities $\frac{1}{2}$, $\frac{1}{2}$, then $x(t)$ will resemble the random telegraph wave of Fig. 1-2, except that state changes are, again, separated by integral multiples of Δt ("coin-tossing" sample-hold process).

We shall consider only the case where different samples of q are statistically independent. In this case,

$$
\left.
\begin{aligned}
R_{xx}(\tau) &= [E\{q\}]^2 = [E\{x\}]^2 = \xi^2 \qquad (|\tau| > \Delta t) \\
R_{xx}(\tau) &= E\{q^2\} \,\text{Prob}\,[t,\, t + \tau \text{ are in same sampling interval}] \\
&\quad + [E\{q\}]^2 \,\text{Prob}\,[t,\, t + \tau \text{ are not in same sampling interval}] \\
&= \text{Var}\,\{x\}\left(1 - \frac{|\tau|}{\Delta t}\right) + \xi^2 \qquad (|\tau| < \Delta t)
\end{aligned}
\right\}
$$

$$(1\text{-}51)$$

and hence

$$
\Phi_{xx}(\omega) = \text{Var}\,\{x\}\,\Delta t \left[\frac{\sin\,(\omega\,\Delta t/2)}{\omega\,\Delta t/2}\right]^2 + \xi^2\delta(\omega) \qquad (1\text{-}52)
$$

Figure 1-3 compares $R_{xx}(\tau)$ and $\Phi_{xx}(\omega)$ for a random telegraph wave and a coin-tossing sample-hold process with equal mean count rates $\alpha = \frac{1}{2}\Delta t$, zero mean, and $E\{x^2\} = a^2$.

REFERENCES AND BIBLIOGRAPHY

1. Doob, J. L.: *Stochastic Processes*, Wiley, New York, 1953.
2. Laning, J. H., and R. H. Battin: *Random Processes in Automatic Control*, McGraw-Hill, New York, 1956.
3. Davenport, W. B., Jr., and W. L. Root: *Introduction to Random Signals and Noise*, McGraw-Hill, New York, 1958.
4. Bendat, J. S.: *Principles and Applications of Random-noise Theory*, Wiley, New York, 1958.
5. Lee, Y. W.: *Statistical Theory of Communication*, Wiley, New York, 1960.
6. Middleton, D.: *An Introduction to Statistical Communication Theory*, McGraw-Hill, New York, 1960.
7. Korn, G. A., and T. M. Korn: *Mathematical Handbook for Scientists and Engineers*, McGraw-Hill, New York, 1961.
8. Harman, W. W.: *Principles of the Statistical Theory of Communication*, McGraw-Hill, New York, 1963.
9. Rideout, V. C.: Random-process Studies, in Huskey, H. D., and G. A. Korn, *Computer Handbook*, McGraw-Hill, New York, 1962.
10. Cramér, H.: *Mathematical Methods of Statistics*, Princeton University Press, Princeton, N.J., 1951.
11. Papoulis, A.: *Probability, Random Variables, and Stochastic Processes*, McGraw-Hill, New York, 1965.

CHAPTER **2**

A REVIEW OF
COMPUTER TECHNIQUES

INTRODUCTION AND SURVEY

2-1. The Role of Computers in Random-process Studies. The most common applications of random-process theory predict unknown statistics (such as sample or time averages) in terms of their expected values and variances. These theoretical quantities are mathematically related to "known," i.e., assumed or estimated (measured) ensemble averages. Electronic computers then serve in a threefold role:

1. *Fast Computation of Weighting-function Integrals.* Special computer techniques conveniently produce the complicated convolution integrals (1-24) to (1-28) needed to relate input and output statistics of linear systems (Chap. 3).

Such methods apply not only to intrinsically linear filters and control systems, but also to the effects of small random perturbations on nonlinear processes (Sec. 2-10). Originally developed for electronic analog computers, weighting-function methods also work with digital computation.

2. *Direct Monte-Carlo-type Simulation of Random Phenomena.* Analytical methods fail where a complex random-input system is essentially nonlinear, or if the problem requires prediction of probabilities rather than just mean-square output or correlation functions. In such situations, repeated simulation of the process in question with analog, digital, or hybrid analog-digital computers is usually the only way out. Such "Monte-Carlo methods" are not restricted to linear systems or stationary random processes (Chaps. 4 and 8).

High-speed, digitally controlled iterative differential analyzers (Secs. 2-12 and 4-2) are especially well suited to fast-time Monte-Carlo simulation. Such machines can take statistics over 1,000 to 10,000 simulated random-process runs in a matter of minutes or seconds and can also optimize system parameters with successive samples.

3. *Measurement of Statistics.* Analog, digital, and hybrid analog-digital computing devices permit sophisticated and relatively inexpensive processing of the often formidable masses of data required in practical studies of real or simulated random processes (Chaps. 5, 6, and 7).

2-2. Digital Techniques. (a) **Digital Operations.** In the most general sense, a *computer* is any physical system designed to represent a mathematical model. Computers serve to implement mathematically defined system functions (control, instrumentation, data processing) as well as for problem solving. *Digital operations*, employed both in purely digital computers and in hybrid analog-digital machines, establish relations between two or more discrete-valued variables, usually *binary variables* capable of taking only *two* values. These values, generally referred to as logical 0 and 1, may correspond to voltage levels, such as 0 and −6 volts (voltage OFF or ON). *Numbers* are represented by sets of 0's and 1's on appropriate lines (*parallel* binary-number representation), or by time sequences of 0's and 1's (*serial* binary-number representation).

Combinatorial logic circuits (gates, inverters) implement the logical AND, OR, and complementing operations of Boolean algebra on binary variables (Fig. 2-1). *Sequential digital logic* combines the storage or memory capacity of flip-flops or magnetic-core circuits with shift registers and counters (Figs. 2-2 and 2-3). Digital computing elements further comprise parallel or serial adders, multipliers, and digital comparators.

(b) **Digital Computers.** Some special-purpose digital computers employ separate digital computing elements for separate operations, but the most common type of digital machine has a single *arithmetic element*, which performs all necessary operations in sequence. In such a computer, a *control unit* refers to a *stored program* previously entered into the computer memory system to command a sequence of mathematical operations on binary numbers taken from memory. The result of each operation is returned to storage for future use. Intermediate results can also act as logical decisions to modify the stored program, so that "branching" and iterative cycles are readily possible. The reader is referred to standard texts[1-7] for the design and operation of digital computers.

2-3. Electronic Analog Computers. (a) **Computers and Machine Variables.** An *analog computer* establishes prescribed mathematical relations between continuously variable physical quantities. Specifically,

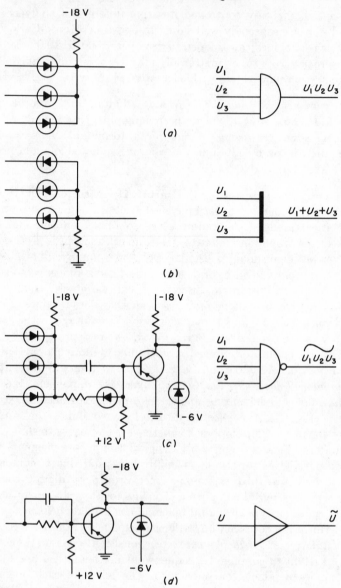

FIG. 2-1. Typical combinatorial-logic modules and block-diagram symbols: AND gate
(a), OR gate (b), NAND gate (c), and inverter (d).

electronic analog computers most frequently represent each problem
variable by a corresponding voltage between ± 100 or ± 10 volts on a
convenient scale (*problem scaling*, Sec. 2-6).   These *machine variables* are
made to obey mathematical relations corresponding to those of the given
problem.   In particular, a *differential analyzer* starts a set of machine

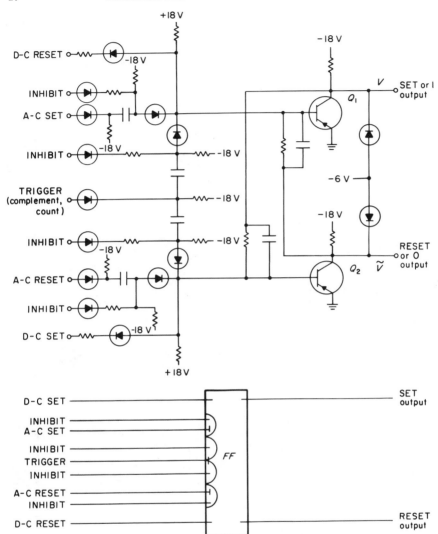

FIG. 2-2. A clamped general-purpose flip-flop with 0-, -6-volt levels, and block-diagram symbol. (*From G. A. Korn and T. M. Korn, Electronic Analog and Hybrid Computers, McGraw-Hill, New York, 1964.*)

variables from specified initial values and employs analog integrators (Sec. 2-3*b*) together with other computing elements to enforce a system of prescribed ordinary differential equations.

(b) Analog Computing Elements. Electronic analog computers establish more or less complex mathematical relationships between machine variables (voltages) $X_o, X_1, X_2, \ldots$, say

$$X_o = 0.02X_1X_2 - 100 \sin 3X_2 = F(X_1,X_2) \qquad (2\text{-}1)$$

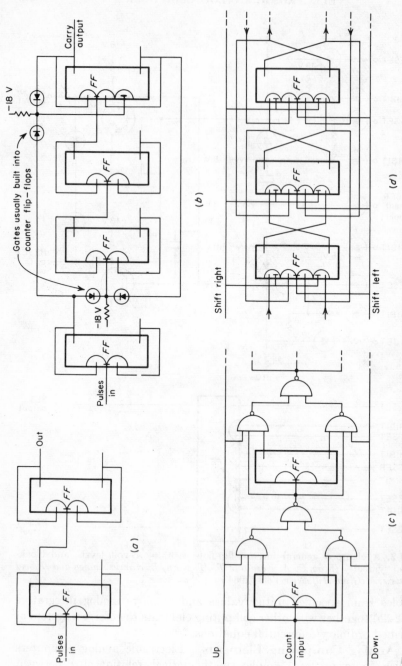

FIG. 2-3. A simple binary counter (*a*), a binary-coded decimal (BCD) counter (*b*), a reversible binary counter (*c*), and a reversible shift register (*d*). D-c reset connections are not shown. (*From G. A. Korn and T. M. Korn, Electronic Analog and Hybrid Computers, McGraw-Hill, New York, 1964.*)

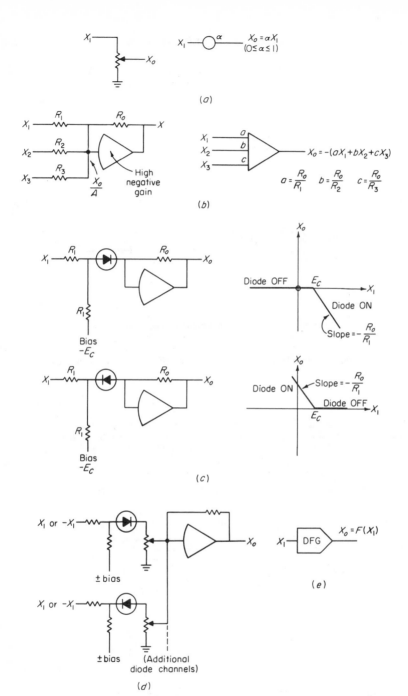

FIG. 2-4a, b, c, d, e. Coefficient-setting potentiometer (a) and summer/phase inverter (b) with their block-diagram symbols. Series-diode limiters with their input-output transfer characteristics (c), a diode function generator (DFG) combining several series-limiter channels to produce straight-line-segment approximations to various functions (d), and block-diagram symbol (e).

19

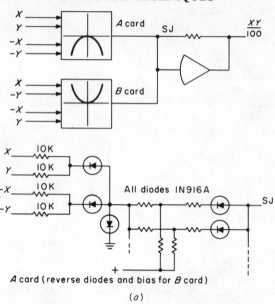

A card (reverse diodes and bias for B card)

(a)

FIG. 2-5a. A quarter-square multiplier employing diode function-generator networks to implement

$$\frac{XY}{100} = \frac{1}{400}\left[(X+Y)^2 - (X-Y)^2\right]$$

The summing-junction current from the A card is proportional to $-(X+Y)^2$, and that from the B card is proportional to $(X-Y)^2$. (*From G. A. Korn and T. M. Korn, Electronic Analog and Hybrid Computers, McGraw-Hill, New York, 1964.*)

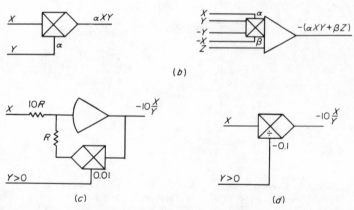

(b)

(c)   (d)

FIG. 2-5b, c, d. Block-diagram symbols for electronic multipliers (b), feedback division circuit (c), and block-diagram symbol for division circuit (d).

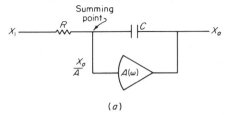

(a)

FIG. 2-6a. Operational-amplifier integrator. The high-gain feedback circuit reduces the summing-point voltage X_o/A to a very small value at frequencies $\omega/2\pi$ such that $|A(\omega)|\omega RC \gg 1$, so that the summing-point node equation

$$\frac{1}{R}\left(X_1 - \frac{X_o}{A}\right) + \frac{1}{C}\int\left(X_o - \frac{X_o}{A}\right) dt = 0$$

implies

$$X_o = -\frac{1}{RC}\int X_o(t)\, dt = -\frac{1}{RC}\int_0^t X_o(t)\, dt + X_o(0)$$

where $X_o(0)$ is the initial voltage on the integrating capacitor (initial-condition voltage). The low-frequency amplifier gain $A(0)$ is real and negative (between -10^4 and -10^8).

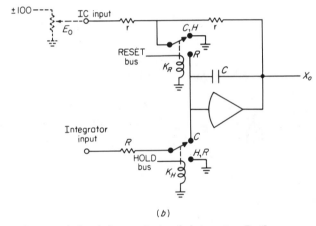

(b)

FIG. 2-6b. Mode-control circuit for an electronic integrator. In the RESET mode, relays K_R and K_H are energized to charge the integrating capacitor to $X_o(0) = -E_o$. If K_H alone is energized, the integrator holds its last output value (HOLD mode). In fast computers, K_R and K_H are replaced by electronic switches.

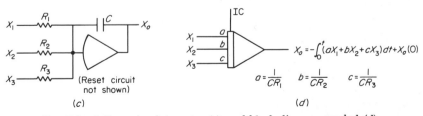

(c)   (d)

FIG. 2-6c, d. Summing integrator (c), and block-diagram symbol (d).

by combining computing elements establishing elementary mathematical operations, usually

Multiplication of a machine variable (voltage) by a constant coefficient
Addition of two or more machine variables
Multiplication of two machine variables
Generation of functions of machine variables

(Figs. 2-4 and 2-5). In addition, analog differential-equation solvers (differential analyzers, Sec. 2-4) employ electronic *integrators* capable of producing the integral of a voltage $x(t)$ with respect to the computer time t, which serves as the independent variable (Fig. 2-6). Conventional electronic analog computers employ separate analog computing elements for each of the operations required by a simulation or data-processing problem. The design and performance of analog computing elements and systems is treated in detail in ref. 12.

(c) **The Computer System.** Besides a set of operational amplifiers and other computing elements and their power supplies, an electronic analog-computer system will comprise:

1. *Interconnections* between computing elements to implement the analog-computer program. Interconnections may involve fixed wiring and switches in special-purpose machines, or *patching* connections in general-purpose computers
2. *Control switches or relays* to place initial conditions on integrators (RESET *condition*) and to start and terminate the computation
3. *Readout devices,* such as oscilloscopes, strip-chart recorders, *xy* recorders, digital voltmeters, and printers
4. *Reference power supplies* to supply accurate *reference voltages* (usually ± 100 or ± 10 volts) required as computing and initial-condition voltages

ANALOG SIMULATION

2-4. Operation of Electronic Differential-equation Solvers. The electronic analog computer represents problem variables by voltages which vary as functions of the time t (*machine time,* used as the independent variable). The *solution of a set of ordinary differential equations* proceeds as follows:

1. With the machine connected up to solve the given problem, the machine variables (voltages) are set to the correct initial conditions prescribed by the problem (RESET *mode*).
2. Computing elements, particularly integrators, are made operative and force the voltages in the machine to vary in a manner prescribed by the given differential equations (COMPUTE *or* OPERATE *mode*).

The voltage variations with time are recorded and constitute solutions of the given problem.

3. The machine is reset to its initial conditions and is ready for the next run with changed coefficients, initial conditions, etc.

"Slow" d-c analog differential-equation solvers admit signal frequencies up to about 50 cps; this is sufficient for simulation of most dynamical systems on a 1:1 time scale.

In a *repetitive* differential-equation solver, the steps of the solution outlined above are repeated automatically at a rapid rate (5 to 1,000 cps) through periodic operation of the integrator mode switches. During each cycle, each machine variable varies in the prescribed manner and is then reset to its initial value. The results can then be presented on an ordinary cathode-ray oscillograph whose sweep frequency equals the computer repetition rate. The rapid operation of such machines permits immediate observation of the effects of parameter changes on the solution. Current trends in electronic analog computation combine repetitive operation with analog memory and hybrid analog/digital automatic program changes to permit automatic decisions and iterative subroutines (Secs. 2-12 to 2-13).

2-5. Programming Differential Equations. Figure 2-7a illustrates the solution of a first-order ordinary differential equation

$$\frac{dX}{dt} \equiv PX = -F(X,t) \tag{2-2}$$

by an analog integrator set up to integrate a voltage $F(X,t)$ obtained by suitable combinations of coefficient potentiometers, summing amplifiers, multipliers, and function generators; here, X is a voltage (machine variable), and the independent variable t is real time (computer time). Note that feedback of the voltage X around the integrator is involved (implicit computation, classical differential-analyzer technique); and that the integrator output starts with a specified *initial-condition voltage*.

In Fig. 2-7b, n integrators similarly solve n simultaneous first-order differential equations

$$\frac{dX_i}{dt} \equiv PX_i = -F_i(X_1,X_2, \ldots ,X_n;t) \qquad (i = 1,2, \ldots ,n) \tag{2-3}$$

We shall transform higher-order differential equations into sets of first-order equations by introducing derivatives $\dot{x}$, $\ddot{x}$, ... as new variables. In particular, a second-order differential equation (e.g., an equation of motion)

$$\frac{d^2x}{dt^2} = f\left(x, \frac{dx}{dt}, \cdots\right) \tag{2-4}$$

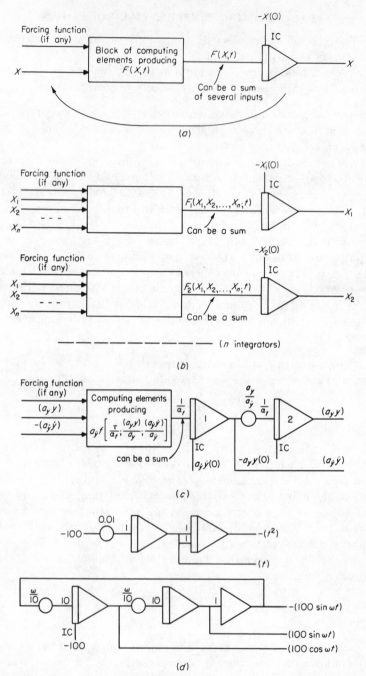

FIG. 2-7. Solution of a first-order differential equation (a), of n first-order equations (b), and scaled computer setup for a second-order equation (c). Figure 2-7d shows how forcing functions (input functions of the computer time t) are obtained as solutions of suitable differential equations.

is transformed into a pair of first-order equations

$$\frac{d\dot{x}}{dt} = f(x,\dot{x}, \cdots) \qquad \frac{dx}{dt} = \dot{x} \qquad (2\text{-}5)$$

(Fig. 2-7c).

Input functions of the computer time t (forcing functions) can themselves be generated by solution of suitable differential equations (Fig. 2-7d), or special signal generators (e.g., sine and square-wave generators) may be used.

2-6. Problem Scaling. (a) **Amplitude Scaling.** Analog computers represent problem variables x, y, . . . by machine variables (usually voltages, currents, or shaft rotations)

$$X = a_x x \qquad Y = a_y y \qquad \cdots \qquad (2\text{-}6)$$

The dimensional *scale factors* a_x, a_y, . . . are chosen so that each machine variable X, Y, . . . is as large as possible without exceeding its maximum permissible excursion $X_{\max}$, $Y_{\max}$, . . . (e.g., 10, 50, or 100 volts) in absolute value.

To scale a given problem for an electronic analog computer capable of supplying ± 100-volt machine variables, one may measure X, Y, . . . in 100-volt *machine units*, but *scaling in volts* is almost universally accepted for such computers. If we scale in volts, we must find new scale factors if we use a ± 10-volt machine. This difficulty is avoided by scaling in terms of *per-cent machine units*. One per-cent machine unit is just one volt for the common ± 100-volt analog computers. Scaling for ± 10-volt computers is then identical to that for ± 100-volt machines, although one per-cent machine unit is now 0.1 volt. We have

$$a_x \le \frac{100}{|x|_{\max}} \frac{\text{volts}}{\text{problem unit}} \qquad (2\text{-}7)$$

where $|x|_{\max}$ is the largest expected excursion of the problem variable x. For convenience, the numerical value of each scale factor is usually a round number of the form 10^n, 2×10^n, 0.25×10^n, 4×10^n, or 5×10^n.

To obtain the correct *machine equations* relating the voltages $(a_x x)$, $(a_y y)$, . . . , write

$$x \text{ as } \frac{1}{a_x}(a_x x) \qquad y \text{ as } \frac{1}{a_y}(a_y y) \qquad \cdots \qquad (2\text{-}8)$$

in each given problem equation. Then set up the block diagram, leaving terms like $(a_x x)$, $(a_y y)$ intact; these terms will appear as voltages whose absolute values cannot exceed 100 volts or 100 per cent of a machine unit. Note that computer setups for second-order differential equations (4), (5) *require separate scale factors for x and $\dot{x}$.* $|x|_{\max}$ and $|\dot{x}|_{\max}$ are estimated from physical considerations or by exploratory computer runs with small scale factors.

(b) Time Scaling. Electronic integrators and computing networks integrate machine variables *with respect to real time*. Therefore, *real time, or machine time t, is the independent machine variable in an electronic differential analyzer*. The *time scale* is established by writing a transformation equation relating the machine time t to the mathematical independent variable t_{PROBLEM}, say,

$$t = \alpha_t t_{\text{PROBLEM}} \tag{2-9}$$

so that the correct machine equations are obtained through the substitution

$$p = \frac{d}{dt_{\text{PROBLEM}}} = \alpha_t \frac{d}{dt} = \alpha_t P \tag{2-10}$$

where the operator $P = d/dt$ denotes the differentiation with respect to the real or machine time t. The dimensional coefficient α_t is the *time-scale factor* or *time scale*. α_t is numerically equal to the number of seconds representing the unit of the independent variable under consideration.

When the time scale is changed, the voltage changes in the computer remain proportional to the corresponding changes of the mathematical variables, but the *rates* at which these voltages change are speeded up or slowed down to improve accuracy or increase the convenience of the computation. A simple way to increase (slow) the time scale is to increase all capacitors in the computer setup proportionately.

If the time t_{PROBLEM} occurs *explicitly* in a given differential equation, t_{PROBLEM} will be represented by a machine variable (voltage) $(a_t t_{\text{PROBLEM}})$ in addition to the machine time t; one must not confuse a_t with the time-scale factor α_t.

2-7. Representation of Dynamical Systems. Figure 2-8 once again illustrates our differential-equation-solving procedure and exhibits features essentially common to all analog-computer representations of dynamical (mechanical) systems:

1. Specific blocks of computing elements implement machine equations corresponding to the *equations of motion* for each "generalized coordinate" of the dynamical system.* The output voltages of these blocks represent *generalized displacements* and/or *velocities*. As a rule, the initial values of these quantities are given. For convenient scaling, it is usually best to rewrite second-order equations of motion as pairs of first-order equations (Sec. 2-5).

* The general formulation of such equations of motion (Lagrange's equations) is discussed, for instance, in R. B. Lindsay and H. Margenau, *Foundations of Physics*, Wiley, New York, 1936.

2. The input voltages "driving" each block will represent *generalized forces* or *accelerations*. In general, each such voltage is a function of the computer time and/or of the machine variables representing generalized displacements and velocities.

3. Coupling forces coupling two degrees of freedom appear as logical interactions between two of the equations of motion and result in corresponding electrical interconnections between two blocks of computing elements.

4. It is usually possible to vary system parameters within reasonable limits and to study the resulting changes in system performance without radical changes in the computer setup.

The functional analogy between components of an actual dynamical system under consideration and blocks of computing elements will not only furnish numerical solutions of the equations of motion but will also

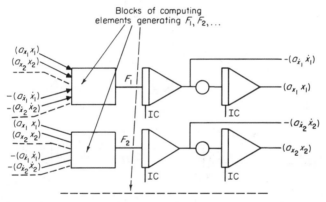

Fig. 2-8. Simulation of a dynamical system by analog-computer implementation of second-order equations of motion.

enhance the investigator's intuitive understanding of the system. In a more general sense, dynamical systems can involve electrical and thermo-dynamic as well as mechanical variables; the corresponding computer setups still relate state changes to forcing functions for each system degree of freedom.

2-8. Example: A Simple Ballistic-trajectory Study. As a simple example of ballistic-trajectory computation in two dimensions, we consider the trajectory of an old-fashioned spherical cannonball with air resistance. This problem does not permit analytical solution in closed form. Referring to Fig. 2-9a, our cannonball is fired with a given muzzle velocity $v(0) = v_0$ and given elevation angle $\vartheta(0) = \vartheta_0$. It is desired to determine the trajectory with respect to a reactangular cartesian coordi-

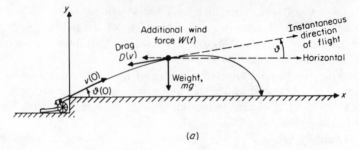

(a)

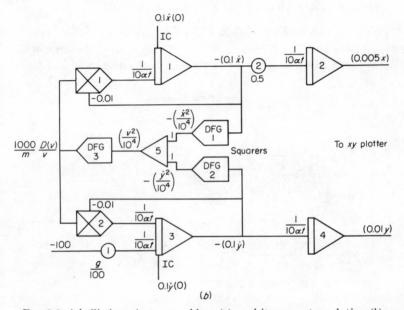

(b)

Fig. 2-9. A ballistic-trajectory problem (a), and its computer solution (b).

nate system with horizontal x axis, vertical y axis, and origin at the cannon muzzle. The only forces acting on the projectile are its weight mg in the vertical direction, and the aerodynamic drag $D(v)$, which opposes the instantaneous-velocity vector. For the velocity range in question, $D(v)$ is approximately proportional to v^2:

$$D(v) \approx rv^2 = 4.7 \times 10^{-5} v^2 \qquad \text{lb} \qquad (2\text{-}11)$$

We introduce the projectile velocity components $\dot{x}$, $\dot{y}$, the instantaneous velocity v, and the angle ϑ between the horizontal x axis and the instantaneous velocity, so that

$$v^2 = \dot{x}^2 + \dot{y}^2 \qquad \cos \vartheta = \frac{\dot{x}}{v} \qquad \sin \vartheta = \frac{\dot{y}}{v} \qquad (2\text{-}12)$$

The projectile equations of motion are

$$m \frac{d\dot{x}}{dt} = -D(v) \cos \vartheta = -\frac{D(v)}{v} \dot{x} \qquad\qquad \left.\frac{dx}{dt} = \dot{x} \right\rbrace$$

$$m \frac{d\dot{y}}{dt} = -D(v) \sin \vartheta - mg = -\frac{D(v)}{v} \dot{y} - mg \qquad \frac{dy}{dt} = \dot{y} \;\; \rbrace \qquad (2\text{-}13)$$

with $x(0) = y(0) = 0 \qquad \dot{x}(0) = v_0 \cos \vartheta_0 \qquad \dot{y}(0) = v_0 \sin \vartheta_0$ (2-14)

Given

$$g = 32.2 \text{ ft/sec}^2 \qquad m = 0.621 \text{ slug (20 lb)}$$
$$v_0 = 900 \text{ ft/sec} \qquad 15 \text{ deg} \le \vartheta_0 \le 20 \text{ deg}$$

we obtain bounds for x, y, ẋ, ẏ, and v for scaling purposes by solving the equations of motion analytically for $D(v) \equiv 0$, *since air resistance will only decrease the maximum values of coordinates and velocity components.* From the resulting simple parabolic trajectory, we find

$$0 < t < 25 \text{ sec} \qquad\quad 100 < v < 900 \text{ ft/sec}$$
$$0 < x < 20{,}000 \text{ ft} \qquad 100 < \dot{x} < 900 \text{ ft/sec}$$
$$0 < y < 6{,}000 \text{ ft} \qquad\; 100 < \dot{y} < 900 \text{ ft/sec}$$

Hence $(0.005x)$, $(0.01y)$, $(0.1\dot{x})$, $(0.1\dot{y})$, and $(0.1v)$ will not exceed 100 per-cent machine units (100 volts for ± 100-volt computers) and are suitable machine variables. The machine equations corresponding to Eqs. (13) and (14) become

$$\frac{d}{dt}(0.1\dot{x}) = -\frac{1}{10\alpha_t}\left\lbrace \frac{1}{100}\left[\frac{1{,}000}{m}\frac{D(v)}{v}\right](0.1\dot{x}) \right\rbrace$$

$$\frac{d}{dt}(0.005x) = \frac{0.5}{10\alpha_t}(0.1\dot{x})$$

$$\frac{d}{dt}(0.1\dot{y}) = -\frac{1}{10\alpha_t}\left\lbrace \frac{1}{100}\left[\frac{1{,}000}{m}\frac{D(v)}{v}\right](0.1\dot{y}) + g \right\rbrace \qquad\qquad (2\text{-}15)$$

$$\frac{d}{dt}(0.01y) = \frac{1}{10\alpha_t}(0.1\dot{y})$$

$$(0.1v)^2 = (0.1\dot{x})^2 + (0.1\dot{y})^2$$

which is implemented by the computer setup of Fig. 2-9*b* on a $\alpha_t:1$ time scale; time-scale changes are easily introduced through integrator-gain changes (Sec. 2-6*b*). Diode function generator 3 produces $1{,}000 D(v)/mv$ as a function of its input voltage $(v^2/10^4)$.

2-9. The Perturbation Method.   (a) Perturbations and Linearization.[5,6] Consider the first-order differential equation

$$\frac{d}{dx}x(t) = f(t,x;\alpha) \qquad\qquad (2\text{-}16)$$

for the state variable $x = x(t)$, where α is a given parameter, initial value, or forcing function; we note that α can be a function $\alpha(t)$ of the independent variable t. We assume that $\alpha(t) = \alpha_0(t) + \delta\alpha(t)$ does not change greatly from its nominal or unperturbed value $\alpha_0(t)$, and that we know the *nominal or unperturbed solution* $x_0(t)$ defined by

$$\frac{d}{dt}x_0(t) = f(t,x_0;\alpha_0) \qquad (2\text{-}17)$$

accurately from analysis or from another computation. Granting suitable differentiability, we introduce $\delta x = x - x_0 = \delta x(t)$ and use the Taylor-series approximation

$$\frac{dx}{dt} = \frac{dx_0}{dt} + \frac{d}{dt}\,\delta x = f(t,x;\alpha)$$
$$= f(t,x_0;\alpha_0) + f_x(t,x_0;\alpha_0)\,\delta x + f_\alpha(t,x_0;\alpha_0)\,\delta\alpha + \cdots \qquad (2\text{-}18)$$

We subtract Eq. (17) to find

$$\frac{d}{dt}\,\delta x = f_x(t,x_0;\alpha_0)\,\delta x + f_\alpha(t,x_0;\alpha_0)\,\delta\alpha + \cdots \qquad (2\text{-}19)$$

Solution of this differential equation yields the exact *perturbation* δx of our nominal solution due to a "perturbation input" $\delta\alpha$. For sufficiently small perturbations $\delta\alpha$, δx, however, we can disregard all but linear terms in these quantities; in this case, Eq. (19) reduces to a *linear* differential equation. Computer solution of such a linear differential equation is simple *if* we can produce the derivatives $f_x(t,x_0;\alpha_0)$, $f_\alpha(t,x_0;\alpha_0)$ which are, in general, functions of time depending on the nominal solution $x_0(t)$. *If $x_0(t)$ is accurately precomputed analytically, digitally, or by accurate "slow" analog computation, then errors in the solution $\delta x(t)$ of Eq. (19) will have a relatively small effect on the total solution $x(t) = x_0(t) + \delta x(t)$.*

Our linear perturbation analysis is easily extended to cases involving n state variables $x_1, x_2, \ldots, x_n$ and r parameters $\alpha_1, \alpha_2, \ldots, \alpha_r$ (which can also be functions of t). Given

$$\left.\begin{array}{l} \dfrac{dx_i}{dt} = f(t;x_1,x_2,\ldots,x_n;\alpha_1,\alpha_2,\ldots,\alpha_r) \\[2mm] \text{with } x_i = x_{0i} + \delta x_i \qquad \alpha_k = \alpha_{0k} + \delta\alpha_k \end{array}\right\}$$
$$(i = 1,2,\ldots,n;\ k = 1,2,\ldots,r) \qquad (2\text{-}20)$$

we find, assuming differentiability and valid linearization,

$$\frac{d}{dt}\,\delta x_i = \sum_{k=1}^{n}\frac{\partial f_i}{\partial x_k}\,\delta x_k + \sum_{k=1}^{r}\frac{\partial f_i}{\partial \alpha_k}\,\delta\alpha_k \qquad (i = 1,2,\ldots,n) \quad (2\text{-}21)$$

This is, again, a linear system with (in general) variable coefficients. Equations (16) and (19) are equivalent to Eqs. (20) and (21) if we regard x, x_0, δx, f as $n \times 1$ matrices, α, α_0, $\delta\alpha$ as $r \times 1$ matrices, f_x as an $n \times n$ matrix, and f_α as an $n \times r$ matrix.

The linear nature of the perturbation equations (19) or (21) can be of the greatest value (Chap. 3).

(b) Application to the Trajectory Study. We will apply the perturbation technique to a study of the effects of a horizontal gust on the ballistic trajectory of Sec. 2-8. We will represent the effect of a gust by a *force*

$$W(t) = \begin{cases} W_0 & (t_1 < t < t_2) \\ 0 & \text{otherwise} \end{cases} \tag{2-22}$$

in the negative x direction (dash line in Fig. 2-9a). A more accurate way to introduce gust effects would be to replace the drag force $D(v) = D(\sqrt{\dot{x}^2 + \dot{y}^2})$ in Eq. (13) by $D(\sqrt{(\dot{x} + w)^2 + \dot{y}^2})$, where $w = w(t)$ is a given wind *velocity*. Our simple wind-force representation is, however, much simpler to implement and will yield good approximations as long as the wind velocity does not exceed $v/10$.

For the velocity range of our cannonball ($v < 900$ ft/sec), it is again reasonable to let $D(v) = rv^2$, so that the projectile equations of motion are

$$m\frac{d\dot{x}}{dt} = -rv\dot{x} - W(t) \qquad \frac{dx}{dt} = \dot{x} \left.\vphantom{\begin{matrix}a\\b\end{matrix}}\right\}$$
$$m\frac{d\dot{y}}{dt} = -rv\dot{y} - mg \qquad \frac{dy}{dt} = \dot{y} \qquad (2\text{-}23)$$
$$v^2 = \dot{x}^2 + \dot{y}^2$$

We introduce

$$x(t) = x_0(t) + \delta x(t) \qquad y(t) = y_0(t) + \delta y(t) \qquad v(t) = v_0(t) + \delta v(t)$$

where $x_0(t)$, $y_0(t)$, $v(t)$ satisfy the nominal or unperturbed system

$$m\frac{d\dot{x}_0}{dt} = -rv_0\dot{x}_0 \qquad \frac{dx_0}{dt} = \dot{x}_0 \left.\vphantom{\begin{matrix}a\\b\end{matrix}}\right\}$$
$$m\frac{d\dot{y}_0}{dt} = -rv_0\dot{y}_0 - mg \qquad \frac{dy_0}{dt} = \dot{y}_0 \qquad (2\text{-}24)$$
$$v_0^2 = \dot{x}_0^2 + \dot{y}_0^2$$

with $\quad x_0(0) = y_0(0) = 0 \qquad \dot{x}_0(0) = v_0(0)\cos\vartheta(0) \qquad \dot{y}_0(0) = v_0(0)\sin\vartheta(0)$ (2-25)

We subtract Eq. (24) from (23) and neglect second-order terms to find

$$m\frac{d}{dt}\delta\dot{x} = -r(\dot{x}_0\,\delta v + v_0\,\delta\dot{x}) - W(t) \qquad \frac{d}{dt}\delta x = \delta\dot{x}$$
$$m\frac{d}{dt}\delta\dot{y} = -r(\dot{y}_0\,\delta v + v_0\,\delta\dot{y}) \qquad \frac{d}{dt}\delta y = \delta\dot{y}$$
$$\delta v = \frac{\dot{x}_0}{v_0}\delta\dot{x} + \frac{\dot{y}_0}{v_0}\delta\dot{y}$$

or

$$\frac{d}{dt}\delta\dot{x} = -\frac{r}{mv_0}[(2\dot{x}_0^2 + \dot{y}_0^2)\,\delta\dot{x} + \dot{x}_0\dot{y}_0\,\delta\dot{y}] - \frac{1}{m}W(t) \left.\vphantom{\begin{matrix}a\\b\\c\end{matrix}}\right\}$$
$$\frac{d}{dt}\delta\dot{y} = -\frac{r}{mv_0}[\dot{x}_0\dot{y}_0\,\delta\dot{x} + (\dot{x}_0^2 + 2\dot{y}_0^2)\,\delta\dot{y}] \qquad\qquad (2\text{-}26)$$
$$\frac{d}{dt}\delta x = \delta\dot{x} \qquad \frac{d}{dt}\delta y = \delta\dot{y} \qquad v_0 = \sqrt{\dot{x}_0^2 + \dot{y}_0^2}$$

This is a time-variable linear system, to be solved for the unknown perturbations δx, δy, $\delta\dot{x}$, $\delta\dot{y}$, which can now take up the full computer scale; the correct initial values are

$$\delta x(0) = \delta y(0) = \delta\dot{x}(0) = \delta\dot{y}(0) = 0 \tag{2-27}$$

The time-variable coefficients in Eq. (26) depend on $\dot{x}_0(t)$ and $\dot{y}_0(t)$. These functions must be either precomputed through numerical solution of the nominal system (24), or the latter is set up on the analog computer and runs concurrently with the perturbation equations (26) to produce $\dot{x}_0(t)$ and $\dot{y}_0(t)$ as functions of time.

2-10. Computer Setups for Linear Transfer Operators. (a) Problem Statement.

The dynamical relationship between the input (stimulus) $x(t)$ and the output (response) $y(t)$ of many control-system components can be represented by a linear differential equation

$$\frac{d^n y}{dt^n} + a_{n-1}\frac{d^{n-1}y}{dt^{n-1}} + \cdots + a_0 y = b_m \frac{d^m x}{dt^m} + b_{m-1}\frac{d^{m-1}x}{dt^{m-1}} + \cdots + b_0 x$$

$$(m \leq n) \quad (2\text{-}28a)$$

with constant coefficients a_i, b_k, or in operator form

$$y(t) = H(p)x(t) = \frac{b_m p^m + b_{m-1}p^{m-1} + \cdots + b_0}{p^n + a_{n-1}p^{n-1} + \cdots + a_0}\,x(t)$$

$$\left(m \leq n;\, p \equiv \frac{d}{dt}\right) \quad (2\text{-}28b)$$

(b) Operational-amplifier Method. Simple operations of the form (28) are readily implemented by the well-known operational-amplifier circuits shown in Fig. 2-10. We note that each two-terminal impedance (Fig. 2-10a) or short-circuit transfer impedance (Fig. 2-10b) $Z_k(j\omega)$ relates an input voltage X_k and an output current i_k by the differential equation

$$X_k = Z_k(p)i_k \qquad \left(p \equiv \frac{d}{dt}\right) \quad (2\text{-}29)$$

In each operational amplifier, high-gain degenerative feedback forces the summing-point voltage E_G close to ground potential ($E_G \approx 0$). Hence, the summing-point node equation

$$\frac{1}{Z_1(p)}\,X_1 + \frac{1}{Z_o(p)}\,X_o = 0 \qquad \left(p \equiv \frac{d}{dt}\right) \quad (2\text{-}30)$$

implies the input-output relation

$$X_o = -\,\frac{Z_o(p)}{Z_1(p)}\,X_1 \qquad \left(p \equiv \frac{d}{dt}\right) \quad (2\text{-}31)$$

The assumption $E_G = 0$ implies infinite operational-amplifier loop gain $|A(j\omega)\beta(j\omega)|$; more precisely, Eq. (31) can be shown to hold within $100/|A(j\omega)|$ per cent for sinusoidal input of circular frequency ω.[5] For typical operational amplifiers, $|A(j\omega)|$ is between 10^4 and 10^8 at zero frequency and reduces to unity between 0.1 to 20 Mc. Figure 2-10c shows simple examples, and Fig. 2-10d shows an operational amplifier with multiple inputs.

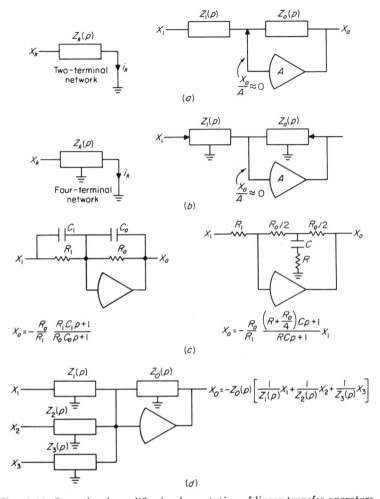

FIG. 2-10. Operational-amplifier implementation of linear transfer operators.

(c) Differential-analyzer Techniques. The operational-amplifier circuits of Fig. 2-10 are most useful in special-purpose computers for instrumentation and control applications. To set up Eq. (28) on a general-purpose electronic differential analyzer, we can

1. Integrate Eq. (28a) n times to obtain

$$y = b_n x + \frac{1}{p}(b_{n-1}x - a_{n-1}y) + \frac{1}{p^2}(b_{n-2}x - a_{n-2}y) + \cdots$$

$$+ \frac{1}{p^n}(b_0 x - a_0 y) \quad (2\text{-}32)$$

which is implemented in Fig. 2-11a.

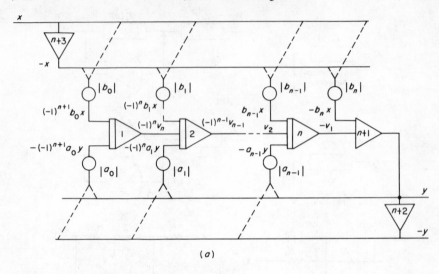

(a)

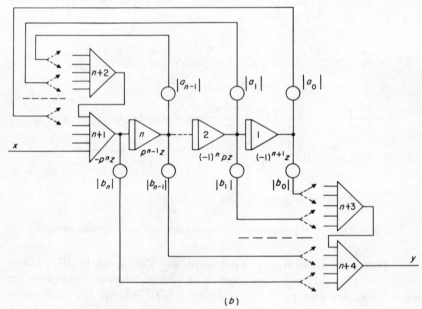

(b)

FIG. 2-11. Differential-analyzer setups representing the relation (28), or

$$y = \frac{b_m p^m + b_{m-1} p^{m-1} + \cdots + b_0}{p^n + a_{n-1} p^{n-1} + \cdots + a_0} x \qquad \left(m \leq n; p \equiv \frac{d}{dt} \right)$$

without explicit differentiation. (*From G. A. Korn and T. M. Korn, Electronic Analog and Hybrid Computers, McGraw-Hill, New York, 1964.*)

2. Rewrite Eq. (28b) as

$$y(t) = (b_n p^n + b_{n-1} p^{n-1} + \cdots + b_0) z(t) \qquad (2\text{-}33)$$

where
$$(p^n + a_{n-1} p^{n-1} + \cdots + a_0) z(t) = x(t) \qquad (2\text{-}34)$$

The computer setup of Fig. 2-11b solves Eq. (34) in the ordinary manner and generates z, $-pz$, $p^2 z$, $\ldots$. These quantities are combined in accordance with Eq. (33) to produce y.

Figure 2-12 shows a useful example. High-order operators (28) are usually factored into lower-order terms. In most practical applications, initial integrator outputs in Fig. 2-11 can be equal to zero. Scaling in these computer setups may require a trial-and-error procedure.[5] Computer setups for operations of the form (28) with *time-variable* coefficients a_i, b_k will be discussed in Sec. 3-5.

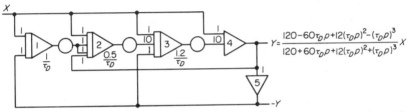

FIG. 2-12. A linear-transfer-operator setup approximating the constant-time-delay operator $e^{-\tau_D p}$, so that $Y(t) \approx X(t - \tau_D)$ for low-frequency input $X(t)$. *(From G. A. Korn and T. M. Korn, Electronic Analog and Hybrid Computers, McGraw-Hill, New York, 1964.)*

(d) The Inpulse Response. It is often important to compute the response $y(t) = w(t,\lambda)$ of a linear system to a (symmetrical) unit-impulse input $x(t) = \delta(t - \lambda)$ applied at the time $t = \lambda$ (Sec. 1-6, Chap. 3, and Sec. 7-11). For a time-invariant linear system (28), $w(t,\lambda) \equiv h(t - \lambda)$, so that we need only compute the response $y(t) = h(t)$ to a unit impulse $\delta(t)$ at $t = 0$. Since both unilateral Laplace transforms and analog computers work only for $t > 0$, either computation method would cut the *symmetrical* impulse input $\delta(t)$ in half. We can, however, compute the system response $w_+(t,0) \equiv h_+(t)$ to an *asymmetrical* unit impulse $\delta_+(t)$, where

$$\mathcal{L}[\delta(t)] = \int_{0+0}^{\infty} \delta(t) e^{-st}\, dt = \tfrac{1}{2} \qquad \mathcal{L}[\delta_+(t)] = \int_{0+0}^{\infty} \delta_+(t) e^{-st}\, dt = 1 \qquad (2\text{-}35)$$

$h_+(t)$ and $h(t)$ are identical wherever they are continuous.[9]

While it is, clearly, impossible to produce impulse voltages in an analog computer, the impulse response $z(t) = h(t)$ of a linear system described by

$$z(t) = \frac{1}{p^n + a_{n-1} p^{n-1} + \cdots + a_0}\, x(t) \qquad \left(n > 0; \ p \equiv \frac{d}{dt}\right) \qquad (2\text{-}36)$$

is bounded and continuous for $t > 0$.   Moreover, Laplace transformation of

$$(p^n + a_{n-1}p^{n-1} + \cdots + a_0)h_+(t) = \delta_+(t)$$
with $h_+, ph_+, p^2h_+, \ldots, p^{n-1}h_+ = 0$ for $t = 0$ $\left. \right\}$ $\left(n > 0; p \equiv \dfrac{d}{dt} \right)$

$$(2\text{-}37)$$

shows that $h_+(t)$ is identical with solution of the problem

$$(p^n + a_{n-1}p^{n-1} + \cdots + a_0)h_+(t) = 0$$
with $h_+, ph_+, p^2h_+, \ldots, p^{n-2}h_+ = 0$ and $p^{n-1}h_+ = 1$ for $t = 0 + 0$ $\left. \right\}$

$$\left(n > 0; p \equiv \dfrac{d}{dt} \right) \quad (2\text{-}38)$$

This is easily implemented by the computer setup of Fig. 2-13.   *We see that the impulse input is simply replaced by an initial-condition setting on a single integrator.*

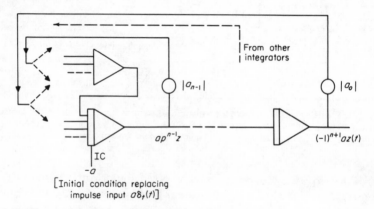

[Initial condition replacing impulse input $a\delta_+(t)$]

FIG. 2-13. Computer setup producing the impulse response

$$(-1)^{n+1}az(t) = \frac{(-1)^{n+1}a}{p^n + a_{n-1}p^{n-1} + \cdots + a_0} \delta_+(t)$$

The same technique applies also to operations of the more general form (28), provided that $n > m$, so that $H(\infty)$ and $h_+(t)$ are bounded.   In this case, we simply generate the impulse response $z(t)$ as in Fig. 2-13 and then produce

$$y(t) = (b_m p^m + b_{m-1}p^{m-1} + \cdots + b_0)z(t) \qquad (m < n)$$

in the manner of Fig. 2-11*b*.

2-11. Analog, Digital, and Hybrid Computation.   Iterative Differential Analyzers.   (a) Appraisal of Analog Methods. As we have seen, electronic analog computers employ distinct computing elements for each mathematical operation required to solve a given problem. Such all-parallel operation permits high computing speeds in differential-equation solvers: most problems, regardless of complication, are solved within two minutes by "slow" electronic analog computers and within fractions of a second by repetitive machines. On the other hand, parallel operation imposes practical limits on the complexity of problems which can be solved. These limits clearly depend on the problem; generally speaking, a 20-amplifier desk-top machine will readily solve the four nonlinear second-order differential equations describing a reasonable four-degree-of-freedom dynamical system, and a medium-sized analog computer (80 amplifiers) can deal with a 10-degree-of-freedom system without special difficulties. Much larger problems, requiring up to 1,000 amplifiers, have been treated successfully at the expense of a massive effort in problem preparation and checkout.

Component accuracies of individual analog computing elements for addition, multiplication, integration, etc., vary between 3 and 0.01 per cent of half-scale (100 or 10 volts). Costs increase rapidly if component accuracies better than 0.2 per cent are desired. Accuracies obtainable in solving a complete problem depend critically on the problem and on the computer setup as well as on the component accuracies, since errors may cancel or be compounded. The overall accuracy can be practically equal to the component accuracy in problems involving linear differential equations with constant coefficients if the solutions comprise only well-damped modes (linear-servo simulation).

The really important contributions of analog computers to modern system development techniques go beyond numerical computation as such, for the analog approach functions as a direct aid to a research worker's thinking process. Analog-computer setups serve as "live mathematical models" which bridge the gap between mathematical symbolism and physical reality. Simple patchcord connections and potentiometer settings create a scale model which permits convenient investigation of the performance and interaction of processes and systems.

The *time scale* of analog computations may be slowed down or speeded up within wide limits at the convenience of the experimenter. In particular, analog-computing speeds are sufficiently high to permit representation of most dynamical and electromechanical processsses on a 1:1 time scale (real-time simulation). With the computer running on a 1:1 time scale, actual physical components of a system under investigation can take the place of a corresponding block of computing elements (partial system testing).

Besides passive networks, modern analog computing elements require only three types of basic electronic components, viz., transistor d-c amplifiers, diode networks (for function generation and multiplication), and electronic switches. The resulting all-solid-state analog computers are substantially more reliable and more easily maintained than their vacuum-tube predecessors.   Nevertheless, the essential advantages of all-parallel electronic analog computation (fast solution of differential equations, simple man-machine interaction) are best realized in small- to medium-sized installations (up to 100 to 150 amplifiers) designed for high computing speed.   In larger installations, the simplicity of the man-machine interface, if not the solution accuracy, is, more often than not, lost to increasing difficulties with programming, problem checkout, and equipment maintenance.

(b) Hybrid Analog-Digital Computation.   Combined Simulation.   *Combined simulation,* say of space vehicles or industrial processes, with analog-digital computers typically employs an electronic analog computer for simulating control-system dynamics while the digital computer is used for accurate generation of multivariable functions and for precise trajectory integration.[9,12]   Such attempts to combine the better features of analog and digital computers have usually arisen from regretable necessity in connection with very complicated real-time simulation problems.   It must be realized that a large combined simulation also combines the *worst* features of both types of computers.   Analog-computer errors and checkout problems are joined to the sampled-data-handling difficulties limiting the speed of the digital computer, and an expensive analog/digital/analog converter system is required to link both machines. While all technical difficulties can be resolved, the combination of a large analog computer, a general-purpose digital computer, and a multichannel linkage is cumbersome and expensive; many such systems are practically sure to be superseded by future all-digital simulators combining some increase of digital computing speed with radically improved display and programming systems, which will permit human operators convenient real-time access to the digital computation.

In the meantime, the experience afforded to computer designers and users by combined analog-digital simulation points the way to more economical hybrid computers of the future.   Such systems are likely to comprise only relatively small (and probably fast) electronic analog computers (up to 100 amplifiers), which do not present a maintenance problem.   Foremost among the truly system-designed hybrid computers is the *digitally controlled iterative differential analyzer,* which combines analog memory and digital logic to give a small- or medium-sized analog computer a measure of program-changing and decision-making ability (Sec. 2-12).   At only slightly increased cost, much of the parallel digital logic can be replaced by a small program-controlled digital computer in the $10,000 to $30,000 class.   Such a machine will not only control iterative analog computation with a minimum of patching and parallel hardware, but can also automate analog-computer "housekeeping" functions such as computation and storage of potentiometer settings.   Only a relatively inexpensive analog-to-digital converter is required to read two to four samples per analog-computer run.   This permits not only digital readout, but also sophisticated digital parameter optimization and statistics computation (Chap. 4) *without requiring high speed in digital computation or conversion.*

2-12. The Iterative Differential Analyzer. Flow Diagrams.[12,17]   An analog computer with integrator-mode and program switches operable by sequence-controlling timers, analog comparators, and/or digital logic will be called an *iterative differential analyzer.*   Such machines can automatically perform successive analog-computer runs utilizing stored results of earlier runs and can, therefore, implement iterative computations converging to a desired solution.   The automatic programming features have many other applications as well.

Iterative differential analyzers, like digital computers, are programmed through a series of subroutines.   A *subroutine* is a sequence of operations, such as an analog-computer run or a number of repetitive-analog-computer runs.   We associate each subroutine with a digital (binary) *control variable* U_i representing the state of a control relay or flip-flop.   The subroutine proceeds when $U_i = 1$; $U_i = 0$ "resets" the computing elements involved in the subroutine (e.g., integrators, counters) for renewed use.   Note that the complementary control variable $\tilde{U}_i$ (0 for $U_i = 1$, 1 for $U_i = 0$) may also define a subroutine.   Subroutines can be "nested," i.e., they may involve component subroutines.

Typical analog-subroutine changes are combinations of the following operations:

1. Switching a group of integrators from RESET to COMPUTE, or from RESET (TRACK) to HOLD, and vice versa (complementary subroutines)
2. Switching to new values of parameter or initial-value settings (e.g., parameter optimization, automatic scale-factor changes)
3. Switching interconnections to produce computer-setup changes

Subroutines start and terminate when the corresponding binary control variables change state as logical functions of (1) external control (switches, relays controlled by external devices), (2) the states of timers or subroutine counters, and (3) analog-comparator decisions.   An *analog comparator* produces a binary 0 or 1 output in accordance with the sign of an analog (voltage) input sum or difference (Fig. 2-14; see also Sec. 8-2). An analog comparator can be regarded as the basic *analog-to-digital conversion* element, just as a simple switch is the basic *digital-to-analog* conversion element.

Appropriate Boolean functions and sequences of binary control variables can be implemented by patched digital-logic circuits (gates, inverters, flip-flops).   For more flexible control and greater problem-changing convenience with complex programs, patched "parallel" digital-logic elements

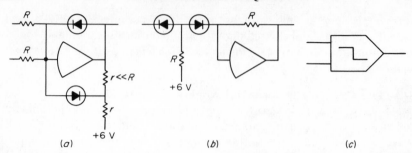

FIG. 2-14. Analog comparators (a), (b), and block-diagram symbol (c). Each output voltage is zero if the input or input sum is negative, and -6 volts if the input is positive.

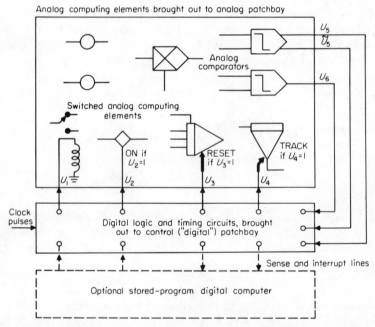

FIG. 2-15. Iterative-differential-analyzer system. Operations (operation boxes) are mainly analog-computer runs "ordered" by electronic switches or relays controlled by binary control variables U_i. Control-variable states are preset by timers and counters and/or "computed" by analog comparators and digital logic. Switches and comparators form the digital-analog and analog-digital interfaces.

can be combined with the stored-program logic of a small general-purpose digital computer in the \$10,000 to \$30,000 class.

The interplay of binary control variables and analog computation gives the iterative differential analyzer a special hybrid analog-digital structure (Fig. 2-15). Because relays or electronic switches implement analog-subroutine changes under control of digital (binary) control variables

U_i, they constitute the digital-to-analog interface of our hybrid computer. Analog solutions, in turn, can modify digital controls. Program sequences of differential-analyzer operations and analog/digital decisions are nicely represented by *flow diagrams* quite similar to those used in digital computation (Fig. 2-16).

Iterative differential analyzers can implement vastly more sophisticated models than ordinary analog computers and still retain some of the

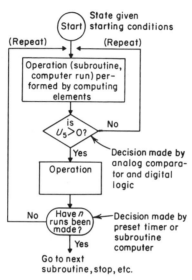

FIG. 2-16. Iterative-differential-analyzer flow chart.   Rectangular boxes specify operations.   Oval decision boxes refer to preset digital-timer and/or counter decisions, while diamond-shaped decision boxes involve analog comparators and/or comparator-actuated digital logic.   *(From H. R. Eckes and G. A. Korn, Digital Program Control for Iterative Differential Analyzers, Simulation, February, 1964.)*

intuitive appeal of the latter.   We start our list of applications with those most peculiarly suited to iterative analog computation.

1. *Iterative Parameter Optimization.*   The machine varies parameters of a simulated system so as to improve performance measured in successive computer runs (Sec. 8-15).
2. *Monte-Carlo Studies of Random Processes.*   (Chaps. 4 and 8).
3. *Real-time and fast-time simulation of sampled-data systems*, including digital computers (Sec. 2-13).

Repetitive analog computation at the highest possible speed is practically indispensable for Monte-Carlo studies of dynamical systems. Parameter optimization benefits most from high computing speed if we are required to *track* optimum-parameter combinations under changing conditions, as in cross-plotting studies or two-time-scale control.

Other interesting applications include:[12]

4. *Approximate solution of partial differential equations.*
5. *Automatic sequencing* of routine computations for plotting families of curves, special displays, cross plotting, etc.
6. *Introduction of artificial errors* into alternate computer runs for purposes of error analysis.
7. *Automatic scale-factor changes.*
8. *Multiplexing expensive computing elements* or blocks of computing elements (e.g., coordinate-transformation circuits).
9. *Special simulation and data-processing circuits*, e.g., patchbay-assembled time-division and sampling multipliers, special function generators, and delays.

2-13. Analog Memory and Sampled-data Operations. **(a) Sample-hold Circuits.** The simple sample-hold circuit (*track-hold circuit, zero-order hold*) of Fig. 2-17a tracks its analog input while the switch S is closed (TRACK mode). If we open the switch at a specific time t_k, the circuit holds its last output voltage $X(t_k)$ without discharging the storage

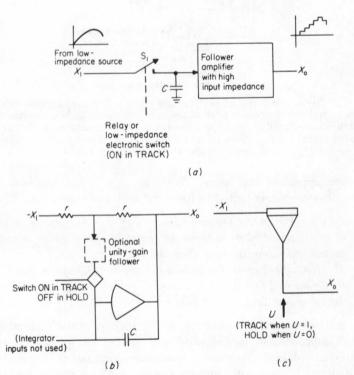

FIG. 2-17. A simple track-hold circuit (*a*), electronic integrator used as a track-hold (*b*), and block-diagram symbol (*c*).

capacitor C (HOLD mode).   This is useful for data processing (analog-to-digital conversion) or for analog storage of the sample during subsequent analog-computer operations or computer runs.

An ideal track-hold circuit would track its input without delay or phase shift, would switch into HOLD instantaneously upon command, and would hold for an indefinite time without drift or offset errors.   In practice, a compromise between these requirements is necessary; the design of track-hold circuits is treated in detail in ref. 12.   Figure 2-17b shows the use of a switched electronic integrator as a track-hold circuit.

(b) Track-hold Pairs and Sampled-data Operations.   The sampled-data output of a simple track-hold circuit is interrupted by TRACK

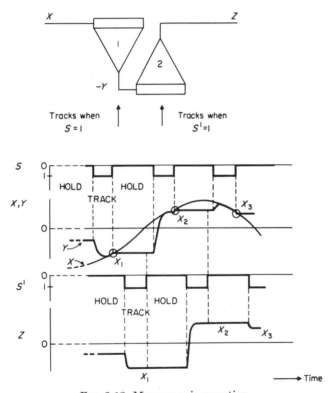

FIG. 2-18. Memory-pair operation.

periods.   Figure 2-18 illustrates the operation of two track-hold circuits as a *track-hold pair*.   The second track-hold circuit "presents" its stored output while the input track-hold is tracking to acquire a new input sample.   Track-hold pairs can, in particular, store analog voltage samples acquired during successive computer runs and introduce them into later computer runs.[12,17]

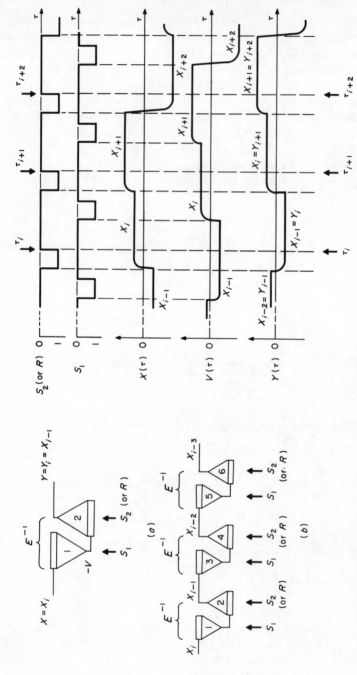

Fig. 2-19. Memory pair with sampled-data input (a), and cascaded memory pairs (b). (From G. A. Korn and T. M. Korn, Electronic Analog and Hybrid Computers, McGraw-Hill, New York, 1964.)

If the input to a track-hold pair is the sampled-data output of a similarly timed track-hold pair (Fig. 2-19), then each track-hold pair acts as a *unit delay operator* which delays its input by one sample, i.e.,

$$Y_i = \mathbf{E}^{-1}X_i = X_{i-1} \qquad (i = 1,2, \ldots) \qquad (2\text{-}39)$$

Feedback circuits involving such track-hold pairs can solve recurrence relations (difference equations)

$$\mathbf{E}Y_i = Y_{i+1} = F_i(Y_i) \qquad (i = 0,1,2, \ldots) \qquad (2\text{-}40)$$

(Fig. 2-20), or systems of such equations, much as analog integrators are used to solve ordinary differential equations (ref. 12).   Note that the initial value Y_0 must be given.

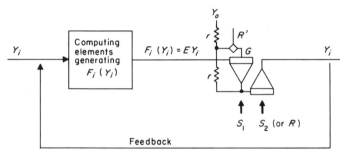

Fig. 2-20. Solution of recursion relations or difference equations.   An extra reset circuit (*initial-reset* circuit operated by the control variable R') establishes the correct initial output Y_0 at the start of computation.

As a specific example, the *sampled-data accumulator circuit* of Fig. 2-21a solves the recurrence relation

$$\mathbf{E}Y_i = Y_i + X_i \qquad (i = 0,1,2, \ldots) \qquad (2\text{-}41)$$

to compute the sum

$$Y_i = \frac{1}{\mathbf{E}-1}X_i = \sum_{k=0}^{i-1} X_k \qquad (i = 1,2, \ldots ; Y_0 = 0) \qquad (2\text{-}42)$$

where $X_0, X_1, X_2, \ldots$ is an analog sampled-data input sequence.   Similarly, the circuit of Fig. 2-21b solves the difference equation

$$\mathbf{E}Y_i = \alpha Y_i + X_i \qquad (0 < \alpha \le 1 ; i = 0,1,2, \ldots) \qquad (2\text{-}43)$$

to compute the sampled-data equivalent of an exponentially-weighted-past average (see also Sec. 5-4):

$$Y_i = \frac{1}{\mathbf{E}-\alpha} X_i = \sum_{k=0}^{i-1} \alpha^{i-k-1} X_k \qquad (i = 1,2, \ldots ; Y_0 = 0) \qquad (2\text{-}44)$$

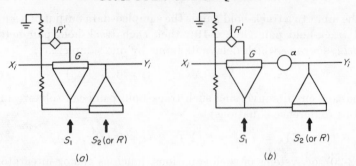

Fig. 2-21. Sampled-data accumulator (a), and exponentially-weighted-past averaging circuit (b).

REFERENCES AND BIBLIOGRAPHY

Digital Computation (published since 1962)

1. Bartee, T. C., et al.: *Theory and Design of Digital Machines*, McGraw-Hill, New York, 1962.
2. Burroughs Corp. Staff: *Digital Computer Principles*, McGraw-Hill, New York, 1962.
3. Chu, Y.: *Digital Computer Design Fundamentals*, McGraw-Hill, New York, 1962.
4. Ledley, R. S.: *Programming and Utilizing Digital Computers*, McGraw-Hill, New York, 1962.
5. Braun, E. L.: *Digital Computer Design*, Academic, New York, 1963.
6. Sherman, P. M.: *Programming and Coding Digital Computers*, Wiley, New York, 1963.
7. Ware, W. H.: *Digital Computer Technology and Design*, Wiley, New York, 1963.

Analog and Hybrid Analog-Digital Computation (published since 1962)

8. Giloi, W., and R. Lauber: *Analogrechnen*, Springer, Berlin, 1963.
9. Huskey, H. D., and G. A. Korn: *Computer Handbook*, McGraw-Hill, New York, 1962.
10. Johnson, C. L.: *Analog Computer Techniques*, 2d ed., McGraw-Hill, New York, 1963.
11. Kogan, B. Y.: *Eectronic Analog Computers*, 2d ed., Fismatgis, Moscow, 1963.
12. Korn, G. A., and T. M. Korn: *Electronic Analog and Hybrid Computers*, McGraw-Hill, New York, 1964.
13. Levine, A.: *Methods for Solving Engineering Problems Using Analog Computers*, McGraw-Hill, New York, 1964.
14. MacKay, D. M., and M. E. Fisher: *Analogue Computing at Ultra-high Speed*, Wiley, New York, 1962.
15. Tomovič, R., and W. J. Karplus: *High-speed Analog Computers*, Wiley, New York, 1962.

Miscellaneous

16. Korn, G. A., and T. M. Korn: *Mathematical Handbook for Scientists and Engineers*, McGraw-Hill, New York, 1961.
17. Eckes, H. R., and G. A. Korn: Digital Program Control for Iterative Differential Analyzers, *Simulation*, February, 1964.

CHAPTER 3

COMPUTER TECHNIQUES IMPLEMENTING STATISTICAL INPUT-OUTPUT RELATIONS

INTRODUCTION

3-1. Introductory Remarks. An important class of applications requires determination of the output autocorrelation function or mean-square output of a linear system when the autocorrelation function or power spectrum of the system input is given. The methods described in this chapter employ analog computers, or digital computers programmed as linear-differential-equation solvers, to implement the requisite relations (1-24) to (1-28) conveniently. In this context, the electronic differential-equation solver does *not* "simulate" a system with random input and output, but furnishes weighting functions for the theoretical relations (1-24) to (1-28). Practically, the most important computer methods will be those producing a system mean-square output (usually a mean-square error) *in a single computer run* (Secs. 3-3, 3-4, and 3-7 to 3-9), so that we can iterate computer runs for automatic parameter optimization (Sec. 2-12).

TIME-INVARIANT LINEAR SYSTEMS WITH STATIONARY INPUTS

3-2. Computation of Output Correlation Functions. We are given an analog-computer setup for a time-invariant linear operation

$$y(t) = H\left(\frac{d}{dt}\right) x(t) = \int_{-\infty}^{\infty} h(t - \lambda) x(\lambda) \, d\lambda \qquad (3\text{-}1)$$

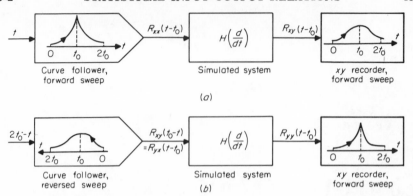

FIG. 3-1. Computer implementation of the Wiener-Lee relations for a time-invariant linear system with stationary input. $R_{xy}(t - t_0)$ and $R_{yy}(t - t_0)$ are successively produced in two computer runs.

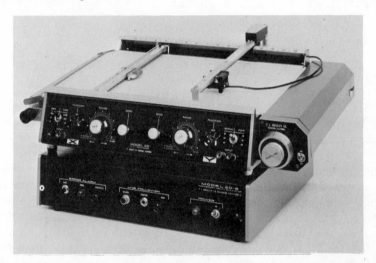

FIG. 3-2. A table-top servo plotter (xy table) incorporating separate y servos for a pen and for a photoelectric curve follower; the x servo can furnish reversible time sweeps for both. With the chart-drive accessory shown, the curve follower can also read $f(t - \tau)$ as the pen records a voltage $f(t)$; if the pen is replaced by a second curve follower, we can read both $f_1(t)$ and $f_2(t - \tau)$ from long records of the functions (time-delay generation in correlation measurements, Sec. 5-7). Chart speeds between 2 and 32 in./sec and adjustable carriage separation yield delays τ between 4 and 420 sec. Servo static accuracy is within 0.1 volt, velocity and acceleration limits are 20 in./sec and 750 in./sec²; small-signal phase shift reaches 5 deg at 3 cps. (*F. L. Moseley Co., Pasadena, Calif.*)

(Sec. 2-10) and the autocorrelation function $R_{xx}(\tau)$ of the stationary input $x(t)$; physical realizability implies $h(t - \lambda) = 0$ for $\lambda > t$. Figure 3-1a and b illustrates a method for computing the output autocorrelation function $R_{yy}(\tau)$. With $R_{xx}(\tau)$ given in the form of a graph, a curve-following servo table (Fig. 3-2) generates $R_{xx}(t - t_0)$ as a function of real time t. The computer setup of Fig. 3-1a then produces $R_{xy}(t - t_0)$ in accordance with the first Wiener-Lee relation (1-27), i.e.,

$$R_{xy}(t - t_0) = \int_{-\infty}^{\infty} h(t - \lambda) R_{xx}(\lambda - t_0) \, d\lambda = \int_{-\infty}^{t} h(t - \lambda) R_{xx}(\lambda - t_0) \, d\lambda \tag{3-2}$$

and records this function with the aid of a second servo plotting table. In Fig. 3-1b, the resulting graph is then read by the first servo table with reversed time sweep to produce the voltage $R_{xy}(t_0 - t) = R_{yx}(t - t_0)$, so that our computer setup implements the second Wiener-Lee relation (1-27) in the form

$$R_{yy}(t - t_0) = \int_{-\infty}^{t} h(t - \mu) R_{xy}(t_0 - \mu) \, d\mu \tag{3-3}$$

This procedure works nicely for random functions whose correlation functions become negligible for $|\tau| > t_0$, where t_0 is some reasonable delay. For processes too fast or too slow for convenient and accurate servo-table operation (0.01 to 2 cps), we must first change the time scale (Sec. 2-6b); we merely replace t by $\alpha_t t$ and d/dt by $(1/\alpha_t) \, d/dt$ in Eqs. (1) and (2).

3-3. Shaping-filter Technique and Mean-square-output Computation. If our stationary input signal $x(t)$ is stationary *white noise* with $R_{xx}(\tau) \equiv \delta(\tau)$, $\Phi_{xx}(\omega) \equiv 1$ (2 volt^2/cps, Sec. 1-7),* then

$$R_{xy}(\tau) \equiv h(\tau) \tag{3-4}$$

and the servo-table output $R_{xx}(\tau)$ in Fig. 3-1a is replaced by a unit impulse $\delta(\tau)$, with $t_0 = 0$. The unit-impulse response $h(t)$, and hence $R_{xy}(t)$ and $R_{yy}(t)$, will be bounded only if $H(\infty) = 0$; in the typical case of an operator

$$H\left(\frac{d}{dt}\right) \equiv H(p) \equiv \frac{b_m p^m + b_{m-1} p^{m-1} + \cdots + b_0}{a_n p^n + a_{n-1} p^{n-1} + \cdots + a_0} \quad \left(p \equiv \frac{d}{dt}\right) \tag{3-5}$$

(Sec. 2-10) this implies $n > m$. *The desired impulse excitation* $\delta(t) \equiv R_{xx}(t)$ *can, therefore, be implemented simply and accurately by an initial-condition setting in the manner of Sec.* 2-10d.† This simplification is especially useful if we require only the mean-square output resulting from our white-noise input; this is very often true when $E\{y^2\}$ is a mean-square control-system error. For $R_{xx}(\tau) = \delta(\tau)$, Eq. (1-25) yields

$$E\{y^2\} = R_{yy}(0) = \int_0^{\infty} h^2(t) \, dt \tag{3-6}$$

where we have replaced $-\mu$ by t; the computer setup of Fig. 3-3a is seen

---

* In accordance with our definition (1-32) of the spectral density $\Phi_{xx}(\omega)$, this means $\Phi_{xx}(\omega) = 1$ volt^2/cps between $\omega = -\infty$ and $\omega = \infty$, or $2\Phi_{xx}(\omega) = 2$ volt^2/cps between $\omega = 0$ and $\omega = \infty$ in Eq. (1-33).

† The initial-condition technique of Sec. 2-10d actually produces the response $h_+(t)$ to the asymmetrical impulse[14] $\delta_+(t)$; but $h(t) = h_+(t)$ wherever it is continuous,[14] which is true for all $t > 0$ if $n > m$.

to produce the desired expression (4) *in a single computer run* of sufficiently long duration.

This convenient and practical procedure can often be applied even when our input signal $x(t)$ is *not* white noise. *As far as output autocorrelation function and mean-square output are concerned*, a system described by

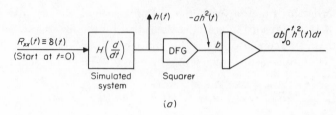

(a)

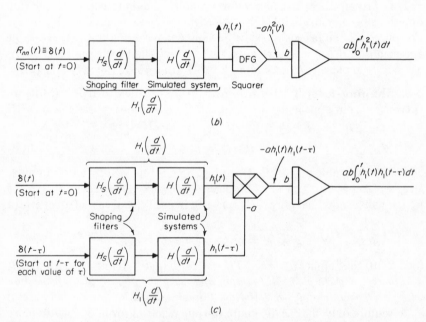

(b)

(c)

FIG. 3-3. Computation of mean-square output for a time-invariant linear system with white-noise input (a), and shaping-filter techniques producing $E\{y^2\}$ and $R_{yy}(\tau)$ (b), (c). Impulse excitation is obtained through suitable initial-condition settings (Sec. 2-10d).

$H(d/dt)$ with stationary input $x(t)$ of given spectral density $\Phi_{xx}(\omega)$ is entirely equivalent to a system described by

$$H_1\left(\frac{d}{dt}\right) \equiv H\left(\frac{d}{dt}\right) H_S\left(\frac{d}{dt}\right) \qquad (3\text{-}7)$$

with stationary white-noise input $n(t)$ of unit spectral density, and

$$|H_S(j\omega)|^2 \equiv \Phi_{xx}(\omega) \qquad (3\text{-}8)$$

In many applications, it is possible to express (or at least approximate) the given input spectral density in the form (8) where $H_S(j\omega)$ is the frequency-response function of a simply realizable *shaping filter*, so that the computer setup of Fig. 3-3b yields $E\{y^2\}$ in one run. Since

$$|H_S(\infty)|^2 = \Phi_{xx}(\infty) = 0$$

in all practical cases, impulse excitation for each shaping filter is obtained simply through an initial-condition setting; this is true even if we have a system operator (5) with $m = n$. Figure 3-4 shows examples of simple shaping filters. Combinations of these filters suffice in many practical situations. If more elaborate spectrum shaping is desired, refs. 2 and 15 describe formal synthesis methods yielding shaping-filter approximations for given power spectra $\Phi_{xx}(\omega)$ or given autocorrelation functions $R_{xx}(\tau)$.

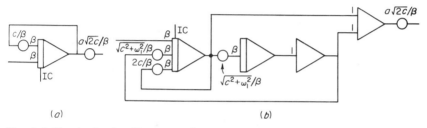

(a)   (b)

FIG. 3-4. Simple shaping-filter setups for

(a) $H_S(d/dt) = \dfrac{-a\sqrt{2c}}{d/dt + c}$ $\Phi_{xx}(\omega) = \dfrac{2a^2 c}{\omega^2 + c^2}$ $R_{xx}(\tau) = a^2 e^{-c|\tau|}$

(b) $H_S(d/dt) = a\sqrt{2c}\,\dfrac{d/dt + \sqrt{c^2 + \omega_1{}^2}}{(d/dt)^2 + 2c(d/dt) + (c^2 + \omega_1{}^2)}$

$\Phi_{xx}(\omega) = 2a^2 c\,\dfrac{c^2 + \omega_1{}^2 + \omega^2}{(c^2 + \omega_1{}^2 - \omega^2)^2 + 4\omega^2 c^2}$

$R_{xx}(\tau) = a^2 e^{-c|\tau|}\cos\omega_1\tau$

Figure 3-3c shows a computer setup producing $R_{yy}(\tau)$ by a generalization of the shaping-filter technique of Fig. 3-3b. This method requires duplicate computer setups for system and shaping filter, and separate computer runs for each specified (positive) value of the delay τ. The desired Wiener-Lee relations (1-27) are implemented in the form

$$R_{ny}(\tau) = R_{yn}(-\tau) = \int_0^\infty h_1(\zeta)\delta(\tau - \zeta)\,d\zeta = h_1(\tau) \left.\right\}$$
$$R_{yy}(\tau) = R_{yy}(-\tau) = \int_0^\infty h_1(t)h_1(t - \tau)\,dt \qquad \left.\right\} \tag{3-9}$$

where $h_1(t - \lambda)$ is the weighting function corresponding to the combined operator (7).

3-4. Time-variable Systems. Simple Problems with Switched Input. (a) The Mean-square Output. We consider a linear system with input $x(t)$ and output

$$y(t) = \int_{-\infty}^{t} w(t,\lambda)x(\lambda)\,d\lambda = \int_0^\infty h(t,\zeta)x(t - \zeta)\,d\zeta$$

where $w(t,\lambda) \equiv h(t, t - \lambda)$ is the response to a unit impulse $\delta(t - \lambda)$ (Sec. 1-6); we assume that $w(t,\lambda) = 0$ when $t < \lambda$ for physical realizability. The input and output autocorrelation functions $R_{xx}(t_1,t_2)$, $R_{yy}(t_1,t_2)$ are related by the generalized Wiener-Lee relations (1-24).   More specifically, the mean-square output is

$$E\{y^2(T)\} = \int_{-\infty}^{T} d\mu \, w(T,\mu) \int_{-\infty}^{T} w(T,\lambda) R_{xx}(\mu,\lambda) \, d\lambda \qquad (3\text{-}10)$$

For a stationary white-noise input with $R_{xx}(t_1,t_2) \equiv \delta(t_1 - t_2)$, this reduces to

$$E\{y^2(T)\} = \int_{-\infty}^{T} w^2(T,\mu) \, d\mu = \int_{0}^{\infty} h^2(T,\zeta) \, d\zeta \qquad (3\text{-}11)$$

(b) Time-invariant Systems with Switched Stationary Source (see also Sec. 3-8).   The simplest type of time-variable-system problem requires us to find the mean-square response $E\{y^2(t)\}$ of a time-invariant linear system to a stationary-source input $x(t)$ *suddenly applied* at the time $t = 0$ (Fig. 3-5a).   Given the weighting function $w(t,\lambda) \equiv h(t - \lambda)$ of our time-invariant system, we shall consider first only the simple (but fre-

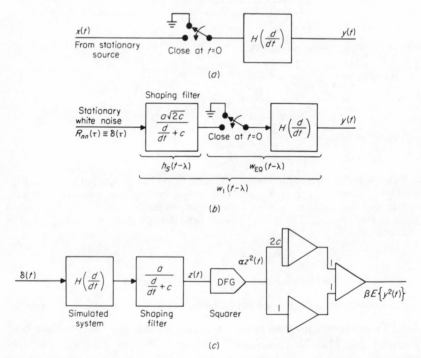

Fig. 3-5. Time-invariant linear system with switched stationary source (a), equivalent system (b), and mean-square error computation (c).   Impulse excitation is again obtained through initial-condition settings.

quently encountered) type of input $x(t)$ such that

$$R_{xx}(\tau) = a^2 e^{-c|\tau|} \qquad \Phi_{xx}(\omega) = \frac{2a^2 c}{\omega^2 + c^2} \qquad (c > 0) \qquad (3\text{-}12)$$

(see also Sec. 1-8). Such an input is equivalent to stationary white noise passed through a simple low-pass shaping filter described by

$$H_S(j\omega) = \frac{a\sqrt{2c}}{j\omega + c} \qquad h_S(t - \lambda) = \begin{cases} a\sqrt{2c}\, e^{-c(t-\lambda)} & (t > \lambda) \\ 0 & (t < \lambda) \end{cases} \qquad (3\text{-}13)$$

(Fig. 3-5b). The combination of switch and $h(t - \lambda)$ corresponds to the time-variable weighting function

$$w_{EQ}(t,\lambda) = \begin{cases} h(t - \lambda) & (t > 0) \\ 0 & (t < 0) \end{cases} \qquad (3\text{-}14)$$

where physical realizability implies $h(t - \lambda) = 0$ for $t < \lambda$.

Our system is, then, equivalent to a white-noise-input system obtained by cascading the systems described by Eqs. (13) and (14). The resulting overall weighting function $w_1(t,\mu)$ is evidently the output generated by w_{EQ} for an input $h_S(t - \mu)$:

$$\begin{aligned} w_1(t,\mu) &= \int_{-\infty}^{t} w_{EQ}(t,\lambda) h_S(\lambda - \mu)\, d\lambda \\ &= a\sqrt{2c} \int_{\mu}^{t} h(t - \lambda) e^{-c(\lambda - \mu)}\, d\lambda \\ &= \begin{cases} a\sqrt{2c}\, e^{c\mu} \int_{0}^{t} h(t - \lambda) e^{-c\lambda}\, d\lambda & (\mu < 0) \\ a\sqrt{2c}\, e^{c\mu} \int_{\mu}^{t} h(t - \lambda) e^{-c\lambda}\, d\lambda & (\mu > 0) \end{cases} \end{aligned} \qquad (3\text{-}15)$$

White-noise input to this system produces the desired mean-square response

$$\begin{aligned} E\{y^2(t)\} &= \int_{-\infty}^{t} w_1^2(t,\mu)\, d\mu = \int_{-\infty}^{0} w_1^2(t,\mu)\, d\mu + \int_{0}^{t} w_1^2(t,\mu)\, d\mu \\ &= z^2(t) + 2c \int_{0}^{t} z^2(t)\, dt \end{aligned}$$

with $$z(t) = a \int_{0}^{t} h(t - \lambda) e^{-c\lambda}\, d\lambda$$

Precisely this output is obtained by impulse excitation (Sec. 2-10d) of the simple computer setup of Fig. 3-5c. *Note that the entire time history of $E\{y^2(t)\}$ is conveniently produced in a single computer run.*

This ingeniously simple procedure, due to Laning and Battin,[2] applies directly only for stationary inputs $x(t)$ with correlation functions of the form (12). More generally, the mean-square response $E\{y^2(t)\}$ to any sum of uncorrelated inputs $x(t)$ satisfying Eq. (12) can be produced through addition of the individual mean-square contributions (Fig. 3-6a). Bendat[3] has derived a similar technique for the widely useful class of sta-

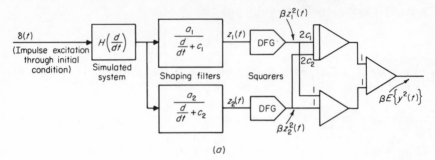

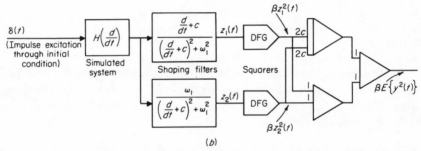

FIG. 3-6. Treatment of systems with switched stationary input $x(t)$ such that $R_{xx}(\tau) = a_1{}^2 e^{-c_1|\tau|} + a_2{}^2 e^{-c_2|\tau|}$ (a), and $R_{xx}(\tau) = a^2 e^{-c|\tau|}\cos\omega_1\tau$ (b).

tionary inputs $x(t)$ such that

$$R_{xx}(\tau) = a^2 e^{-c|\tau|} \cos \omega_1 \tau \qquad (3\text{-}16)$$

(Fig. 3-6b), and hence also for sums of uncorrelated inputs satisfying Eq. (12) and/or (16).

3-5. Time-variable Systems: More General Problems. In most practical applications, time-variable linear systems are described by a set of state variables $y_1(t)$, $y_2(t)$, $\ldots$, $y_n(t)$ which satisfy linear differential equations

$$\frac{dy_i}{dt} = \sum_{k=1}^{n} a_{ik}(t) y_k(t) + \sum_{k=1}^{r} b_{ik}(t) x_k(t) \qquad (i = 1, 2, \ldots, n) \quad (3\text{-}17)$$

with given initial values $y_i(0)$. The $x_k(t)$ are given forcing functions (system inputs), as illustrated by the block diagram of Fig. 3-7. Such linear time-variable systems typically represent

1. Linear systems with switched, sampled, modulated, and/or time-programmed parameters
2. Linearized sensitivity equations yielding output *perturbations* $y_i(t)$ resulting from input and/or parameter perturbations $x_k(t)$ in nonlinear systems (e.g., trajectory perturbations, Sec. 2-9)

Linear superposition permits us to consider the effect of nonzero initial values $y_i(0)$ separately (Sec. 3-10) and to deal with the effect of each input $x_k = x(t)$ one at a time. Formal solution of the operator equation (17) then yields each output $y_i = y(t)$ as the result of a time-variable linear operation on the input $x(t)$:

$$y(t) = H(t,p)x(t) = \frac{1}{p^n + a_{n-1}(t)p^{n-1} + \cdots + a_0(t)} [b_m(t)p^m$$

$$+ b_{m-1}(t)p^{m-1} + \cdots + b_0(t)]x(t) \qquad (p \equiv \frac{d}{dt}; n > m) \quad (3\text{-}18)$$

Note that *time-variable linear operators do not commute;* so the order of operators and coefficients in Eq. (18) must be strictly observed. *Analog-computer setups are best obtained directly from Eq.* (17); the setup methods of Sec. 2-10 do *not* apply to Eq. (18) unless all coefficients $a_i(t)$, $b_k(t)$ are constant.

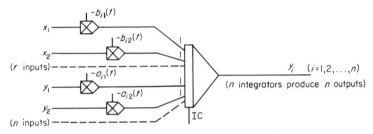

FIG. 3-7. Unscaled computer representation of a time-variable linear system with r inputs $x_k(t)$ and n outputs $y_i(t)$.

Where an input-output relation is specifically given in the form (18), we can still obtain an equivalent first-order system:[2]

$$\left.\begin{aligned}
y &= v_1 + c_0(t)x \\
\frac{dv_i}{dt} &= v_{i+1} + c_i(t)x \qquad (i = 1, 2, \ldots, n-1) \\
\frac{dv_n}{dt} &= -\sum_{k=0}^{n-1} a_k(t)v_{k+1} + c_n(t)x
\end{aligned}\right\} \qquad (3\text{-}19)$$

where the $c_i(t)$ are given by the recurrence relations

$$c_0 = b_n \qquad c_i = b_{n-i} - \sum_{k=0}^{i-1}\sum_{s=0}^{i-k} \binom{n+s-i}{n-i} a_{n-i+k+s} \frac{d^s c_k}{dt^s}$$

$$(i = 1, 2, \ldots, n) \quad (3\text{-}20)$$

For $n > m$, we have $c_0(t) = 0$, and impulse excitation* can be replaced by initial conditions $v_i(0+0) = c_i(0+0)$ $(i = 1, 2, \ldots, n)$ in the manner of Sec. 2-10d.

* See footnote to Sec. 3-3.

3-6. Direct Method Producing $R_{yy}(t_1,t)$ and $E\{y^2(T)\}$. Given a time-variable linear system (17) or (18) and records of input autocorrelation function $R_{xx}(t_1,t)$ against the computer time t for different t_1, computer setups analogous to Fig. 3-1 can implement Eq. (18) to produce $R_{xy}(t_1,t)$ for each separate value of t_1. The results can be cross-plotted to yield the input records $R_{yx}(t_1,t) \equiv R_{xy}(t,t_1)$ required to generate $R_{yy}(t_1,t)$ in a second series of computer runs with the same computer setup.

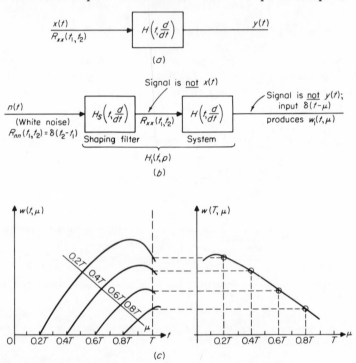

Fig. 3-8. Time-variable linear system with stationary and nonstationary input (a), shaping-filter setup generating $w_1(t,\mu)$ as a function of t (b), and cross-plotting technique producing $w_1(t,\mu)$ as a function of μ (c).

Since the autocorrelation function for a white-noise input $n(t)$ is simply $R_{nn}(t_1,t_2) \equiv \delta(t_2 - t_1)$, we can, again, dispense with records of $R_{xx}(t_1,t_2)$ if we can design a (now possibly time-variable) shaping filter yielding the desired autocorrelation function $R_{xx}(t_1,t_2)$ for white-noise input. Very frequently, the given input $x(t)$ is stationary, so that the desired shaping filter is still time-invariant.

Fortunately, most applications require us to find only the mean-square output at the time T, or

$$E\{y^2(T)\} = R_{yy}(T,T) = \int_{-\infty}^{T} w_1^2(T,\mu)\, d\mu \qquad (3\text{-}21)$$

where the weighting function $w_1(T,\mu)$ includes the effect of a suitable shaping filter. To obtain $E\{y^2(T)\}$, we excite the simulated system with a unit impulse $\delta(t - \mu)$ at the time $t = \mu$ (Sec. 2-10d) and record the system output $w_1(T,\mu)$ at the time $t = T$. We must repeat this procedure for a sufficient number of values of μ to enable us to compute the expression (21) by squaring and approximate integration (Fig. 3-8).

3-7. The Modified-adjoint-system Method.[2-6,9] If we had a computer setup producing $w_1(T,t)$ as a function of the computer time t, then the desired integral (21) could be obtained directly by squaring and

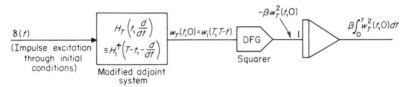

FIG. 3-9. Modified-adjoint-system setup producing $E\{y^2(T)\}$ in a single computer run for each value of T.

integration *in a single analog-computer run.* The so-called *adjoint system* with the required impulse response

$$w_1\dagger(t,T) = w_1(T,t) \tag{3-22}$$

is not physically realizable, since the realizability condition

$$w_1\dagger(t,\lambda) = 0 \ (t < \lambda)$$

would imply $w_1(t,\lambda) = 0 \ (t > \lambda)$. Substitution of $T - t$ for t in the differential equations defining the adjoint system, however, does yield a realizable system, the *modified adjoint system.* Its response

$$w_T(t,0) = w_1\dagger(T - t, \ T) = w_1(T, \ T - t) = h_1(T,t) \tag{3-23}$$

to a unit impulse $\delta(t)$ applied at the computer time $t = 0$ can be directly squared and integrated to produce the desired output

$$E\{y^2(T)\} = \int_{-\infty}^{T} w_1{}^2(T,\mu) \ d\mu = \int_0^{\infty} w_T{}^2(t,0) \ dt \tag{3-24}$$

in a single computer run for each specified value of T (Fig. 3-9). Each run starts at $t = 0$; with the usual type of system, $w_T{}^2(t,0)$ decays as t increases, so that a finite integration time is sufficient.

It remains to construct the modified adjoint system, i.e., the linear system with the desired impulse response (23), for a given linear system and shaping filter. We note that each linear operator $H_1(t,d/dt)$ is constructed by addition, multiplication, and inversion* of simpler linear (real) operators $A = A(t,d/dt)$, $B = B(t,d/dt)$, . . . , all ultimately reducible to the elementary operators $\alpha(t)$ and $p \equiv d/dt$ corresponding to the

---

* Inverses of differential operators are defined uniquely only when suitable initial conditions determine all constants of integration.

(symbolic) weighting functions $\alpha(t)\delta(t - \lambda)$ and $(d/dt)\delta(t - \lambda)$. We assume the existence of weighting functions (possibly with delta-function terms) $w_A(t,\lambda)$, $w_B(t,\lambda)$, . . . such that

$$A\left(t, \frac{d}{dt}\right)u(t) = \int_{-\infty}^{\infty} w_A(t,\lambda)u(\lambda)\,d\lambda$$

$$B\left(t, \frac{d}{dt}\right)u(t) = \int_{-\infty}^{\infty} w_B(t,\lambda)u(\lambda)\,d\lambda \qquad \cdots \quad (3\text{-}25)$$

for reasonable inputs $u(t)$ and define *adjoint operators* $A\dagger = A\dagger(t,d/dt)$, $B\dagger = B\dagger(t,d/dt)$, . . . by their weighting functions

$$w_A\dagger(t,\lambda) = w_A(\lambda,t) \qquad w_B\dagger(t,\lambda) = w_B(\lambda,t) \qquad \cdots \qquad (3\text{-}26)$$

The definitions (25) imply

$$w_{A+B}(t,\lambda) = w_A(t,\lambda) + w_B(t,\lambda) \qquad w_{AB}(t,\lambda) = \int_{-\infty}^{\infty} w_A(t,\mu)w_B(\mu,\lambda)\,d\mu$$
$$(3\text{-}27)$$

We combine Eqs. (26) and (27) to derive

$$(A + B)\dagger \equiv A\dagger + B\dagger \qquad (AB)\dagger \equiv B\dagger A\dagger \qquad (A^{-1})\dagger \equiv (A\dagger)^{-1} \quad (3\text{-}28)$$

$$[\alpha(t)]\dagger \equiv \alpha(t) \qquad \left(\frac{d}{dt}\right)^{\dagger} \equiv -\frac{d}{dt} \qquad (3\text{-}29a)$$

and hence

$$\left[\alpha(t)\frac{d}{dt}\right]^{\dagger} = -\frac{d}{dt}[\alpha(t)\cdot] = -\left[\alpha(t)\frac{d}{dt} + \frac{d\alpha(t)}{dt}\right] \qquad (3\text{-}29b)$$

(see also ref. 9). We obtain the modified adjoint system from the adjoint system by substituting $T - t$ for t (and thus again d/dt for $-d/dt$) in each operator. These relations neatly justify Laning and Battin's topological-transformation method[2,9] for deriving modified-adjoint-system computer setups from existing linear-system setups (Fig. 3-10).

To find the mean-square output $E\{y_{jk}{}^2(t)\}$ of a time-variable linear system (17) to a single white-noise input $x_k(t)$ with $R_{x_k x_k}(t_1,t_2) = \delta(t_1 - t_2)$, we perform our topological transformation on Fig. 3-7 to obtain the modified-adjoint setup of Fig. 3-11. Impulse excitation through a single initial-condition setting produces the desired weighting function for squaring and integration.

The computer setup of Fig. 3-11 represents the system

$$y_{jk}\dagger = \sum_{i=1}^{n} b_{ik}(T - t)\eta_i \qquad (3\text{-}30)$$

$$\left.\begin{aligned} \frac{d\eta_i}{dt} &= \sum_{h=1}^{n} a_{hi}(T - t)\eta_h + x_{ik}\dagger \\ \text{with} \qquad x_{ik}\dagger &= \begin{cases} 0 & (i \neq j) \\ x_k\dagger(t) \equiv \delta_+(t) & (i = j) \end{cases} \end{aligned}\right\} \qquad (3\text{-}31)$$

where i and j can take values between 1 and n, and k runs from 1 to r.

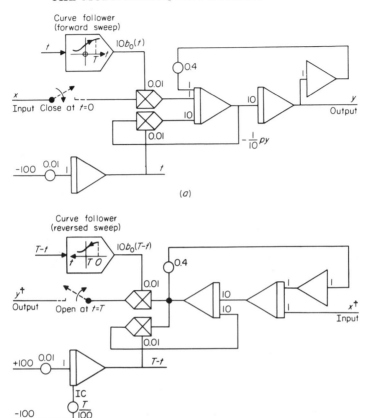

FIG. 3-10. Analog-computer setup (a) for

$$\frac{d^2y}{dt^2} + \frac{t}{10}\frac{dy}{dt} + 4y = b_0(t)\,x$$

and the corresponding modified-adjoint-system setup (b), which implements

$$\frac{d^2y\dagger}{dt^2} + \frac{d}{dt}\left[\frac{T-t}{10}\,y\dagger\right] + 4y\dagger = b_0(T-t)\,x\dagger$$

The modified-adjoint-system setup can be derived from the "direct" computer setup for each given system by the following procedure:

1. Write the block diagram so that no potentiometer or multiplier has more than one output (repeat computing elements where needed). We associate amplifier gains with the input lines rather than with the amplifiers themselves.
2. Reverse the signal flow through each computing element, except for the multiplier inputs $a_i(t)$, $b_k(t)$. It is often possible to reverse an entire block of computing elements together.
3. Replace each time input t (input voltage or curve-follower sweep) to the coefficient functions $a_i(t)$, $b_k(t)$ by $T - t$.

If the process under consideration starts at $t = 0$ rather than at $t = -\infty$, then we must stop the output integration at $t = T$ by a switch or hold circuit. This is indicated by the switches shown in dash lines; these switches really act as two additional coefficient multipliers multiplying by the step functions $U(t)$ and $U(T - t)$ [$U(t) = 0$ for $t < 0$, $U(t) = 1$ for $t > 0$].[9]

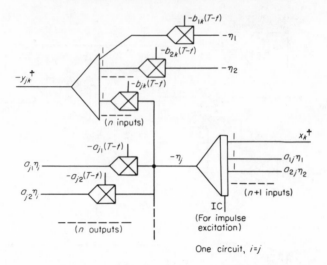

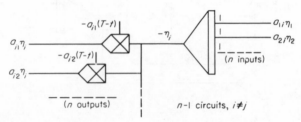

Fig. 3-11. Modified-adjoint-system setup relating the output y_j and the (single) input x_k of a linear system represented by

$$\frac{dy_i}{dt} = \sum_{k=1}^{n} a_{ik}(t)\, y_k + \sum_{k=1}^{r} b_{ik}(t)\, x_k \qquad (i = 1, 2, \ldots, n)$$

This computer setup is obtained through straightforward topological transformation of Fig. 3-7 if we consider x_k as the only input and y_j as the only output.

For linear systems specifically given in the form (18), we can also derive a modified-adjoint-system setup *directly*.[9] We simply apply our rules (28) and (29) to the operator $H(t,d/dt)$ in Eq. (18) and substitute $T - t$ for t, $-p$ for p to obtain

$$\left.\begin{aligned} w_T(t,0) = H\dagger(T - t, -p)\delta(t) &= \{p^m[b_m(T - t)\,\cdot] + p^{m-1}[b_{m-1}(T - t)\,\cdot] \\ &+ \cdots + b_0(T - t)\} \frac{1}{p^n + p^{n-1}[a_{n-1}(T - t)\,\cdot] + \cdots + a_0(T - t)} \delta(t) \\ \text{with} \qquad p^r[c(t)\,\cdot] &= \sum_{k=0}^{r} \binom{r}{k} \frac{d^k c}{dt^k}\, p^{r-k} \qquad (r = 1,2,\ldots) \end{aligned}\right\} \quad (3\text{-}32)$$

This relation is, in general, *easier* to implement than Eq. (18), for we can now employ a computer setup analogous to Fig. 2-11b, with multipliers replacing coefficient-setting potentiometers where necessary (Fig. 3-12).[9] Since $n > m$, the impulse input is, again, simply replaced by a single initial condition in the manner of Sec. 2-10d.   But Eq. (32), like Eq. (19), still requires us to obtain derivatives of coefficients $a_i(t)$ and/or $b_k(t)$, which is very inconvenient unless the coefficients are simple analytic functions.   Whenever possible, therefore, we ought to start with the first-order system (17) and apply the topological transformation in the manner of Fig. 3-11, so that no differentiation of coefficients is required.

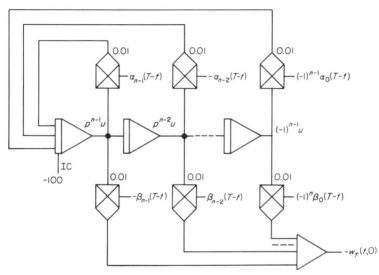

FIG. 3-12. Unscaled analog-computer setup implementing Eq. (32) in the form

$$w_T(t,0) = \frac{1}{100}[\beta_m(T-t)\,p^m + \beta_{m-1}(T-t)\,p^{m-1} + \cdots + \beta_0(T-t)]u(t)$$

$$u(t) = \frac{10^4}{100p^n + \alpha_{n-1}(T-t)p^{n-1} + \cdots + \alpha_0(T-t)}\,\delta(t)$$

where $m < n$.   One obtains the new coefficients α_i, β_k by performing the product differentiations in Eq. (32).

3-8.   Modified-adjoint Systems with Shaping Filters.   A frequently

pleasant feature of modified-adjoint systems is the fact that our relation (28) inverts the order of adjoint system and shaping filter, so that a single computer run can yield the mean-square output $E\{y^2(T)\}$ for two or more types of system input $x(t)$; we can also study the superposition of two uncorrelated inputs through squaring and addition (Fig. 3-13a).

Many practical applications deal with stationary inputs $x(t)$, so that we have time-invariant shaping filters; these are, conveniently, identical with their modified-adjoint counterparts.   Another case of frequent interest is that of a time-variable system with a stationary input switched on at $t = 0$ (this is a generalization of the situation studied in Sec. 3-4b). Figure 3-13b shows the corresponding modified-adjoint system.   Such a computer setup requires a switch opening at $t = T$.   This is easily implemented in modern analog computers incorporating a digital-counter timing system (Sec. 8-2). Otherwise, we can employ a comparator (Sec. 2-12) driven by an integrator producing $T - t = - \int_o^t dt + T$; the comparator opens a relay or electronic switch when the integrator output $T - t$ goes through zero.

For switched stationary inputs with correlation functions of the form (12) or (16), or for uncorrelated sums of such inputs, we can, in fact,

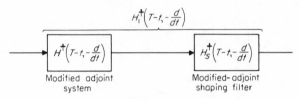

Fig. 3-13a. Modified-adjoint system for a system with shaping filter.

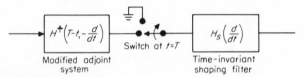

Fig. 3-13b. Modified-adjoint system for a time-variable system with switched stationary input.

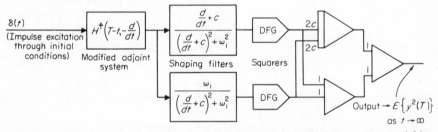

Fig. 3-13c. Modified-adjoint-system setup producing $E\{y^2(T)\}$ for a time-variable system with switched stationary input $x(t)$ having the autocorrelation function $R_{xx}(\tau) = a^2 e^{-c|\tau|} \cos \omega_1 \tau$. Similar computer setups analogous to Figs. 3-5c and 3-6a apply for input autocorrelation functions $a^2 e^{-c|\tau|}$ and $a_1^2 e^{-c_1|\tau|} + a_2^2 e^{-c_2|\tau|}$.

eliminate the necessity for switching at $t = T$ and employ computer setups analogous to those of Figs. 3-5c and 3-6 (Fig. 3-13c). The derivation, due to Bendat,[3] is completely analogous to that presented in Sec. 3-4b for *time-invariant* systems with switched stationary input.

3-9. Systems with Multiple Inputs and Outputs. Consider a system (17) with multiple inputs $x_k(t)$; assume that the system includes shaping filters permitting us to regard each input as white noise with autocorrelation function $\delta(t_1 - t_2)$. Note that we need only add extra summers and multipliers to Fig. 3-11 to compute the contributions (30) from each individual input $x_k\dagger(t) = \delta_+(t)$ all in a single computer run. If our random inputs $x_k(t)$ are mutually uncorrelated, we can, then, produce the complete mean-square output $E\{y_j{}^2(T)\}$ due to all r white-noise inputs in one run by squaring, adding, and integrating the r voltages

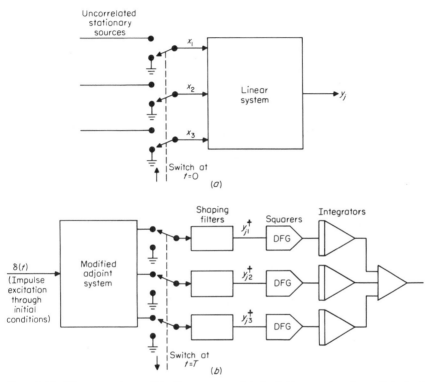

FIG. 3-14. Linear system with three uncorrelated stationary inputs switched at $t = 0$ (a), and modified-adjoint system producing individual and combined mean-square outputs due to the various inputs in a single computer run (b). Note that the modified-adjoint system has one input and three outputs. Individual integrators are needed only if it is desired to measure the individual mean-square contributions simultaneously; otherwise, a single summing integrator suffices.

$y_{jk}\dagger(t)$ (Fig. 3-14). The same computer setup will, moreover, generate each of the $E\{y_j{}^2(T)\}$ in turn if we apply the impulse excitation to each of the n integrators.

In matrix notation, our system (17) becomes

$$\frac{dy}{dt} = A(t)y + B(t)x \tag{3-33}$$

where x, y are now column matrices $\{x_1, x_2, \ldots, x_r\}$, $\{y_1, y_2, \ldots, y_n\}$. $A(t) \equiv [a_{ik}(t)]$ is an $n \times n$ matrix, and $B(t) \equiv [b_{ik}(t)]$ is an $n \times r$ matrix. We have

$$y = \left[I \frac{d}{dt} - A(t) \right]^{-1} B(t)x = H\left(t, \frac{d}{dt} \right) x = \int_{-\infty}^{t} w(t,\lambda)x(\lambda) \, d\lambda \qquad (3\text{-}34)$$

where I is the identity matrix; $H(t,d/dt)$ is the $n \times r$ matrix operator producing the output y, and $w(t,\lambda) \equiv [w_{ik}(t,\lambda)]$ is an $n \times r$ weighting-function matrix (Green's matrix).[9]

By analogy with Sec. 3-7, we introduce the adjoint matrix operator $H\dagger(t,d/dt)$ with weighting-function matrix $w\dagger(t,\lambda) \equiv \tilde{w}(\lambda,t)$, where the tilde denotes matrix transposition. It may be shown[9] that our matrix operators satisfy the rule (28) for forming adjoint operators, while

$$A\dagger(t) \equiv \tilde{A}(t) \qquad \left(I \frac{d}{dt} \right)^{\dagger} \equiv -I \frac{d}{dt} \qquad (3\text{-}35)$$

takes the place of Eq. (29). Equations (28), (33), and (35) yield

$$H\dagger\left(t, \frac{d}{dt} \right) \equiv \left\{ \left[I \frac{d}{dt} - A(t) \right]^{-1} B(t) \right\}^{\dagger} \equiv -\tilde{B}(t) \left[I \frac{d}{dt} + \tilde{A}(t) \right]^{-1} \qquad (3\text{-}36)$$

We again replace t by $T - t$ to obtain a modified adjoint operator, and

$$y\dagger = H\dagger\left(T - t, -\frac{d}{dt} \right) x\dagger = \tilde{B}(T - t) \left[I \frac{d}{dt} - \tilde{A}(T - t) \right] x\dagger \qquad (3\text{-}37)$$

corresponds precisely to Eqs. (30) and (31) for row-matrix inputs

$$x\dagger \equiv (x_1\dagger, x_2\dagger, \ldots, x_r\dagger)$$

such that only a single $x_k\dagger$ differs from zero.

As a matter of academic interest, it may be possible to compute each mean-square output $E\{y_i^2(t)\}$ of a given system (17) continuously as a function of t. Consider a system with shaping filters such that each system input $x_k(t)$ is stationary white noise with autocorrelation function $\delta(t_1 - t_2)$ and uncorrelated with all other inputs. Then

$$E\{y_i(t)x_k(t)\} = w_{ik}(t,t) \qquad (i = 1,2, \ldots, n; k = 1,2, \ldots, r) \qquad (3\text{-}38)$$

We now substitute the given system equations (17) into

$$\frac{d}{dt}(y_i y_k) = y_i \frac{dy_k}{dt} + \frac{dy_i}{dt} y_k \qquad (i,k = 1,2, \ldots, n)$$

and average to obtain $n(n + 1)/2$ linear first-order equations relating the $n(n + 1)/2$ unknown functions $E\{y_i(t)y_k(t)\}$ to the forcing functions (38). In the case of system[8] given in the form (18), this procedure is applied to the set of first-order equations (19).[2]

Reference 13 describes an extension of the modified-adjoint-system method yielding correlation functions as well as mean-square errors.

3-10. Effect of Random Initial Conditions.[3,13]

Effects of random initial-condition settings on the mean-square output of time-variable linear systems are of particular interest in trajectory-perturbation studies (Sec. 2-9). We shall assume that the initial-condition inputs are uncorrelated with respect to each other and all other random inputs, so that the mean-square output effects simply add and can be treated

separately. In this case, the contribution of each individual random
initial value $y_k(0)$ to the mean-square output $E\{y_i{}^2(t)\}$ is simply

$$e_i{}^2(t) = E\{y_i{}^2(0)\}y_{ik}{}^2(t) \qquad (i = 1,2, \cdots ,n) \qquad (3\text{-}39)$$

where $y_{ik}(t)$ is the simulator solution $y_i(t)$ obtained for $y_k(0) = 1$, with all
other $y_i(0)$ and all inputs $x_k(t)$ set equal to zero.

REFERENCES AND BIBLIOGRAPHY

1. Bennett, R. R.: Analog Computing Applied to Noise Studies, *Proc. IRE*, October, 1953.
2. Laning, J. H., and R. H. Battin: *Random Processes in Automatic Control*, McGraw-Hill, New York, 1956.
3. Bendat, J. S.: *Principles and Applications of Random-noise Theory*, Wiley, New York, 1958.
4. Rideout, V. C.: Random-process Studies, in Huskey, H. D., and G. A. Korn, *Computer Handbook*, McGraw-Hill, New York, 1962.
5. Fifer, S.: *Analogue Computation*, McGraw-Hill, New York, 1960.
6. Levine, L.: *Methods for Solving Engineering Problems Using Analog Computers*, McGraw-Hill, New York, 1964.
7. Aseltine, J. A., and R. R. Favreau: Weighting Functions for Time-varying Feedback Systems, *Proc. IRE*, October, 1954.
8. Matyas, J.: Methods of Analog-computer Solution of Linear Differential Equations with Variable Coefficients, *Automatika i Telemekhanika*, July, 1959.
9. Korn, G. A.: Adjoint Linear Systems in Analog Computation: A New Look, *Ann. AICA*, October, 1962.
10. Meissinger, H. F.: Parameter-influence Coefficients and Weighting Functions Applied to Perturbation Analysis of Dynamic Systems, *Proc. 3d AICA Conf.*, Opatija, Yugoslavia, 1961, Presses Académiques Européennes, Brussels, 1962.
11. Giloi, W.: Ein Verfahren zur Berechnung von Optimalfiltern auf dem Analogrechner, *Elektron. Rechenanlagen*, April, 1961.
12. ——— and R. Lauber: *Analogrechnen*, Springer, Berlin, 1963.
13. Isaac, M. G., and V. T. DeBuono: Deterministic and Stochastic Response of Linear Time-variable Systems, *IEEETEC*, October, 1963.
14. Korn, G. A., and T. M. Korn: *Mathematical Handbook for Scientists and Engineers*, McGraw-Hill, New York, 1961.
15. Mazelsky, B., and H. B. Amey, Jr.: On the Simulation of Random Excitation for Airplane Response Investigations on Analog Computers, *J. Aeron. Sci.*, September. 1957.

CHAPTER 4

DIRECT SIMULATION OF RANDOM PHENOMENA: INTRODUCTION TO MONTE-CARLO TECHNIQUES AND NOISE GENERATORS

INTRODUCTION

4-1. Direct Simulation. Direct computer simulation of random phenomena permits estimation of a much wider variety of statistics than the essentially analytical methods of Chap. 3 and is not restricted to linear systems. Direct analog simulation of random processes requires generation of random signals with known statistical properties (random-noise generation, Secs. 4-7 to 4-12); these noise signals serve as forcing functions or yield random parameters and/or random initial conditions for computer-simulated systems.

The simplest direct-simulation methods involve time-invariant linear or nonlinear systems with stationary random-noise-generator inputs; output statistics are measured as *finite-time averages* (Secs. 1-4 and 5-1). Figure 4-1 shows a simple example; another possibly significant application is the simulation of noise-generating mechanisms in various electronic devices (microwave tubes, solid-state junctions) or radiation-propagation media to check physical theories.

The time-averaging technique, which attempts to estimate random-process parameters *from a single experiment considered as sufficiently typical*, is clearly restricted to phenomena which are stationary and ergodic (or approximately so). Prediction of estimate variances can be quite difficult (Secs. 5-4, 5-7, and 5-11). A by far more powerful computing technique simulates *repeated independent experiments yielding classical random-sample statistics.* Such *Monte-Carlo methods* have long been used with digital computers,[1-6] but they have really come into their own with the advent of hybrid analog-digital interative differential analyzers (Secs. 2-12 and 8-2). Such machines combine extraordinarily fast

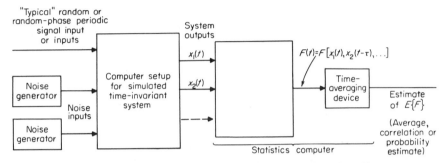

Fɪɢ. 4-1. Time-average measurements on a simulated time-invariant linear or nonlinear system with jointly stationary signal and noise inputs. The measured time average $\langle f \rangle_T$ or $[f]_n$ may estimate mean value, mean square, correlation function, or probability; bias and fluctuations of the estimate must be investigated by the methods of Chap. 5.

analog simulation with very flexible digital logic and arithmetic. A fast iterative differential analyzer can, in particular

1. Solve the complicated nonlinear differential equations describing a simulated space-vehicle flight, chemical process, or radar detection 50 to 1,000 times *per second*, so that large statistical samples become quickly available.
2. Employ patched or stored-program digital logic to implement problem logic such as rules for simulated games and automatic program changes as well as the digital computation, readout, and plotting of statistics.
3. Produce *automatic optimization routines* permitting system-parameter changes minimizing or maximizing statistics (e.g., control-system mean-square error) computed over successive samples of 100 to 10,000 computer runs. Instead, the machine can also compute statistics over the results of many optimization subroutines (see also Sec. 8-2).

**MONTE-CARLO SIMULATION WITH
ANALOG/HYBRID COMPUTERS**

4-2. The Computer System. The *iterative-analog-computer Monte-Carlo technique*, probably first suggested by Hall[7] and Van der Velde[10] at MIT, is best understood by reference to Fig. 4-2. A simulated dynamical system, such as a control system, space vehicle, or communication sys-

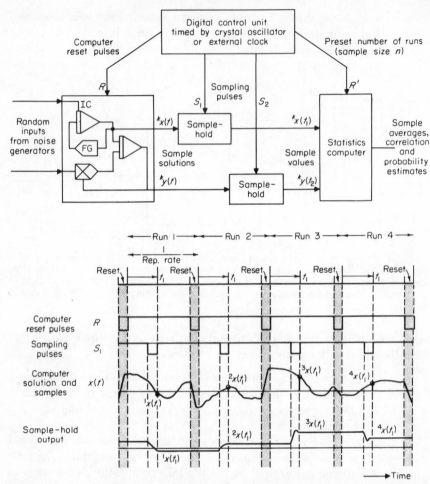

FIG. 4-2a. A fast iterative differential analyzer implements Monte-Carlo techniques by simulating a random-input dynamical or communication system 10 to 2,000 times per second.

Digitally controlled track-hold units read out samples of dynamic variables $X(t)$, $Y(t)$ at thumbwheel-selected times t_1, t_2 after the start of each computer run. The statistics computer averages functions of successive sample values to produce estimates of mean-square values, correlation functions, probabilities, etc., for nonstationary as well as stationary processes.

tem, is simulated repetitively (usually on a fast time scale, see also Sec. 2-6b). Statistically independent random forcing functions, initial conditions, and/or parameters for successive computer runs are obtained from random-noise generators, which supply appropriate voltages to the analog-computer setup. In this manner, we generate statistically independent sample functions $^kx(t)$, $^ky(t)$, . . . of random processes (Sec. 1-1) as

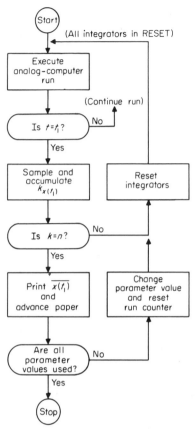

FIG. 4-2*b*. Flow diagram for Monte-Carlo computation of

$$\overline{x(t_1)} = \frac{1}{n} \sum_{k=1}^{n} {}^{k}x(t_1)$$

with automatic printout for a set of parameter values (e.g., different values of servo damping). Completely preset operation is shown; but, instead of sampling ${}^{k}x(t)$ at a fixed time $t = t_1$, one could readily let analog comparators and digital logic determine each sampling time as a function of computer variables (see, e.g., Sec. 4-4).

computer solutions once per computer run.* Referring again to Fig. 4-2, track-hold circuits produce samples such as ${}^{k}x(t_1)$, ${}^{k}y(t_2)$, ${}^{k}z(t_1) = \int_0^{t_1} {}^{k}x^2(t)\, dt, \ldots$ in the course of the kth computer run. These samples are then read into analog or hybrid-analog-digital computing

* Noise generators and computers are carefully designed and tested so as to produce statistically independent computer runs (Sec. 4-7). Some special computing techniques, however, introduce artificially produced correlation between results of different random-input computer runs (Secs. 4-6 and 8-5).

elements set up to produce statistics in the form of *sample averages* (Sec.
1-5) like $\overline{x(t_1)} = \sum\limits_{k=1}^{n} {}^k x(t_1)/n$ or $\overline{f(t_1,t_2)} = \overline{x(t_1)y(t_2)} = \sum\limits_{k=1}^{n} {}^k x(t_1)^k y(t_2)/n$
accumulated over a preset or computed number n of computer runs.

Statistically independent computer runs constitute independent similar
experiments, and sample averages used as estimates of ensemble averages
(Sec. 1-5) are classical random-sample statistics. It follows that *the well-
established classical theory of random-sample statistics can be brought to bear
on the critical question of estimate fluctuations;* in particular, sample averages
computed from large samples can often be considered as approximately
normal random variables, so that the classical t test, analysis of variance,
etc., apply (Sec. 5-7). Note also that the use of stationary-noise generators in no sense restricts our simulation to stationary random phenomena, since suitable computer operations (e.g., multiplication by time
functions) readily produce time-variable functions of the input noise
during each computer run.

In principle, any electronic differential analyzer can be used for Monte-
Carlo-type random-process studies if suitable noise generators and
measuring devices are available. There is, however, a considerable
premium on high computing speed, since system optimization studies may
require samples of 100 to 10,000 computer runs for *each* of many different
system-parameter combinations. On the other hand, the squaring,
multiplication, etc., and addition of sample values required to produce
sample averages like $\overline{x(t_1)}$, $\overline{x(t_1)y(t_2)}$, etc., takes place only once per
computer run. Hence, relatively slow and inexpensive analog and digital
computing devices can compute statistics from sample values (Secs. 5-4,
5-8, 5-9, 5-13 to 5-16, and 8-2).

4-3. Survey of Applications. *Monte-Carlo-type simulation applies to
nonstationary and nonlinear phenomena and readily yields distribution
estimates and test statistics as well as simple averages.* The Monte-Carlo
technique is, therefore, often the *only* way to study a process involving
random inputs or parameters. The most important applications, some
of which will be described in more detail in Chap. 8, include

1. *Error studies for control and guidance systems* subject to random
   inputs, initial conditions, and/or parameters (component tolerances);
   in particular, prediction of missile hit probabilities and mean-square
   miss errors (Sec. 4-4).
2. *Operations-analysis studies*, especially of queuing problems (e.g.,
   effects of machine failures in factories, traffic problems, duels, and
   games (Secs. 8-12).
3. *Simulation of communication and detection systems*, an extraordinarily
   powerful technique deserving additional popularity (Secs. 4-5 and
   8-8 to 8-10).

With suitable computer systems, Monte-Carlo techniques can be convenient and fast as well as powerful. At times, it may actually pay to recast a problem not primarily concerned with random phenomena so that complicated integrals can be estimated by Monte-Carlo computation of statistical averages. Analog/hybrid computer applications of this type include an attempt to solve partial differential equations (Sec. 8-14) and, rather more significantly, random-search methods for finding optimum parameter combinations in system design (Sec. 8-15). Last but not least, Monte-Carlo-type simulation is a very powerful teaching aid for courses in statistics and random-process theory.

The *scaling of random variables*, such as Gaussian noise-generator outputs, requires some caution, for the ± 10 or ± 100 volts voltage limits of an analog computer must necessarily clip the tails of Gaussian and similar voltage distributions. As a rule of thumb, one should attempt to scale so that the computer dynamic range just accommodates deviations $|x - E\{x\}|$ from the mean up to between $3 \sqrt{\text{Var } \{x\}} = 3\sigma$ and 4σ for each Gaussian variable x. The probability of a larger absolute deviation from the mean is 0.3 per cent for 3σ and 0.01 per cent for 4σ (see also Table 5-2). The resulting statistical errors will be proportionately small in most applications, although each individual case deserves a little cautious scrutiny (see also Sec. 5-5).

4-4. Example: Effects of Random Wind Forces and System Tolerances on a Ballistic Trajectory. (a) Direct Method. Some of the earliest applications of hybrid-computer Monte-Carlo simulation dealt with the effects of random wind forces and production tolerances on weapon trajectories.[9,10] As an instructive as well as simple example, we will study such effects in connection with the eighteenth-century weapon system (cannon and cannonball) already introduced in Chap. 2. Referring to Sec. 2-8 and Fig. 4-3a, we again write the vehicle equations of motion

$$m \frac{d\dot{x}}{dt} = -D(v) \cos \vartheta - W(t) \qquad \frac{dx}{dt} = \dot{x} \left. \right\}$$

$$m \frac{d\dot{y}}{dt} = -D(v) \sin \vartheta - mg \qquad \frac{dy}{dt} = \dot{y} \qquad \left. \right\} \qquad (4\text{-}1)$$

$$\cos \vartheta = \frac{\dot{x}}{v} \qquad \sin \vartheta = \frac{\dot{y}}{v} \qquad v^2 = \dot{x}^2 + \dot{y}^2 \left. \right\}$$

with

$$x(0) = y(0) = 0 \qquad \dot{x}(0) = v(0) \cos \vartheta(0) \qquad \dot{y}(0) = v(0) \sin \vartheta(0) \quad (4\text{-}2)$$

where $W(t)$ is a random disturbing force due to horizontal wind gusts (see also Sec. 2-9b). For our spherical projectile and wind velocities less than $v/10$, the wind force can be approximately represented as a Gaussian random variable with zero mean and a power spectral density obtainable with a simple shaping filter (Fig. 4-3a; see also Sec. 3-3). In more com-

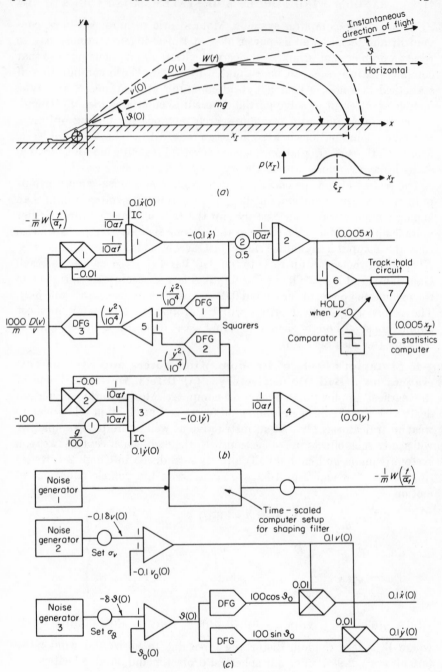

FIG. 4-3. Monte-Carlo study of a ballistic trajectory (see text).

plicated situations, we must introduce random variables representing horizontal and vertical gust *velocities* into the computation of the aerodynamic drag and lift.[51,52]

As an added complication, we will also consider the effects of system tolerances. Random variations in the powder charge and in gunpowder quality and condition cause random variations $\delta v(0)$ in the vehicle initial velocity $v(0)$. Production tolerances in our eighteenth-century cannon cause the cannonball to bounce back and forth in the gun barrel; this introduces a perturbation $\delta\vartheta(0)$ in the initial elevation angle $\vartheta(0)$. We write

$$v(0) = v_0(0) + \delta v(0) \qquad \vartheta(0) = \vartheta_0(0) + \delta\vartheta(0) \qquad (4\text{-}3)$$

and assume $\delta v(0)$ and $\delta(0)$ to be normally distributed with zero mean and variances $\sigma_v{}^2$ and $\sigma_\vartheta{}^2$.

Given such random forcing functions and initial conditions, we desire to find the resulting probability distribution of the impact coordinate x_I, say in terms of its probability density $p(x_I)$ (Fig. 4-3a). Alternatively, it may be sufficient to determine merely the probability that x_I does not differ by more than a given distance $\Delta x/2$ from the nominal impact coordinate x_{I0} obtained when $W(t) \equiv 0$, $\delta v(0) = \delta\vartheta(0) = 0$ (*hit probability* for a target extending from $x_{I0} - \Delta x/2$ to $x_{I0} + \Delta x/2$; see also Sec. 5-12). Referring to Sec. 2-8, we again write scaled machine equations

$$
\left.
\begin{aligned}
\frac{d}{dt}(0.1\dot{x}) &= -\frac{1}{10\alpha_t}\left\{\frac{1}{100}\left[\frac{1{,}000}{m}\frac{D(v)}{v}\right](0.1\dot{x}) + \frac{1}{m}W\left(\frac{t}{\alpha_t}\right)\right\} \\
\frac{d}{dt}(0.1\dot{y}) &= -\frac{1}{10\alpha_t}\left\{\frac{1}{100}\left[\frac{1{,}000}{m}\frac{D(v)}{v}\right](0.1\dot{y}) + g\right\} \\
\frac{d}{dt}(0.005x) &= \frac{0.5}{10\alpha_t}(0.1\dot{x}) \qquad \frac{d}{dt}(0.01y) = \frac{1}{10\alpha_t}(0.1\dot{y})
\end{aligned}
\right\} \qquad (4\text{-}4)
$$

Figure 4-3b shows the corresponding analog-computer setup, which is identical to that in Fig. 2-9b except for the addition of the random wind force $W(t)$. A comparator senses impact $(y = 0)$ and actuates a track-hold circuit, which reads $0.005x_I$ once per computer run. This track-hold output voltage is fed to a simple amplitude-distribution analyzer which computes $p(x_I)$ and/or Prob $[|x_I - x_{I0}| < \Delta x/2]$ (Secs. 5-12 and 5-13).

Figure 4-3c shows the generation of the necessary random voltages $-W(t/\alpha_t)/m$ and

$$
\begin{aligned}
0.1\dot{x}(0) &= 0.1[v_0(0) + \delta v(0)]\cos[\vartheta_0(0) + \delta\vartheta(0)] \\
0.1\dot{y}(0) &= 0.1[v_0(0) + \delta v(0)]\sin[\vartheta_0(0) + \delta\vartheta(0)]
\end{aligned}
$$

Note that the wind-force voltage $-W(t/\alpha_t)/m$ must be continuously supplied during the entire computer run, while each run requires only one sample each of $-0.1\delta v(0)$ and $-\delta\vartheta(0)$ to produce random initial-condition settings.

(b) Perturbation Method. If the random disturbances $W(t)$, $\delta v(0)$, $\delta \vartheta(0)$ are small, the resulting changes $\delta x_I = x_I - x_{I0}$ will also be small, and the accuracy of our amplitude-distribution analysis of δx_I will suffer from unfavorable scaling. If greater accuracy is required, we may be able to apply the perturbation technique of Sec. 2-9 to our Monte-Carlo computation. As noted earlier, perturbation computation is usually most convenient if we can consider perturbations from a simple analytical solution for the nominal (unperturbed) trajectory. Otherwise, the nominal trajectory must be precomputed or run concurrently with the perturbation calculation, and this may require a rather formidable analog-computer setup. *Monte-Carlo simulation of random perturbations is most readily justified if it is possible to consider exact (nonlinear) perturbations* (Sec. 2-9), *rather than linear approximations.* With *linear* homogeneous perturbation equations, Gaussian inputs with zero mean will produce Gaussian outputs with zero mean. Hence, each output distribution is completely defined by its mean square; each mean-square output may be computed (usually in a single computer run) by the weighting-function methods of Chap. 3.

4-5. Example: Monte-Carlo Simulation of Matched-filter Detection. In an experiment simulating a proposed multiplex telemetering system,[18,19] B. K. Conant[20] implemented matched-filter generation and detection of signals with the computer setup of Fig. 4-4. The circuit of Fig. 4-4a generates a linear combination

$$as(t) = -a[a_0 s_0(t) + a_1 s_1(t) + a_2 s_2(t) + a_3 s_3(t)] \qquad (4-5)$$

of the four polynomials*

$$\left.\begin{array}{ll} s_0(t) = P_0\left(2\,\dfrac{t}{T} - 1\right) = 1 & s_1(t) = P_1\left(2\,\dfrac{t}{T} - 1\right) = 2\,\dfrac{t}{T} - 1 \\[2mm] s_2(t) = P_2\left(2\,\dfrac{t}{T} - 1\right) = 6\left(\dfrac{t}{T}\right)^2 - 6\,\dfrac{t}{T} + 1 \\[2mm] s_3(t) = P_3\left(2\,\dfrac{t}{T} - 1\right) = 20\left(\dfrac{t}{T}\right)^3 - 30\left(\dfrac{t}{T}\right)^2 + 12\,\dfrac{t}{T} - 1 \end{array}\right\} \qquad (4-7)$$

derived from the well-known Legendre polynomials[50] $P_k(x)$.

* Additional polynomials $s_k(t) = P_k[2(t/T) - 1]$ can be obtained from the same filter chain with the aid of the recurrence relation

$$s_n(t) = \frac{2}{T}(n-1)\int_0^t s_{n-1}(t)\,dt + s_{n-2}(t) \qquad (n = 2,3,\ \ldots) \qquad (4-6)$$

but scaling becomes increasingly unfavorable; it might be more profitable to employ separate filters for higher-order polynomials.

Note that orthogonal-polynomial filter synthesis can also be used to approximate matched filters for nonpolynomial signals[22-21] and may be easier to implement on analog computers than the conventional delay-line synthesis.

The four outputs $y_i(t)$ of the linear filter circuit in Fig. 4-4b are *matched-filter* outputs designed to yield weighting functions $h_i(t)$, respectively proportional to $s_i(T - t)$. If, say, $s_2(t)$ alone is transmitted ($a_0 = a_1 = a_3 = 0$, $a_2 > 0$) with additive white Gaussian noise $n(t)$, our matched-

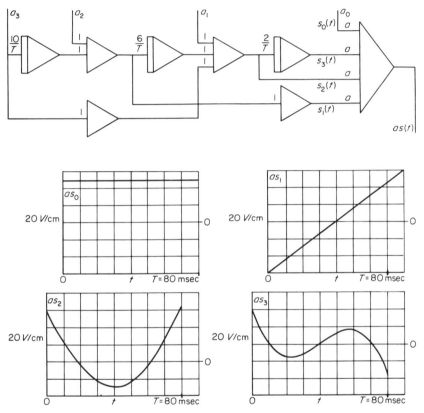

FIG. 4-4a. Polynomial-generating circuit and output signals obtained for $a = 50$ volts and $n(t) \equiv 0$ (ASTRAC I data, University of Arizona; based on ref. 20).

filter output is

$$y_2(t) = \int_0^t h_2(t - \lambda)[s_2(\lambda) + n(\lambda)] \, d\lambda$$

$$= \text{const} \left[\int_0^t s_2{}^2(\lambda) \, d\lambda + \int_0^t s_2(\lambda)n(\lambda) \, d\lambda \right] \qquad (4\text{-}8)$$

It can be shown[21] that our choice of the weighting function maximizes the *detection probability* $1 - \beta$ that $y_2(T)$ exceeds any given positive comparator threshold y_c at the end of the observation time T (Fig. 4-4c, d). The threshold y_c is selected to yield an acceptable *false-alarm probability* α when noise alone is received. In Fig. 4-4d, $1 - \beta$ and α appear as areas under normal-probability-density curves and can be found with the aid of normal-distribution tables if a_2, y_c, and the noise power σ_n^2 are given.[21] Conant measured $1 - \beta$ and α by counting comparator responses in a sample of 1,000 computer runs at 10 computer runs per second and was able to check theoretical values within 0.5 per cent.

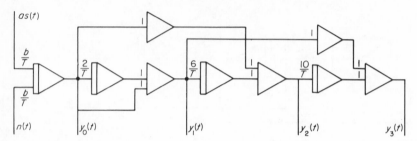

FIG. 4-4b. Matched-filter setup for optimum detection of the signals generated in Fig. 4-4a.

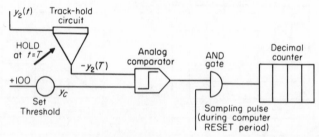

FIG. 4-4c. Circuit used to estimate detection probability (with signal present) and false-alarm probability (with signal absent) in the presence of noise.

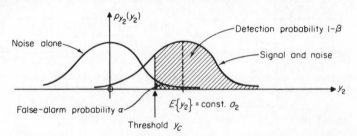

FIG. 4-4d. Definition of detection probability and false-alarm probability.

For *orthogonal-signal multiplexing*, we transmit a linear combination (5) of the $s_k(t)$, with a_0, a_1, a_2, a_3 representing, say, samples of four channels of telemetered data during successive transmission periods of length T. The orthogonality property of Legendre polynomials[50] implies

$$\int_0^T h_i(T - \lambda)s_k(\lambda)\, d\lambda = \int_0^T s_i(\lambda)s_k(\lambda)\, d\lambda = 0 \qquad (i \neq k) \qquad (4\text{-}9)$$

so that the four "receiver" outputs $y_i(T)$ will be respectively proportional to the transmitted values a_0, a_1, a_2, a_3 at the end of each transmission period.

4-6. Special Techniques. In general, we resort to direct simulation, and especially to Monte-Carlo techniques, when analytical methods fail. This should, however, not imply that we abandon critical mathematical supervision of the computation. In particular, we must attempt to predict the statistical fluctuations of measured statistics, i.e., variances and/or confidence limits of estimates. This is, as a rule, easiest (or least difficult) if we employ statistically independent computer runs (Chap. 5); in this case, standard deviations (rms errors) of estimates are usually inversely proportional to $\sqrt{n}$, where n is the sample size. It is, then, necessary to increase the number of computer runs a hundredfold to reduce rms errors by a factor of 10. To prevent statistical fluctuations due to spurious periodic line-frequency pickup, we can make the computer repetition rate incommensurable with the line frequency (check for moving oscilloscope display with line-frequency sweep).

Statistical measurements will be discussed in detail in Chaps. 5 to 7, with emphasis on the reduction of statistical fluctuations of estimates. In Sec. 8-3, we will introduce new Monte-Carlo techniques involving concurrent computation of estimate variances or other measures of dispersion for each estimate. This will permit display of confidence intervals and/or confidence levels for each computed result or, in fact, computation can be stopped when a certain confidence level and accuracy are reached.

Looking to the future, we want to remark that simple independent-sample simulation may not always be the fastest method of arriving at the desired goal. Especially in problems where random initial conditions or parameters change only once per differential-analyzer run, the problem requires us to select samples of these input random variables according to a specified probability distribution. *We are, however, still left with considerable choice in introducing random or even deterministic relationships between different input-noise samples with a view to reducing statistical fluctuations in our estimates.* This is a problem in the design of experiments. We can, for instance, prevent chance accumulation of input samples in some region of low probability by predesigning a complete *pseudo-random sample* more likely to be "typical" of the theoretical probability distribution than a true random sample of the same size. As a less radical measure, we can still employ random sampling, but ensure that predetermined fractions of the total sample fall into selected class intervals (*stratified sampling*).[1-6] Stratified sampling also permits problem rescaling for different subsamples, which may be useful in view of the large ratio of range and mean for many noise distributions. At least in theory, striking reductions of estimate variances can also be effected through *artificial positive or negative correlation* of successive sample values without any change in their first-order probability distribution.[3,6] We shall return to this question in Sec. 8-5.

We shall exhibit several further interesting examples of Monte-Carlo studies in Chap. 8. Still, it is surely fair to say that existing applications of hybrid-computer Monte-Carlo simulation have hardly broken the surface of well-established possibilities, for a vast accumulation of existing knowledge on the design of statistical experiments applies directly to Monte-Carlo simulation. While most simple analog-hybrid computer techniques produce only relatively simple averages and statistical relative frequencies, more advanced techniques require computation of more sophisticated statistics, such as Student's t, variance ratios, or Fisher's z. In low-cost computers, such statistics could be obtained with suitably patched "slow" analog computing elements; it is, in particular, quite feasible to employ relatively slow ± 100-volt computing elements in conjunction with fast ± 10-volt computing elements used for the fast Monte-Carlo simulation itself. For extensive and sophisticated statistical studies involving, say, comparison of test statistics obtained with different samples, and parameter optimization on the basis of measured statistics, it would appear best to employ a small stored-program digital computer in conjunction with a fast ± 10-volt analog Monte-Carlo simulator and some patched digital logic. The digital computer and the associated analog-digital linkage equipment need not be very fast or very accurate, for samples of statistics would be required at most at kilocycle rates. A 10- to 12-bit accuracy would be ample, and *three- to four-bit analog-to-digital conversion is sufficient in many important cases* (Chap. 6). The stored-program computer could conveniently take over many of the functions of present hybrid-computer control circuitry, such as control of sample sizes, parameter changes, and optimization logic. The flexibility of the stored-program computer would permit very efficient sequential-analysis routines, convenient program changes, and a pleasing presentation of printed or plotted results.

RANDOM-NOISE GENERATORS

4-7. Random-noise-generator Specifications. Random-noise generators for random-process and statistical studies with analog and hybrid analog-digital computers should produce stationary noise signals whose amplitude distribution, d-c unbalance, spectrum, and rms level are specified within the computer-accuracy limits (0.1 to 2 per cent) in the sense of averages measured over, say, a period equal to 100 or 1,000 computer runs with at least 95 per cent confidence. In addition, the power spectrum should be flat within 0.1 to 0.3 db from d-c to 100 cps for "slow" electronic analog computers, and up to at least 100 times the highest repetition rate for repetitive/iterative machines. Finally, the noise must be free from periodic components due to line-frequency pickup and other sources. Noise samples must be essentially uncorrelated for delays exceeding, say, one-hundredth to one-thousandth of a typical computer run. Failures to meet such specifications will often show up

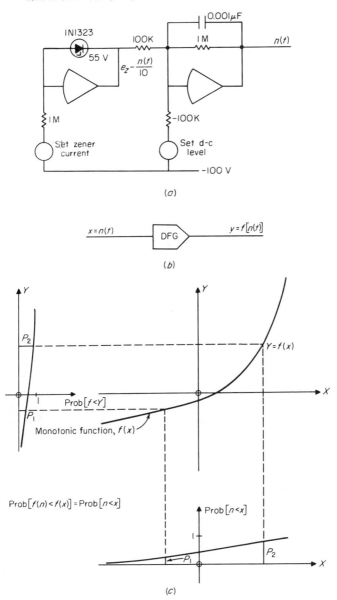

FIG. 4-5. A simple and inexpensive zener-diode noise generator (a), and use of a diode function generator to modify noise-generator amplitude distribution (b), (c).

clearly in statistical averaging studies involving large samples or long integration times.[25]

A given flat-spectrum noise generator can readily produce other reasonable spectra with the aid of shaping filters (see also Sec. 3-3). Time-variable filters, attenuators, and modulators can produce a wide variety of nonstationary noise (see also Sec. 8-9). Suitably selected diode function generators can be used to change the amplitude distribution (Fig. 4-5);[29] note that this will also affect the power spectrum.

4-8. Analog Random-noise Generators (see also Table 4-1). Gaussian noise can be obtained from noisy diodes, zener diodes,[40] photocells, or thyratrons (Figs. 4-5 and 4-7). To ensure zero mean (i.e., zero d-c level), the noise generator can be followed by a d-c blocking filter with the transfer function $T_0s/(T_0s + 1)$, whose time constant T_0 must be

Table 4-1. Typical Noise-generator Specifications

Type	Amplitude distribution	Power spectrum	rms output	Long-term d-c unbalance
Noise from thyratron in magnetic field plus filter and AGC circuit	Gaussian within ± 2 per cent	Flat within 0.5 db, 10–25,000 cps	15 volts ± 0.5 per cent	A-c coupled
Demodulator type (Elgenco type 321A)	Gaussian within ± 1 per cent of probability; dynamic range $\pm 5\sigma$	Flat within 0.1 db, 0–105 cps	12 volts ± 0.2 per cent	<50 mV at 95 per cent confidence level
Pseudo-random-noise generator, 25 stages; period = 33,554,431 bits*	Binary; obtain approximately Gaussian distribution by low-pass filtering	Line spectrum, flat within 0.1 db from d-c to 8 per cent of the 0 to 4 Mc shift-pulse frequency. Can be changed at will	6 volts ± 0.3 per cent, 20–40 deg C	<20 mV 20–40 deg C

* Or 4 uncorrelated 8,388,608-bit sequences.

sufficiently large to permit output fluctuations at the lowest frequency of interest (Fig. 4-6). To be sure of stationary noise-generator output, we may need an automatic-gain-control circuit (with a similarly large time constant) to control the mean-square output or mean absolute output. Such gain control requires detector circuits which must be carefully designed for low long-term drift.[25,26]

The noise-generator system shown in Fig. 4-6, widely used for low-frequency analog-computer applications, combines an elaborate AGC system with a frequency-shifting technique designed to yield a flat power spectrum starting at zero frequency. An accurately symmetrical band-pass filter selects a noise band around 400 to 1,000 cps, where the thryatronnoise power spectrum is quite flat; a 400-cps chopper acts as a frequency-shifting demodulator, and stationary zero-mean noise all the way down to d-c is obtained at the output of a low-pass filter.[25,26] Such noise generators, unfortunately, rarely yield a useful bandwidth much greater than 150 cps. $\sigma = 12$ volts is a typical rms output.

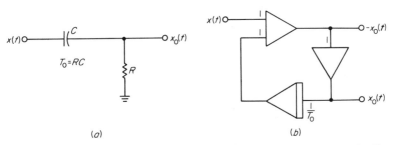

FIG. 4-6. D-c blocking filters. The frequency-response function of each filter is $j\omega T_0/(j\omega T_0 + 1)$; circuit (b) is used for time constants T_0 greater than 1 sec.

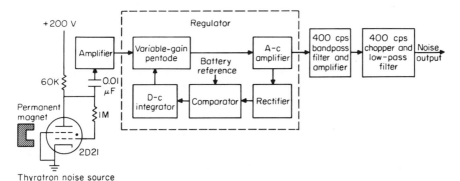

FIG. 4-7. Demodulator-type noise generator (ref. 26). Noise from a thyratron placed in a transverse magnetic field to prevent resonance peaks is first amplified by an a-c regulator amplifier whose gain is accurately controlled for constant rms output. A bandpass amplifier selects a noise band about 100 cps wide and centered accurately about 400 cps. The resulting regulated, band-limited noise is demodulated by a 400-cps chopper and filtered to produce an output spectrum flat within 0.2 db between d-c and 35 cps. Demodulation eliminates any low-frequency fluctuations introduced in the noise source and low-level amplifier stages.

A possibly more useful type of noise signal is *binary noise* with output levels $\pm a$ volts. Such a signal may have a naturally flat spectrum all the way to d-c and is readily filtered to produce Gaussian noise.[33,34] Binary noise, moreover, is highly useful in its own right, for it can operate analog and digital switching circuitry to simulate random events, machine failures, etc., and permits direct correlation with other signals without any need for analog multipliers.[8,35–37] In particular, a flip-flop triggered by random pulses from a Geiger counter or photomultiplier painted with radioactive paint (Fig. 4-8) will produce a random telegraph wave with

Poisson-distributed zero crossings (Sec. 1-11).[28,36,37] Alternatively, comparator-sampled diode or thyratron noise can yield positive or negative outputs during successive clock intervals at 100-cps to 1-Mc bit rates (Fig. 4-9).

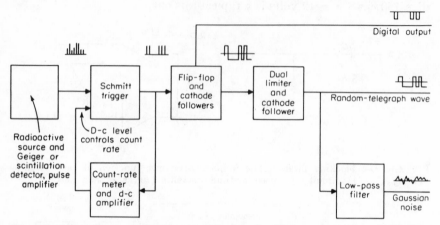

FIG. 4-8. Pulses from a radioactive-particle detector (Geiger counter or scintillation-detecting photomultiplier) trigger a flip-flop to produce a random telegraph wave. With a mean count rate α, the probability of k zero crossings in T sec is $(\alpha T)Ke^{-\alpha T}/K$: (Poisson distribution); a count-rate feedback loop keeps α within about 1 per cent of its design value between 1 and 100 Kc. With $\pm a$ volts output, we have

$$E\{x\} = 0 \qquad R_{xx}(\tau) = a^2 e^{-2\alpha|\tau|} \text{ volt}^2 \qquad \Phi_{xx} = \frac{4\alpha a^2}{\omega^2 + (2\alpha)^2} \text{ volt}^2/\text{cps}$$

(see also Sec. 1-11).

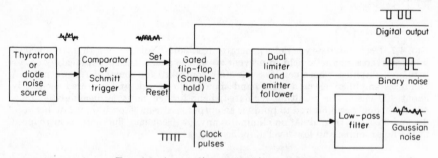

FIG. 4-9. A sampling-type noise generator.

An especially simple way to obtain uniformly distributed random numbers *once per computer run* (e.g., for random intial conditions or system parameters) is to sample a triangular or sawtooth waveform (Sec. 8-9) whose frequency is not commensurable with the computer repetition rate ("wheel of fortune" principle).[39] To obtain a random initial condition, the sampling is simply done with the *IC* input of the integrator in question, while a separate integrator without input in COMPUTE (track-hold circuit, Sec. 2-13) produces a constant random parameter during an entire computer run. A simple oscilloscope check will test the triangle oscillator for inadvertent synchronization with the computer repetition rate.

HYBRID ANALOG-DIGITAL
PSEUDO-RANDOM-NOISE GENERATORS

4-9. Background. Introduction to Shift-register Sequences. Binary-noise waveforms permit relatively simple control of d-c level and rms output through accurate clamping of the binary output levels (Sec. 4-11), but the stationarity and randomness properties of the noise-generating mechanism will still require careful attention.   In particular,

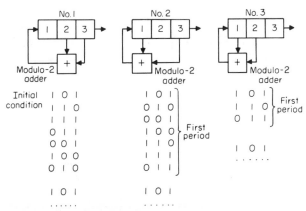

Fig. 4-10. Three-stage shift-register circuits ($n = 3$) generating a maximum-length sequence, its reverse, and a non-maximum-length sequence.[41,47]

the random-telegraph-wave generator of Fig. 4-8 is prone to changes of the count rate α through drift in the Schmitt-trigger level and the photomultiplier plate voltage.   Since this affects the noise spectrum (Sec. 1-11 and Fig. 4-8), one requires a fairly elaborate count-rate control loop;[36,37] even so, it is difficult to keep α from changing by less than 0.5 per cent for a 15 deg C temperature change.   These difficulties tend to increase with increasing noise-bandwidth requirements.

An entirely different approach was chosen to provide noise for the University of Arizona ASTRAC II computer, which must be able to take statistics on 1,000 random-input differential-analyzer runs per second.[46,47] True analog random-noise generation was abandoned frequently in favor of a *digital shift-register sequence generator*, which can produce binary *pseudo-random-noise sequences* at any reasonable clock rate up to 4 Mc. Referring to Fig. 4-10, an *n*-bit digital shift register whose output is "scrambled" by suitable digital logic and fed back to recirculate will produce periodic binary sequences. The maximum period length obtainable with "linear" (modulo-2-adder) feedback is $2^n - 1$ bits; for an n-bit shift register can have 2^n different states, but one of these states will merely reproduce itself (000 in the circuits of Fig. 4-10).

Shift-register sequences have been studied extensively in connection with communication and radar applications,[41-43] It is, in particular, possible to show[41] that feedback of the modulo-2 sum of two shift-register-stage outputs (Figs. 4-10 and 4-11) will yield *maximum-length sequences* of period $2^n - 1$ bits if the feedback is taken from the stages specified in Table 4-2. Table 4-3 is a truth table defining the modulo-2-adder (EXCLUSIVE-OR) logic, and Fig. 4-13a illustrates the implementation of a

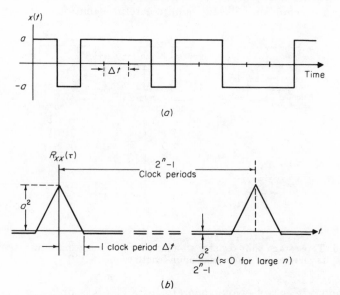

FIG. 4-11. Waveform (a), and autocorrelation function (b) of a pseudo-random-noise voltage.

modulo-2 adder with NAND gates. Maximum-length shift-register sequences obtained in this manner behave, in many ways, like the random sequences obtained by independent trials with Prob [0] = Prob [1] = $\frac{1}{2}$; also, each shift-register sequence is necessarily periodic. In particular, each binary maximum-length shift-register sequence generated by modulo-2 feedback can be shown to have three significant "pseudo-randomness" properties,[41] which often justify substitution of such sequences for true random sequences:

Pseudo-random-noise Property 1. In each period of a maximum-length sequence, the shift register assumes every possible "state" (binary number in the register), except for the all-zero state.

Table 4-2. Some Maximum-length Shift-register-sequence Generators Requiring a Single Modulo-2 Adder

(Feedback from shift-register stages n and m to modulo-2 adder, which feeds stage 1). In each case, substitution of $n - m$ for m also yields a maximum-length sequence, which is the delayed exact *reverse* of the original sequence (see also Fig. 4-10).[41]   The table is based on the theory of ref. 41.

n	m or $n - m$	$2^n{}_{-1}$	n	m or $n - m$	$2^n{}_{-1}$
3	1	7	18	7	262,143
4	1	15	20	3	1,048,575
5	2	31	21	2	2,097,151
6	1	63	22	1	4,194,303
7	1 or 3	127	23	5 or 9	8,388,607
9	4	511	25	3 or 7	33,554,431
10	3	1,023	28	3, 9, or 13	268,435,455
11	2	2,047	31	3, 6, 7, or 13	2,147,483,647
15	1, 4, or 7	32,767	33	13	8,589,934,591

Table 4-3. Truth Table for Modulo-2 Addition $(A + B)_{\mathrm{mod}\,2}$ **(EXCLUSIVE OR, see also Fig. 4-13a)**

B \ A	0	1
0	0	1
1	1	0

In each period of $p = 2^n - 1$ bits, the number of 1's is, therefore, 2^{n-1} and exceeds the number of 0's by exactly one.

Pseudo-random-noise Property 2.   In every period, one-half of all the *runs* (i.e., subsequences containing only 0's or only 1's) are of length 1 (0 or 1), one-fourth are of length 2 (00 or 11), etc.; and for each run of 0's, there is a run of 1's of equal length.

Pseudo-random-noise Property 3.   Let successive output bits (0 or 1) be denoted by $a_1, a_2, \ldots$.   Then

$$\Psi(k) = \frac{1}{2^n - 1} \sum_{i=1}^{2^n - 1} a_i a_{i+k}$$

$$= \begin{cases} \dfrac{2^{n-1}}{2^n - 1} & [k = 0, \pm(2^n - 1), \pm 2(2^n - 1), \ldots] \\ \dfrac{-2^{n-2}}{2^n - 1} & \text{otherwise} \end{cases} \qquad (4\text{-}10)$$

i.e., the "discrete autocorrelation function" $\Psi(k)$ is periodic and assumes only two values.

Closely related to the last property is the fact that term-by-term modulo-2 addition of a maximum-length shift-register sequence $\{a_i\}$ obtained through modulo-2 feedback and a delayed sequence $\{a_{i+k}\}$ yields another delayed (but otherwise identical) sequence $\{a_{i+m}\}$ (*shift-and-add property*).

Different initial shift-register states produce identical but delayed maximum-length sequences. Different modulo-2 feedback configurations, on the other hand, yield different sequences (Fig. 4-10). Specifically, an n-bit register with modulo-2 feedback can generate $\varphi(p)/n$ different maximum-length sequences, where $\varphi(n)$ (*Euler's number*) is the number of positive integers less than n and relatively prime to n.[41] Generation of some of these sequences requires two or more modulo-2 adders. Note that Table 4-2 lists only circuits with a single modulo-2 adder; more extensive tables will be found in refs. 41 and 43.

4-10. Pseudo-random Analog Noise.

To obtain binary analog "noise" from a shift-register sequence, we shift and clip the output levels of the shift-register flip-flop to produce a *pseudo-random square wave* $x(t)$ varying between $-a$ and $+a$ volts (Fig. 4-11a). Assuming periodic shift-pulse input every Δt sec, $x(t)$ is periodic with period $(2^n - 1) \Delta t$. In view of our pseudo-random properties, our periodic waveform has the time average

$$\langle x \rangle = \frac{a}{2^n - 1} \tag{4-11}$$

and the time autocorrelation function

$$\langle x(t)x(t + \tau) \rangle = \begin{cases} a^2 \left[1 - \dfrac{|\tau - k(2^n - 1) \Delta t|}{\Delta t} \right] \text{ if} \\ |\tau - k(2^n - 1) \Delta t| \leq \Delta t \ (k = 0, \pm 1, \pm 2, \ldots) \\ \dfrac{a^2}{2^n - 1} \quad \text{otherwise} \end{cases} \tag{4-12}$$

which is necessarily also periodic with period $(2^n - 1) \Delta t$ (Fig. 4-11b). Note that $a/(2^n - 1)$ and $a^2/(2^n - 1)$ become very small for large n. If $x(t)$ can be regarded as a sample function of a periodic random-phase process (Sec. 1-10), then the time averages (11) and (12) equal the corresponding ensemble averages $E\{x\}$ and $R_{xx}(\tau)$ with probability 1.

$2^n - 1$ increases dramatically with the number n of shift-register stages. For $n = 25$, for instance, the shift-register sequence will repeat only after producing $2^{25} - 1 = 33,554,431$ effectively uncorrelated bits. This would be enough for, say, over 2,500 computer runs at 12,000 bits per computer run.

For observation times shorter than one shift-register period, the first- and second-order probability distributions of a maximum-length pseudo-random square wave are essentially identical to those of true random binary noise generated by sampling independent (Bernoulli) trials yielding $-a$ and $+a$ with equal probability (Sec. 1-13). Even for higher-order distributions, the nonrandomness (interdependence of samples) is not easy to detect, if we assume n and 2^{n-1} to be relatively prime,[57] the sum s of $m < n \ll 2^n - 1$ consecutive bits (0 or 1) of a maximum-length shift-register sequence has, for all practical purposes, the binomial distribution associated with s successes in m independent trials; hence, simple counters can be used to produce binomial and, for larger m, approximately Gaussian digital random numbers. Again, *low-pass filtering of the pseudo-random waveform yields essentially first-order Gaussian output* if the filter time constant is large compared to Δt but does not exceed $n \, \Delta t$. For reasonably large values of n ($n > 10$), such pseudo-binomial and pseudo-Gaussian *first-order* distributions are readily verified experimentally by χ^2 tests at high confidence levels.[47] To the best of the writer's knowledge, however, the distribution of summed or filtered pseudo-random noise has not been derived theoretically (see refs. 33 and 34 for analogous work on true random binary waveforms). It is, clearly, *not* possible to employ the central-limit theorem in this connection. Higher-order distributions need *not* be Gaussian.[57]

The *power spectrum* of our periodic pseudo-random square wave is necessarily a *line spectrum*. If we consider $x(t)$ as a sample function of a random-phase process, transformation of the periodic autocorrelation function (12) yields

$$\Phi_{xx}(\omega) = 2\pi \left(\frac{a}{2^n - 1}\right)^2 \left\{ -(2^n - 1)\delta(\omega) \right.$$
$$\left. + \sum_{k=-\infty}^{\infty} 2^n \left[\frac{\sin k\pi/(2^n - 1)}{k\pi/(2^n - 1)}\right]^2 \delta\left[\omega - \frac{2\pi k}{(2^n - 1)\,\Delta t}\right]\right\} \quad (4\text{-}13)$$

Spectral lines are separated by the reciprocal of the period $(2^n - 1)\,\Delta t$, and their power contributions are proportional to $(\sin \frac{1}{2}\omega \,\Delta t / \frac{1}{2}\omega \,\Delta t)^2$, which is constant within 0.1 db out to about $\omega = 1/2\,\Delta t$. For large values of n, the spectral lines are spaced very closely. No system simulated during a computer run which is short compared to the pseudo-random-noise period $(2^n - 1)\,\Delta t$ can resolve adjacent spectral lines (in other words, all transients die out before the noise sequence repeats). Hence, *the pseudo-random noise acts essentially like band-limited white noise flat within* 0.1 *db out to about* $1/4\pi \,\Delta t$ *cps or* 8 *per cent of the shift-pulse rate* $1/\Delta t$. The -3-db point is at about $0.6/\Delta t$ cps. Shaping filters readily yield various other power spectra (Sec. 3-3).

4-11. Design of a Practical Pseudo-random-noise Generator with Multiple Outputs.[46,47] Figures 4-12 and 4-13 illustrate the design of a complete pseudo-random-noise-generator system. Figure 4-12 is a system block diagram. The *sequence generator* (Fig. 4-13a), comprising a 25-stage shift register and a single modulo-2 adder, can be driven at any periodic clock rate between 0 and 4 Mc, or nonperiodic shift pulses can be

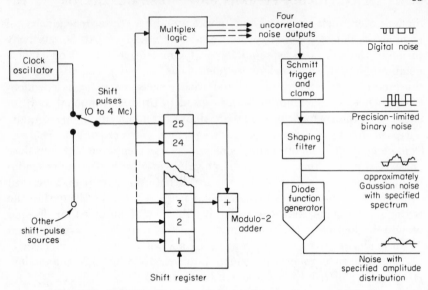

FIG. 4-12. A practical pseudo-random-noise-generator system.[46,47]

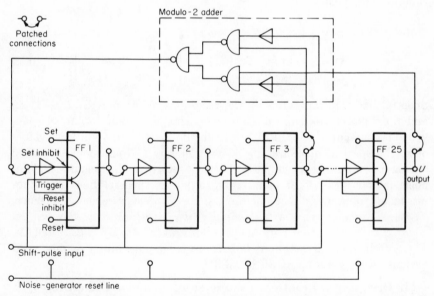

FIG. 4-13a. Noise-generator shift register with modulo-2-adder feedback. Shift pulses are usually 1 Kc to 4 Mc computer clock pulses, but need not be periodic. Flip-flop reset inputs are patched on a small noise-generator patchbay, so that a desired initial pattern can be reset at any computer-selected time. Redundant logic inverters greatly simplify patching of different shift registers and multiple noise generators. (*University of Arizona; see also ref. 47.*)

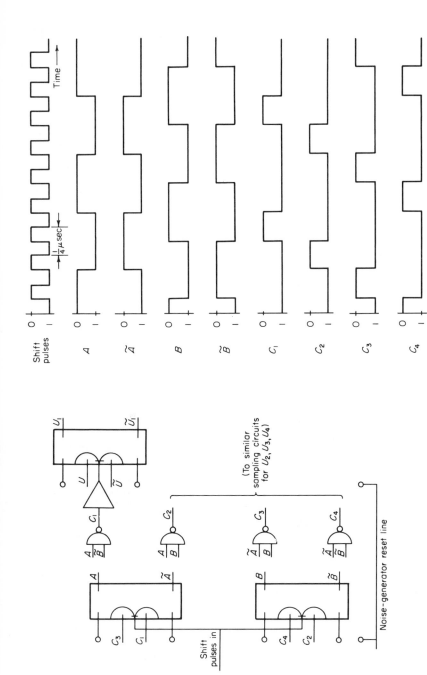

Fig. 4-13b. Multiplexer logic yielding four pseudo-random sequences U_1, U_2, U_3, U_4 from a single shift-register sequence U. Each of the four output sequences is identical to U; they are staggered by $2^n/4$ bits of U, so that they will remain uncorrelated during one full period of U, or for $1/4(2^n - 1)$ output bits. A desired initial phase pattern of the four sequences can be reset by suitable patching.[47]

supplied singly or in bursts by external digital logic. Shift-register stage outputs and reset inputs are terminated on a small noise-generator patchbay with storable patchboards; suitable patching permits selection of initial states, which can be reset whenever ordered by digital pulses on the noise-generator reset line. Patching also permits different feedback connections. Finally, with spare modulo-2 adders available in the patchbay, the register can be split into two or more independent smaller registers; this is especially useful for correlation experiments (Sec. 7-12).

The *multiplex logic* (Fig. 4-13b) samples the shift-register sequence to yield four pseudo-random sequences U_1, U_2, U_3, U_4 at one-fourth the shift

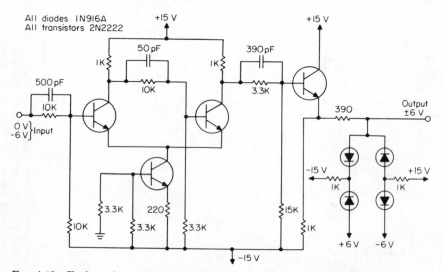

Fig. 4-13c. Each analog output circuit for the shift-register noise generator comprises a fast Schmitt trigger, an output emitter follower, and a temperature-compensating four-diode limiter circuit[49] which clamps the output accurately to ±6 volts. 4-Mc operation is possible. (*University of Arizona.*)

rate of the main sequence U. The four output sequences are identical maximum-length sequences, they are staggered by $2^n/4$ bits of U. Only one-fourth of each output sequence, or $\frac{1}{4}(2^n - 1)$ output bits, are used during one period of U, so that the four outputs remain uncorrelated during this period. Patching permits one to set a desired initial phase pattern for the four output sequences.

Figure 4-13c shows one of the four *analog output circuits* designed to generate ±6 volts pseudo-random square waves following each digital sequence. Each output circuit comprises a fast Schmitt trigger (60 nsec rise time), a level-shifting emitter follower, and a pair of output shunt limiters clamping the analog output to −6 and +6 volts. Each clamp is an accurate two-diode circuit designed for temperature compensation[49] and will maintain its clamping level well within ± 20 mV between 20 and 40 deg C.   Clamping establishes both d-c level and mean-square output.

4-12. Pseudo-random Noise vs. True Random Noise.[44–48]   Suitably designed pseudo-random noise generators offer a number of striking advantages, which are not shared by the analog noise generators discussed in Sec. 4-8.

1. *Pseudo-random noise is produced by reliable and easily maintained digital circuits.*   The analog noise output is unaffected by the physical environment except for the temperature-compensated output clamping levels.
2. *The binary-noise bandwidth is simply proportional to the shift-pulse rate.*
3. *The shift register can be reset at any time to repeat a sequence of random events exactly.*   We can reset once per computer run, once per sample of, say, 1,000 computer runs, or on command.   This permits repetitive computation, synchronized oscilloscope displays, and convenient checks of results and equipment.   With additional logic, the noise sequence can also be reversed (see Table 4-2).
4. *Digital multiplexing (Sec. 4-10) yields multiple uncorrelated pseudo-random outputs from a single shift register at only slight additional cost per output.*
5. The hybrid noise generator produces digital pseudo-random numbers with approximately binomial or Gaussian distribution as well as analog noise.
6. Parallel readout or D/A conversion of the shift-register contents yields uniformly distributed pseudo-random numbers.[57]
7. The binary serial output permits logical or analog multiplication by simple switching.

On the other hand, the pseudo-random nature of shift-register noise requires judgment and caution in the design of experiments.   No particular difficulties arise if we are interested only in mean and mean-square outputs or input-output cross-correlation (Sec. 7-12) of time-invariant linear systems.   Such results depend only on the autocorrelation function of the pseudo-random input which, in this respect, approximates white noise very well.   Statistical results from nonlinear systems, however, may be affected by the second- and higher-order distributions of the pseudo-random noise, which are *not* necessarily Gaussian.

In Monte-Carlo practice, shift-register sequences are used essentially as ergodic random-phase periodic processes (Sec. 1-10).   To obtain low-variance estimates (Secs. 5-2, 5-11, and 8-5c), it may be wise to design experiments so that statistical averaging takes place over a complete shift-register period or over an integral number of periods.   The noise-generator circuit of Fig. 4-13a was especially designed to permit convenient patching of shift registers of different length.

The possibility of binary multiplication is especially useful in correlation applications (Sec. 7-11). In this connection, the shift-and-add property of maximum-length shift-register sequences (Sec. 4-9) can be used to implement time delays with digital logic,[44] but it may be simpler to employ duplicate shift registers and to delay one sequence by shift-pulse timing (Sec. 7-12).

REFERENCES AND BIBLIOGRAPHY

Monte-Carlo Methods, General

1. *Proc. Symposium on Monte Carlo Methods*, Wiley, New York, 1956.
2. Brown, G. W.: Monte Carlo Methods, in Beckenbach, E. F., *Modern Mathematics for the Engineer*, First Series, McGraw-Hill, New York, 1956.
3. Hammersley, J. M., and D. C. Handscomb: *Monte Carlo Methods*, Methuen, London, 1964; see also *Proc. Cambridge Phil. Soc.*, 449 and 476, 1956.
4. Cashwell, E. D., and C. J. Everett: *A Practice Manual on the Monte Carlo Method*, Pergamon Press, New York, 1959.
5. Ulam, S. M.: Monte Carlo Calculations in Problems of Mathematical Physics in Beckenbach, E. F., *Modern Mathematics for the Engineer*, Second Series, McGraw-Hill, New York, 1961.
6. Schreider, Yu: *Method of Statistical Testing (Monte Carlo Method)*, translated from Russian, Elsevier, Amsterdam, 1964.

Analog and Hybrid Computer Monte-Carlo Techniques
(see also Chap. 8)

7. Hall, E.: Analog Simulation for Noise Analysis in Control Systems, *MIT Instrumentation Lab. Rept.* R7-74, May, 1954.
8. Two Applications of GEDA Computers to Statistical Problems of Operation Research, Goodyear Aircraft Corp. *Rept. GER* 6729, Akron, Ohio, 1955.
9. Van Horne, T. B.: An Analog Method for the Solution of Probability of Hit and Related Statistical Problems, *IRETEC*, September, 1957.
10. Van der Velde, W. E.: Make Statistical Studies on Analog Simulations, *Control Eng.*, June, 1960.
11. Cameron, W. D.: Determination of Probability Distributions Using Hybrid-computer Techniques, *NASA Ames Res. Ctr. Mem.*, Moffett Field, Calif., 1963. See also *Proc. Intern. Symposium on Analog and Digital Techniques Applied to Aeronautics*, Liege, Belgium, September, 1963.
12. McGhee, R. B., and A. Levine: Determination of Optimum Production Techniques by Analog Simulation, *Proc. Eastern Joint Computer Conf.* 1959.
13. Chuang, K., et al.: A Stochastic Method for Solving Partial Differential Equations Using an Electronic Analog Computer, *Project Michigan Rept.* 2900-91T, Willow Run Laboratories, University of Michigan, June, 1960.
14. Streets, R. B.: A Note on Arbitrary Non-mean-square Error Criteria, *ACL Memo* 55, Electrical Engineering Department, University of Arizona, 1962; see also *IEEE Trans. PGAC*, September, 1963.
15. Sage, A. P., R. B. Streets, and M. J. Wozny: Statistical Experiments with the APE Hybrid Computer System, *ACL Memo* 60, Electrical Engineering Department, University of Arizona, 1962.
16. Korn, G. A.: Simple Hybrid Analog-digital Computer Teaching Aids for Courses

in Statistics and Random-process Theory, *Instruments and Control Systems*, August, 1963.

17. Levine, L.: *Methods for Solving Engineering Problems Using Analog Computers*, McGraw-Hill, New York, 1964.

Computer Setups for Orthogonal Polynomials and Matched Filters

18. Ballard, A. H.: A New Multiplex Technique for Telemetry, *Proc. Natl. Telemetering Conf.*, 1962.
19. ———: A Real-time Function Analyzer-synthesizer Using Orthogonal Polynomials, *Proc. WESCON*, 1962.
20. Conant, B. K.: ASTRAC I Study of an Orthogonal-function Multiplex System Using Matched Filters, *ACL Memo* 70, University of Arizona, 1963; *Ann. AICA*, July, 1965.
21. Helstrom, C. W.: *Statistical Theory of Signal Detection*, Pergamon Press, New York, 1960.
22. Lampard, D. G.: A New Method of Determining Correlation Functions of Stationary Time Series, *Proc. IEE*, p. C, March, 1955.
23. Otterman, J.: Time-domain Synthesis for an Analog-computer Setup, *Proc. Natl. Simulation Conf.*, 1956.
24. Gilbert, E. G.: Linear-system Approximation by Differential-analyzer Simulation of Orthonormal Approximation Functions, *IRETEC*, June, 1959.

Random-noise Generators

25. Bennett, R. R., and A. S. Fulton: The Generation and Measurement of Low-frequency Random Noise, *J. Appl. Phys.*, September, 1951.
26. Beecher, D. E., R. R. Bennett, and H. Low: Stabilized Noise Source for Air-weapons Design, *Electronics*, July, 1954.
27. Winter, D. F.: A Gaussian Noise Generator for Frequencies Down to 0.001 cps, *IRE Natl. Convention Record*, 1954.
28. Random-noise Generator for Simulation Studies, Goodyear Aircraft Corp. *Rept.* GER-6436, Akron, Ohio, 1954.
29. Diamantides, N. D.: Analog-computer Generation of Probability Distributions for Operations Research, *Trans. AIEE* Paper 56-148, 1956.
30. ——— and C. E. McCray: Generating Random Forcing Functions for Control-system Simulation, *Electronics*, Aug. 18, 1961.
31. Slater, N. T.: A Low-frequency Noise Generator, *Electronic Eng.*, August, 1960.
32. Rainal, A. J.: Sampling Technique for Generating Gaussian Noise, *Rev. Sci. Instr.*, March, 1961.
33. McFadden, J. A.: The Probability Density of the Output of a Filter, *IRE Natl. Convention Record*, 1959.
34. ———: The Probability Density of the Output of a Filter, *IRE Trans. PGIT*, December, 1959.
35. Anderson, G. W., et al.: A Self-adjusting System, *IRE Natl. Convention Record*, 1958.
36. Manelis, J. B.: Generating Random Noise with Radioactive Sources, *Electronics*, Sept. 8, 1961.
37. Handler, H.: A Simple Noise Generator for Random-process Studies, *ACL Memo*. 35, University of Arizona, February, 1962.
38. Martin, J. W., et al.: A Method of Obtaining Noise Sources of Variable Correlation on the PACE Analogue Computer, *Ann. AICA*, July, 1962.
39. Anderson, T. C.: Fortune-wheel Process for Generating Pseudo-random Numbers, *Instruments and Control Systems*, January, 1962.

40. Zener-diode Noise Generator, *Programming Hints* 1, Applied Dynamics, Inc., Ann Arbor, Mich., 1964.

Hybrid Analog-Digital Pseudo-random-noise Generators

41. Golomb, S. W.: Sequences with Randomness Properties (Internal Rept.), Glenn L. Martin Co., Baltimore, Md., June 14, 1955.
42. Sterling, J. T.: An Introduction to Pseudo-noise Codes and Correlators, General Electric Co. *Rept.* R 62 DSD 34, Syracuse, N.Y., 1962.
43. Kepcke, J. J., et al.: GEESE Techniques for Pseudo-noise Generation, General Electric Co., *Rept.* R 62 DSD 64, Syracuse, N.Y., 1962.
44. Poortvliet, D. C. J.: The Measurement of System Impulse Response by Cross-correlation with Binary Signals, Technical University, *Rept.* Delft, Netherlands, 1962.
45. Horton, D.: Shift Counters, Computer Control Co., *Rept.* 3C 013-6, Framingham, Mass., 1962.
46. Hampton, R., G. A. Korn, and B. A. Mitchell: Hybrid Analog-Digital Random-noise Generation, *IEEETEC*, August, 1963.
47. Hampton, R.: A Hybrid Analog-digital Pseudo-random-noise Generator, M.S. Thesis, University of Arizona, 1964; *Proc. Spring Joint Computer Conf.*, 1964.
48. Roberts, T. A.: Analysis and Synthesis of Linear and Nonlinear Shift-register Generators, *Proc. Intern. Telemetering Conf.*, vol 1, London, September, 1963.

Miscellaneous Topics

49. Rogers, E. J.: Ideas for Design, *Electronic Design*, Apr. 27, 1964.
50. Korn, G. A., and T. M. Korn: *Mathematical Handbook for Scientists and Engineers*, McGraw-Hill, New York, 1961.
51. Bendat, J. S.: Mathematical Analysis and Analog Simulation of Atmospheric-turbulence Gust Velocities, *J. Aeron. Sci.*, January, 1957.
52. ———: *Principles and Applications of Random-noise Theory*, Wiley, New York, 1958.
53. Kavanagh, R. J., and R. C. Nolan: Generation of Random Signals with a Specified Spectral-density Matrix, *IEEE Trans. PGAC*, July, 1964.
54. Boulton, P. I., and R. J. Kavanagh: A Method of Producing Multiple Noncorre-lated Random Signals from a Single Gaussian Noise Source, *IEEE Trans. Appl. Ind.*, March, 1963.
55. Petternella, M.: A Low-frequency White-noise Generator with Artificial Source, *Proc. 4th AICA Conf.*, Brighton, England, 1964; Presses Académiques Européennes, Brussels, 1965.
56. Golomb, S. W.: *Digital Communications with Space Applications*, Prentice-Hall, Englewood Cliffs, N.J., 1964.
57. Tausworthe, R. C.: Random Numbers Generated by Linear Recurrence Modulo Two, *Math. of Computation*, April, 1965.

CHAPTER 5

MEASUREMENT OF TIME
AND SAMPLE AVERAGES,
CORRELATION FUNCTIONS,
AND AMPLITUDE DISTRIBUTIONS

AVERAGING AND STATISTICAL FLUCTUATIONS

5-1. Simple Continuous Time-average Measurements. Suitably designed linear filters ("averaging filters," Fig. 5-1a) produce weighted finite-time averages

$$z(T) = \int_0^T h(T - \lambda)f(\lambda) \, d\lambda = \int_0^T h(\zeta)f(T - \zeta) \, d\zeta \qquad (5\text{-}1)$$

which can serve as estimates of the ensemble average $E\{f\}$ of a stationary (or approximately stationary) input $f(t)$ with finite "power" $E\{f^2\}$. Such averaging devices act as low-pass filters attempting to reduce output fluctuations. In particular, the integrator shown in Fig. 5-1b is a linear averaging filter with the weighting function $h(\zeta) = 0$ for $\zeta < 0$, $h(\zeta) = \text{const}$ for $\zeta > 0$. We make the integrator gain equal to the reciprocal $1/T$ of the desired integration time T to obtain the finite-time average

$$\langle f \rangle_T = \frac{1}{T} \int_0^T f(\lambda) \, d\lambda = \frac{1}{T} \int_0^T f(T - \zeta) \, d\zeta \qquad (5\text{-}2)$$

(Sec. 1-4). $\langle f \rangle_T$ is an unbiased estimate of the desired ensemble average $E\{f\}$, i.e.,

$$E\{\langle f \rangle_T\} = E\{f\} \qquad (5\text{-}3)$$

For each of the simple averaging filters in Fig. 5-1c, we have

$$H(j\omega) = \frac{1}{j\omega T_0 + 1} \qquad h(\zeta) = \frac{1}{T_0} e^{-\zeta/T_0} \qquad (\zeta > 0) \qquad (5\text{-}4)$$

Such a filter produces the *exponentially-weighted-past (EWP) average*[6]

$$z(T) = \frac{1}{T_0} \int_0^T e^{-(T-\lambda)/T_0} f(\lambda) \, d\lambda = \frac{1}{T_0} \int_0^T e^{-\zeta/T_0} f(T - \zeta) \, d\zeta \qquad (5\text{-}5)$$

In view of the exponential weighting, values $f(T - \zeta)$ more than $\zeta = 4T_0$ to $\zeta = 10T_0$ in the past will have negligible effect on $z(T)$. In practice,

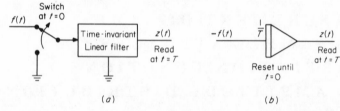

FIG. 5-1a, b. Switched time-invariant averaging filter (a), and simple integrator (b).

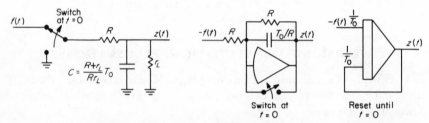

FIG. 5-1c. Three simple averaging filters producing exponentially weighted averages.

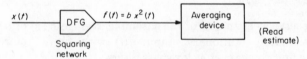

FIG. 5-1d. Measurement of mean square.

we shall always use integration times T longer than 4 to 10 filter time constants T_0; we can then replace Eq. (5) by

$$z(T) = \langle f \rangle_{\text{EWP}} = \frac{1}{T_0} \int_{-\infty}^T e^{-(T-\lambda)/T_0} f(\lambda) \, d\lambda$$

$$= \frac{1}{T_0} \int_0^\infty e^{-\zeta/T_0} f(T - \zeta) \, d\zeta \qquad (5\text{-}6)$$

For sufficiently large T, $z(t)$ is, therefore, a *stationary* random function of T with

$$E\{\langle f \rangle_{\text{EWP}}\} = E\{f\} \qquad (5\text{-}7)$$

We thus have an unbiased estimate of $E\{f\}$ for all sufficiently large T; unlike the integrator output in Fig. 5-1b, our exponentially weighted average can be read continuously, and not only at a specific instant of time.

Statistical fluctuations will cause different readings for $\langle f \rangle_T$ in repeated experiments, and the stationary filter output (6) can actually be observed to fluctuate with time. The fluctuations of an estimate are most frequently measured by its variance (mean-square deviation from the mean, see also Sec. 5-5). For unbiased estimates, the estimate variance equals the square of the rms error due to statistical fluctuations. We have, in particular,

$$\left. \begin{array}{l} \text{Var } \{\langle f \rangle_T\} = \dfrac{2}{T} \displaystyle\int_0^T \left(1 - \dfrac{\lambda}{T}\right) \text{Cov } \{f(0), f(\lambda)\} \, d\lambda \\[2mm] \text{with} \quad \text{Cov } \{f(0), f(\lambda)\} = R_{ff}(\lambda) - [E\{f\}]^2 = R_{f-E\{f\}, f-E\{f\}}(\lambda) \end{array} \right\} \quad (5\text{-}8)$$

as already derived in Sec. 1-4, while the variance of the stationary estimate (4) is obtained most easily with the aid of Eqs. (1-31) and (1-33):

$$\begin{aligned} \text{Var } \{\langle f \rangle_{\text{EWP}}\} &= E\{\langle f \rangle_{\text{EWP}}^2\} - [E\{\langle f \rangle_{\text{EWP}}\}]^2 \\ &= \int_{-\infty}^{\infty} |H(j\omega)|^2 \Phi_{ff}(\omega) \, \frac{d\omega}{2\pi} - [E\{f\}]^2 \\ &= \int_{-\infty}^{\infty} \frac{1}{(\omega T_0)^2 + 1} \, \Phi(\omega) \, \frac{d\omega}{2\pi} \end{aligned} \quad (5\text{-}9)$$

where $\Phi(\omega)$ is the power spectral density of $f(t) - E\{f\}$. In either case, the integration time T or filter time constant T_0 required to reduce the estimate variance to a specified value is seen to depend on the power spectrum of our signal $f(t)$. Signals with predominant low-frequency components often require disconcertingly long averaging periods; note, in this connection, that excessively long observation times may well endanger our stationarity assumptions.

NOTE. If $f(t)$ is a stationary random-phase periodic process (Sec. 1-10), then $R_{ff}(\tau)$ is also periodic; hence the variance (8) vanishes whenever the averaging time T equals an integral number of periods.

5-2. An Example. (a) Measurement of Mean Value. We want to measure the mean value $E\{x\} = \xi$ of a stationary random voltage $x(t)$ with

$$R_{xx}(\tau) = a^2 e^{-\alpha|\tau|} + \xi^2 \qquad \Phi_{xx}(\omega) = \frac{2\alpha a^2}{\omega^2 + \alpha^2} + 2\pi \xi^2 \delta(\omega) \quad (5\text{-}10)$$

(white noise passed through a simple filter with -3-db bandwidth $\alpha/2\pi$ cps, or random telegraph wave with counting rate $\alpha/2$, Sec. 1-11). In this case, Eqs. (6) and (7) yield

$$\text{Var } \{\langle x \rangle_T\} = \frac{2a^2}{T} \int_0^T \left(1 - \frac{\lambda}{T}\right) e^{-\alpha\lambda} \, d\lambda$$

$$= \frac{2a^2}{(\alpha T)^2} (\alpha T - 1 + e^{-\alpha T}) \leq \frac{2a^2}{\alpha T} \quad (5\text{-}11)$$

$$\text{Var } \{\langle x \rangle_{\text{EWP}}\} = \frac{a^2\alpha}{\pi} \int_{-\infty}^{\infty} \frac{d\omega}{[(\omega T_0)^2 + 1](\omega^2 + \alpha^2)} = \frac{a^2}{\alpha T_0 + 1} \leq \frac{a^2}{\alpha T_0} \quad (5\text{-}12)$$

For a specified estimate variance e_{RMS}^2, we shall require

$$T \geq \frac{1}{\alpha} \frac{2a^2}{e_{\text{RMS}}^2} \qquad T_0 \geq \frac{1}{\alpha} \frac{a^2}{e_{\text{RMS}}^2} \quad (5\text{-}13)$$

If our input spectrum Φ_{xx} has a -3-db bandwidth $\alpha/2\pi = 100$ cps (for a random telegraph wave, this would imply a count rate $\alpha/2$ of about 314 cps), an rms error within 1 per cent of the input dispersion $\sqrt{\text{Var } \{x\}} = a$ requires

$$T \geq \frac{100}{\pi} \text{ sec} \approx 31.8 \text{ sec} \qquad T_0 \geq \frac{100}{2\pi} \text{ sec} \approx 15.9 \text{ sec}$$

But to reduce the rms error by a factor of *ten*, we must increase T or T_0 *a hundredfold;* we should want $T \geq 3,180$ sec $= 53$ min, or almost a full hour. In many d-c measurements, it is, of course, more satisfactory to specify rms error requirements in volts rather than in per cent of a.

(b) Measurement of Mean Square (Power). We next want to measure the mean square $E\{x^2\}$ for stationary Gaussian noise $x(t)$ described by Eq. (10). We use a diode squaring network (Sec. 2-3b) or multiplier to form a voltage proportional to $f(t) = x^2(t)$ at the input of our integrator or averaging filter (Fig. 5-1d). Reference to Eq. (56) shows that*

$$\left. \begin{array}{l} R_{ff}(\tau) = 2a^4 e^{-2\alpha|\tau|} + (a^2 + \xi^2)^2 \\[2mm] \Phi_{ff}(\tau) = \dfrac{8\alpha a^2}{\omega^2 + (2\alpha)^2} + 2\pi(a^2 + \xi^2)^2 \delta(\omega) \end{array} \right\} \quad (5\text{-}14)$$

which is of the same general form as Eq. (10). By analogy with the relations derived in Sec. 5-2a, we find, therefore,

$$\text{Var } \{\langle x^2 \rangle_T\} = \frac{a^4}{(\alpha T)^2} (2\alpha T - 1 + e^{-2\alpha T}) \leq \frac{2a^4}{\alpha T} \quad (5\text{-}15)$$

$$\text{Var } \{\langle x^2 \rangle_{\text{EWP}}\} = \frac{2a^4}{2\alpha T_0 + 1} \leq \frac{a^4}{\alpha T_0} \quad (5\text{-}16)$$

If rms errors in our estimate for $E\{x^2\}$ are expressed in per cent of a^2, then averaging-time requirements for a specified percentage error will be the same as those derived in Sec. 5-2a.

* Note that Eq. (14) applies to Gaussian noise but *not*, say, to a random telegraph wave $x(t)$ described by Eq. (10).

5-3. More General Averaging Filters.[4,5] We return to the case of a general time-invariant averaging filter, preceded by a switch closed between $t = 0$ and $t = T$ (Fig. 5-1a). We shall assume $h(\zeta)$ to be bounded and rewrite Eq. (1) as

$$z(T) = \int_{-\infty}^{T} h_T(T - \lambda)f(\lambda) \, d\lambda = \int_{0}^{\infty} h_T(\zeta)f(T - \zeta) \, d\zeta \qquad (5\text{-}17)$$

where
$$h_T(\zeta) = \begin{cases} h(\zeta) & (0 \le t < T) \\ 0 & \text{otherwise} \end{cases} \qquad (5\text{-}18)$$

Hence

$$E\{z(T)\} = E\{f\} \int_{0}^{T} h_T(\zeta) \, d\zeta = a(T)E\{f\} \qquad (5\text{-}19)$$

so that $z(T)/a(T)$ is an unbiased estimate of $E\{f\}$.

Although our filter and switch surely constitute a *time-variable* linear system, the expression (17) looks like that for the output $z(t)$ of a *time-invariant* filter with weighting function $w(t,\lambda) \equiv h_T(t - \lambda)$. Such a filter would continuously produce the stationary *finite-time running average*

$$z(t) = \int_{t-T}^{t} h_T(t - \lambda)f(\lambda) \, d\lambda = \int_{0}^{T} h_T(\zeta)f(t - \zeta) \, d\zeta \qquad (5\text{-}20)$$

over the past T sec, but is not, in general, realizable with a finite number of lumped circuit elements.* The variance of our switched-filter output $z(T)$ is, however, equal to Var $\{z(t)\}$ and can, therefore, be obtained with the aid of Eqs. (1-28) and (1-29):

$$\text{Var } \{z(T)\} = E\{[z(t) - E\{z(t)\}]^2\}$$
$$= \int_{-\infty}^{\infty} \varphi_{h_T h_T}(\lambda)\{R_{ff}(\lambda) - [E\{f\}]^2\} \, d\lambda \qquad (5\text{-}22)$$

where
$$\varphi_{h_T h_T}(\lambda) = \int_{-\infty}^{\infty} h_T(\zeta)h_T(\zeta + \lambda) \, d\zeta \qquad (5\text{-}23)$$

With increasing averaging time $T \to \infty$, Eq. (19) shows that $a(T) \to H(0)$. The estimate variance (22) will not in general go to zero but, rather, approaches the stationary output variance

$$\text{Var } \{z(\infty)\} = \int_{-\infty}^{\infty} \varphi_{hh}(\lambda)\{R_{ff}(\lambda) - [E\{f\}]^2\} \, d\lambda$$
$$= \int_{-\infty}^{\infty} |H(j\omega)|^2 \Phi(\omega) \frac{d\omega}{2\pi} = 2|H(0)|^2 \Phi(0) B_{EQ} \qquad (5\text{-}24)$$

---

* As an interesting example, the finite-time integration in Fig. 5-1b is described by Eq. (26); the transfer function of the corresponding time-invariant filter

$$H_T(s) = \int_{0}^{T} h_T(\zeta)e^{-\zeta s} \, d\zeta = \frac{1}{sT}(1 - e^{-Ts}) \qquad (5\text{-}21)$$

cannot be realized with lumped-parameter networks, although various useful approximations are possible.[5]

if this quantity exists. Here, $\Phi(\omega)$ is, again, the power spectral density of $f(t) - E\{f\}$, and

$$B_{\text{EQ}} = \frac{1}{2|H(0)|^2} \int_{-\infty}^{\infty} |H(j\omega)|^2 \frac{d\omega}{2\pi} \qquad (5\text{-}25)$$

is the bandwidth of an equivalent "rectangular" low-pass filter having the frequency response

$$H_{\text{EQ}}(j\omega) = \begin{cases} H(0) & (|\omega| \leq 2\pi B_{\text{EQ}}) \\ 0 & (|\omega| > 2\pi B_{\text{EQ}}) \end{cases}$$

B_{EQ} is a useful measure of the variance-reducing properties of a given averaging filter.[4,5]

For the switched integrator of Fig. 5-1b,

$$h_T(\zeta) = \begin{cases} h(\zeta) = \dfrac{1}{T} & (0 \leq t < T) \\ 0 & \text{otherwise} \end{cases} \qquad (5\text{-}26)$$

so that

$$\varphi_{h_T h_T}(\lambda) = \frac{1}{T}\left(1 - \frac{|\lambda|}{T}\right) (|\lambda| \leq T) \qquad (5\text{-}27)$$

again yields the expression (6) for Var $\{z(T)\}$ = Var $\{\langle f \rangle_T\}$. As $T \to \infty$, we obtain the asymptotic relation

$$\text{Var } \{\langle f \rangle_T\} \cong \frac{2}{T} \int_0^{\infty} \{R_{ff}(\lambda) - [E\{f\}]^2\}\, d\lambda = \frac{\Phi(0)}{T} \to 0 \text{ as } T \to \infty \qquad (5\text{-}28)$$

where $\Phi(\omega)$ is, once again, the power spectral density of $f(t) - E\{f\}$. Periodic components of $f(t)$ will be "integrated out" eventually as T increases. Comparison of Eqs. (24) and (28) yields the equivalent filter bandwidth $B_{\text{EQ}} = 1/2T$ for the switched integrator, although the definition (25) does not apply directly.

For the simple RC filters of Fig. 5-1c, we find

$$\left. \begin{aligned} a(T) &= 1 - e^{-T/T_0} \\ \varphi_{h_T h_T}(\lambda) &= \frac{1}{2T_0}\left(e^{-|\lambda|/T_0} - e^{(|\lambda|-2T)/T_0}\right) (|\lambda| \leq T) \\ B_{\text{EQ}} &= \frac{1}{4T_0} \end{aligned} \right\} \qquad (5\text{-}29)$$

Other frequently encountered averaging devices are damped mass-spring systems (meter or recorder movements, accelerometers, and many other transducers). Table 5-1 lists equivalent filter bandwidths for such systems (see also refs. 4 and 5).

If the input-signal power spectrum has pronounced components near certain known frequencies, we can, clearly, improve our estimate variance by employing filter sections "tuned" so as to suppress selected frequency ranges. From a more general point of

Table 5-1. Second-order Averaging Filters

	$H(j\omega)$	B_{EQ}
Overdamped system.............	$\dfrac{1}{(j\omega T_1 + 1)(j\omega T_2 + 1)}$	$\dfrac{1}{4(T_1 + T_2)}$
Critically damped system.........	$\dfrac{1}{(j\omega T_0 + 1)^2}$	$\dfrac{1}{2T_0}$
Underdamped system.............	$\dfrac{\alpha^2 + \omega_1^2}{(j\omega + \alpha)^2 + \omega_1^2}$	$\dfrac{\alpha^2 + \omega_1^2}{8\omega_1}$

view, the design of a linear averaging filter which minimizes Var $\{z(T)\}$ for a given input power spectrum $\Phi_{ff}(\omega)$ is a mean-square error-optimization problem which reduces to a Wiener-type filter design as $T \to \infty$.[4] The even more general theory of signal extraction[4] attempts to minimize the estimate variance by employing nonlinear as well as linear signal processing tailored to take advantage of all available information about the input random process $f(t)$ (e.g., about its amplitude distribution and its power spectrum). It can be shown[4] that suitably chosen *linear* filters are optimal for stationary Gaussian input; in particular, the simple integrator is optimal for averaging white (or wideband) Gaussian noise added to a d-c signal. Simple integrators and low-pass averaging networks suffice for most general-purpose-measurement applications, where there is relatively little a priori knowledge about the nature of the signal. Line-frequency-suppression filters are also often useful.

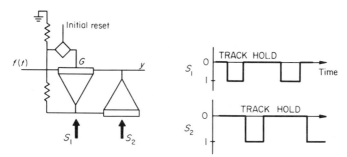

Fig. 5-2a. A track-hold-pair accumulator implementing

$$y_{n+1} = y_n + f(t_n) = \sum_{k=1}^{n} f(t_k)$$

at the time $t = t_k$ ($n = 0, 1, 2, \ldots$). The $f(t_k)$ can be either samples of the same function $f(t)$ (sampled-data time averaging), or samples $^k f(t_1)$ obtained in successive Monte-Carlo-type simulations (random-sample averaging, Fig. 4-1). The initial-reset circuit ensures zero input to track-hold 2 during the INITIAL RESET period prior to computation, so that $y_0 = 0$ (see also Secs. 2-13 and 8-4).

5-4. Sampled-data Averaging. The sampled-data averaging devices of Figs. 5-2 and 5-3 can compute *finite-time sampled-data averages*

$$[f]_n = \frac{1}{n} \sum_{k=1}^{n} f(t_k) \tag{5-30}$$

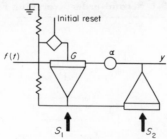

FIG- 5-2b. A track-hold-pair circuit computing on exponentially-weighted-past sampled-data average by implementing the difference equation

$$y_n = \alpha y_{-n1} + f(t_{n-1}) = \sum_{k=1}^{n-1} \alpha^{n-k-1} f(t_k) \qquad (n = 1, 2, \ldots ; \quad 0 < \alpha < 1; y_0 = 0)$$

Timing is the same as in Fig. 5-2a; $\lim\limits_{n \to \infty} E\{y_n\} = E\{f\}/(1 - \alpha)$.

(Sec. 1-4) from single data records in various instrumentation applications. t_k may or may not be an integral multiple $k \, \Delta t$ of a constant time interval Δt (periodic sampling). The same circuits can also average samples ${}^k f(t_1)$ from successive independent experiments or Monte-Carlo simulations to produce *sample averages*

$$\bar{f} = \frac{1}{n} \sum_{k=1}^{n} {}^k f(t_1) \qquad\qquad (5\text{-}31)$$

(Secs. 1-5 and 4-2); note that $\bar{f}$ estimates $E\{f[t_1]\}$ for nonstationary as well as for stationary $f(t)$. The sample size n is treated as a fixed scale factor and is usually taken to be a convenient power of 10.

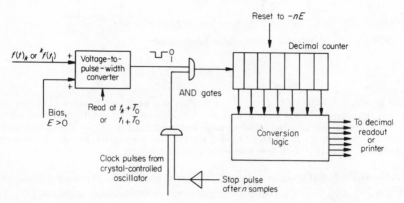

FIG. 5-3a. A hybrid analog-digital sample-averaging circuit for computing $n[f]_n$ or $n\bar{f}$. A bias voltage $E > 0$ ensures positive input to the voltage-to-pulse-width converter. The simple unidirectional counter resets to $-nE$, so that the bias is subtracted out digitally; a conversion matrix produces correct positive or negative readout.

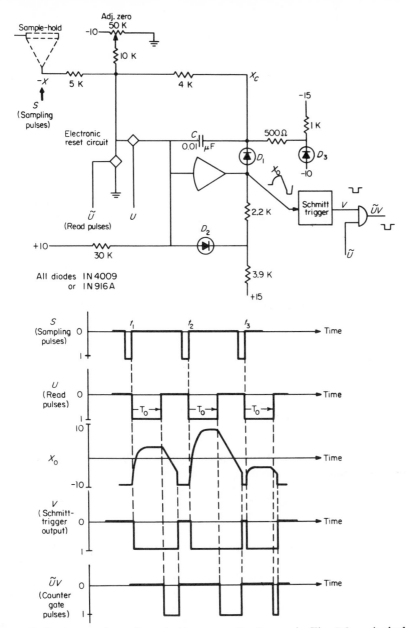

FIG. 5-3b. An inexpensive voltage-to-time converter for use in Fig. 5-3a. A single transistor d-c amplifier serves as both comparator and integrator. The electronic reset circuit functions exactly like the reset relay K_R of Fig. 2-6b to charge the integrating capacitor C initially to $X_C = 0.8$ $(X + 10)$ volts. At $t = t_{\text{READ}}$, the integrator begins to integrate downward at $10^5/3$ volts/sec. When X_C reaches a fixed threshold near -8 volts, diode D_1 ceases to conduct; loss of feedback causes X_o to decrease abruptly until limited by D_2. This marks the end of a time interval accurately proportional to $X + $ const. An extra silicon-junction diode D_3 compensates for breakpoint drift of D_1 with temperature changes. Accuracy is within 20 mv or 0.2 per cent of half scale $(-10$ to $+10$ volts) between 20 and 50 deg C. (*ASTRAC II computer, University of Arizona; based on ref. 22.*)

The *analog accumulator circuits* of Fig. 5-2 combine analog addition with sample-hold operation and are easily patched on modern analog computers. Unfortunately, such accumulators tend to accumulate errors due to switching spikes and amplifier drift (see also Sec. 5-5). *Hybrid analog-digital sample-averaging circuits* of the type shown in Fig. 5-3 are more accurate and convenient. They have served well especially for the computation of sample averages (31) in Monte-Carlo simulation (see also Sec. 4-2).

The sampled-data average (30) is an unbiased estimate of $E\{f\}$ for a stationary process. Assuming periodic sampling (constant Δt), the output variance of the sample-averaging device is then given by Eq. (1-15), i.e.,

$$\left. \begin{aligned} \text{Var } [f]_n &= \frac{1}{n^2} \sum_{i=1}^{n} \sum_{k=1}^{n} \text{Cov } \{f(i\,\Delta t)f(k\,\Delta t)\} \\ &= \frac{1}{n} \text{ Var } \{f\} + \frac{2}{n} \sum_{k=1}^{n-1} \left(1 - \frac{k}{n}\right) \text{Cov } \{f(0)f(k\,\Delta t)\} \end{aligned} \right\} \quad (5\text{-}32)$$

with $\quad \text{Cov } \{f(0)f(k\,\Delta t)\} = R_{ff}(k\,\Delta t) - [E\{f\}]^2$

which reduces to Var $\{f\}/n$ for uncorrelated samples. For large sample sizes n, Eq. (32) reduces to

$$\text{Var } \{[f]_n\} \approx \frac{2}{n} \sum_{k=1}^{n-1} \left(1 - \frac{k}{n}\right) R_{ff}(k\,\Delta t) - [E\{f\}]^2 \quad (5\text{-}33)$$

If $R_{ff}(k\,\Delta t)$ decreases as k increases, we may be able to justify the cruder approximation

$$\text{Var } \{[f]_n\} \approx \frac{2}{n} \sum_{k=1}^{n-1} R_{ff}(k\,\Delta t) - [E\{f\}]^2 \quad (n \gg 1)$$

Care must be taken to avoid pickup of spurious periodic signals at the sampling frequency, its harmonics, or subharmonics. A random-phase signal repeating at the sampling rate (e.g., line-frequency pickup for 60-cps sampling) will add its mean-square value to the estimate *variance*, while fixed-phase disturbances (e.g., sampling-switch spikes) will add a bias to our *average*. Unfortunately, it may be difficult to predict the variance (32) or (33) for correlated samples: $R_{ff}(\tau)$ is often unknown, and its estimation is itself subject to fluctuation errors (see also Sec. 5-9). A low sampling frequency can yield uncorrelated samples but is usually wasteful of data. Fast sampling approximates continuous time averaging (Sec. 1-4).

More sophisticated types of sampled-data time-averaging circuits employ *weighted* averaging, which permits various "digital-filtering" schemes.[4] Figure 5-2b shows a very simple example (see also Secs. 2-13 and 7-2d).

5-5. Some Practical Considerations (see also Secs. 5-4, 8-3, and 8-4). Each of the averaging devices described in Secs. 5-1 to 5-4 can average functions like $f(t) = x^2(t)$, $f(t) = x(t - \tau)y(t)$, etc., to produce mean-square values, correlation-function estimates, and probability estimates (Secs. 5-8 to 5-15). It is usually advisable to have any sample-hold operation precede the required function generator, so that the latter can work with the relatively slow sample-hold output. For sampled-data averaging (but not for Monte-Carlo-type sample averaging), we must then suppress frequencies higher than one-half the sampling rate before sampling to prevent "aliasing" errors caused by spurious high-frequency components.[37] A low-pass smoothing filter immediately ahead of the sampler will, in any case, permit the use of slower (and thus less expensive) track-hold circuits for time averaging.

Note carefully that *all* averaging devices involving d-c amplifiers and/or electronic switches must be calibrated for zero as well as for gain *over a full averaging period* to minimize the effect of accumulating drift, switching-spike errors, and/or conversion errors. This calibration should include the sampling circuits.

The *dynamic range* required of measurement circuits for Gaussian or approximately Gaussian variables x should accommodate deviations $|x - E\{x\}|$ from the mean up to between $3\sqrt{\mathrm{Var}\,\{x\}} = 3\sigma$ and 4σ (see also Sec. 4-3). Note, in particular, that *clipping of a Gaussian random variable x with mean zero and variance σ^2 reduces the ideal mean-square value σ^2*

By 7.9 per cent for clipping at $x = \pm 2\sigma$
By 2.2 per cent for clipping at $x = \pm 2.5\sigma$
By 0.5 per cent for clipping at $x = \pm 3\sigma$
By less than 0.1 per cent for clipping at $x = \pm 4\sigma$

5-6. Error Probabilities and Confidence Limits.   As we have seen, statistical estimates are subject to random fluctuations; the practical design of any measurement procedure and/or apparatus requires us to gauge the extent of these fluctuations, which often impose a practical limit on the need for equipment accuracy. It makes little sense to employ instruments or computers accurate to within 0.1 per cent to determine, say, a voltage average subject to 0.8 per cent rms fluctuations caused by unavoidable restrictions on the observation time or number of observations.

Our previous analysis dealt with fluctuations in terms of estimate variances or rms errors. We may also be interested in the probability of excessive deviations $|z - \zeta|$ of an estimate z from its expected value $\zeta = E\{z\}$. Given only the variance $\mathrm{Var}\,\{z\} = \sigma_z{}^2$ of our estimate, *Chebychev's inequality*

$$\mathrm{Prob}\,[|z - \zeta| \geq a] \leq \frac{\sigma_z{}^2}{a^2} \tag{5-34}$$

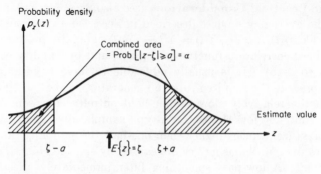

Fig. 5-4a. A symmetrical tolerance interval $(\zeta - a, \ \zeta + a)$ such that Prob $[|z - \zeta| \geq a] \leq \alpha$.

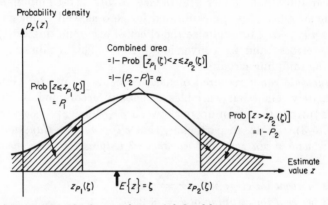

Fig. 5-4b. A more general tolerance interval defined by

$$\text{Prob } [z_{P1}(\zeta) < z \leq z_{P2}(\zeta)] = P_2 - P_1 = 1 - \alpha$$

Observed estimate values z outside the tolerance limits reject the hypothetical mean $E\{z\} = \zeta$ with a false-rejection probability (level of significance) α.

provides coarse but generally applicable bounds on fluctuation probabilities;* note that $\zeta = E\{z\} = E\{f\}$ and $\sigma_z = e_{\text{RMS}}$ if z is an unbiased estimate of $E\{f\}$.

If, in addition to the variance of our estimate z, we also know that its probability density has a single maximum (mode) at $z = \zeta_{\text{MODE}}$, then we may employ the inequality[37]

$$\text{Prob } [|z - \zeta| \geq a] \leq \frac{4}{9} \frac{\sigma_z{}^2 + (\zeta - \zeta_{\text{MODE}})^2}{(a - |\zeta - \zeta_{\text{MODE}}|)^2} \qquad (5\text{-}35)$$

* Chebychev's inequality follows directly from

$$\sigma_z{}^2 = \int_{-\infty}^{\infty} (z - \zeta)^2 p_z(z) \, dz \geq \int_{-\infty}^{z-a} (z - \zeta)^2 p_z(z) \, dz + \int_{\zeta+a}^{\infty} (z - \zeta)^2 p_z(z) \, dz$$

$$\geq a^2 \int_{-\infty}^{\zeta-a} p_z(z) \, dz + a^2 \int_{\zeta+a}^{\infty} p_z(z) \, dz$$

which is stronger than the Chebychev inequality (34) for small $\zeta - \zeta_{\text{MODE}}$ (e.g., symmetrical unimodal distributions). To find the actual value of

$$\alpha = \text{Prob} \left[|z - \zeta| \geq a\right] = 1 - \int_{\zeta-a}^{\zeta+a} p_z(z)\, dz \qquad (5\text{-}36)$$

for different deviations a (Fig. 5-4a), we require more specific knowledge about the amplitude distribution of the estimate z. If, in particular, z is normally distributed (or approximately so), then we can use published tables of the standardized normal distribution (u distribution)[38] listing "tolerance limits" $|u|_{1-\alpha} = u_{1-\alpha/2} = a/e_{\text{RMS}}$ for different values of

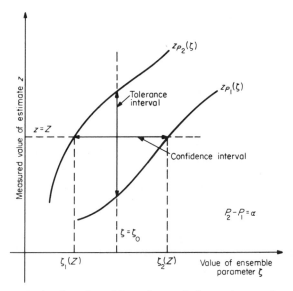

FIG. 5-4c. Derivation of confidence intervals from tolerance intervals.

α or $1 - \alpha$. Table 5-2 gives typical tolerance limits for normal distributions. The corresponding bounds obtained from the inequalities (34) and (35) are also shown for comparison; note that these bounds are quite coarse.

Table 5-2. Probability That an Absolute Deviation
from the Mean Exceeds a

a	Normal distribution, Eq. (36)	From Eq. (35) with $\|\zeta - \zeta_{\text{MODE}}\| \approx 0$	From Chebychev inequality (34)
σ_z	0.32	≤ 0.44	≤ 1
$2\sigma_z$	0.045	≤ 0.11	≤ 0.25
$3\sigma_z$	0.003	≤ 0.049	≤ 0.11
$4\sigma_z$	0.0001	≤ 0.028	≤ 0.063

The relations (34) to (36) predict or bound the probability α that the estimate z will not deviate from its mean ζ by more than a. Estimate values z outside the symmetrical "tolerance interval" $(\zeta - a, \zeta + a)$ are said to *reject the hypothesis* $E\{z\} = \zeta$ *at the level of significance* α; i.e., the probability of a false rejection equals α (test of significance, refs. 37 and 38). More generally, tolerance limits need not be symmetrical about $z = \zeta$. It may be possible to define closer tolerances $z_{P_1}(\zeta)$, $z_{P_2}(\zeta)$ for a hypothetical mean ζ by

$$\text{Prob } [z_{P_1}(\zeta) < z \leq z_{P_2}(\zeta)] = \text{Prob } [z \leq z_{P_2}(\zeta)] - \text{Prob } [z \leq z_{P_1}(\zeta)]$$
$$= P_2 - P_1 = 1 - \alpha \quad (5\text{-}37)$$

(Fig. 5-4b). Test values of z outside the tolerance interval (z_{P_1}, z_{P_2}) again reject the hypothetical value $E\{z\} = \zeta$ at the level of significance α; note that there will be many possible choices of $z_{P_1}(\zeta)$ for a given value of α.

The actual value of $E\{z\} = \zeta$ is usually a fixed and *nonrandom* (though unknown) parameter; it is, then, *not* possible to define an "inverse" probability that ζ differs by less than a from a given measured estimate value $z = Z$. Given a set of tolerance intervals for hypothetical ζ values, we can, however, define lower and upper *confidence limits* $\zeta_1(Z)$, $\zeta_2(Z)$ such that the observed $z = Z$ leads us to accept every hypothetical ζ in the *confidence interval* between $\zeta_1(Z)$ and $\zeta_2(Z)$ at the level of significance α (Fig. 5-4c). We call $1 - \alpha$ the *confidence coefficient* for our class of confidence intervals.

If z is known to be normally distributed with mean ζ and variance $\sigma_z{}^2$, Eq. (36) yields symmetrical tolerance limits

$$z_1(\zeta) = \zeta - u_{1-\alpha/2}\sigma_z \qquad z_2(\zeta) = \zeta + u_{1-\alpha/2}\sigma_z \qquad (5\text{-}38)$$

at the level of significance α. The corresponding confidence limits for a confidence coefficient $1 - \alpha$ are

$$\zeta_1(z) = z - u_{1-\alpha/2}\sigma_z \qquad \zeta_2(z) = z + u_{1-\alpha/2}\sigma_z \qquad (5\text{-}39)$$

In this important special case, the width of the symmetrical confidence interval corresponding to any measured value of z does not depend on z but only on Var $\{z\} = \sigma_z{}^2$. Since z is also an unbiased estimate of ζ, the curves in Fig. 5-4c reduce to straight lines.

5-7. Amount of Data Required. Data taking and computation costs time and effort, and excessive observation times may endanger the validity of stationarity assumptions with respect to environment and/or measuring apparatus. It is, therefore, important to determine the smallest observation time T or sample size n required to produce specified estimate variances Var $\{z\}$ or confidence intervals (see also Sec. 5-2).

If z is, say, an estimate $\langle f \rangle_T$, $\langle f \rangle_{\text{EWP}}$, $[f]_n$, or $\bar{f}$ of an ensemble average $E\{f\}$, the desired relationship between Var $\{z\}$ and T or n is expressed by relations like Eq. (8), (9), (22), or (32); unfortunately, Var $\{z\}$ will depend on Var $\{f\}$ and/or $R_{ff}(\tau)$, *and these quantities are rarely known in practice* (see also Secs. 5-11 and 5-14).

Sometimes, the easiest way out will be to employ very rough estimates of Var $\{f\}$ and/or $R_{ff}(\tau)$ in our expression for Var $\{z\}$ and to accept the resulting large observation times or sample sizes.   If practical, we can, instead, make repeated (and, we hope, independent) estimates z_1, z_2, . . . , z_n of z, so that Var $\{z\}$ can be estimated by the variance between samples

$$
\left.
\begin{aligned}
S_z{}^2 &= \frac{1}{N-1} \sum_{k=1}^{N} (z_k - \bar{z})^2 = \frac{1}{N-1} \sum_{k=1}^{N} z_k{}^2 - \frac{N}{N-1} \bar{z}^2 \\
\bar{z} &= \frac{1}{N} \sum_{k=1}^{N} z_k
\end{aligned}
\right\}
\tag{5-40}
$$

$S_z{}^2$, though, is itself a random variable, whose distribution depends upon further unknown quantities.

This classical statistical dilemma is brilliantly resolved if our N estimates z_1, z_2, . . . , z_N constitute a *normal random sample*, i.e., if they are statistically independent and have identical normal distributions with mean ζ and variance $\sigma_z{}^2$.   In this case, $(N-1)S_z{}^2/\sigma_z{}^2$ has a χ^2 *distribution with $N-1$ degrees of freedom*,[37] so that we can obtain confidence intervals for $\sigma_z{}^2$ from

$$
1 - \alpha = P_2 - P_1 = \text{Prob}\left[\frac{N-1}{\chi_{P_1}{}^2} S_z{}^2 \leq \sigma_z{}^2 \leq \frac{N-1}{\chi_{P_2}{}^2} S_z{}^2 \right]
\tag{5-41}
$$

where $\chi_{P_1}{}^2$, $\chi_{P_2}{}^2$ are χ^2 fractiles taken from published tables.   Even more important is the fact that each of the statistics

$$
\frac{z_k - \zeta}{S_z} \quad (k = 1,2, . . ,N) \quad \text{and} \quad \frac{\bar{z} - \zeta}{S_z/\sqrt{N}}
$$
(STUDENT'S RATIO)   (5-42)

has the widely tabulated *Student's t distribution with $N-1$ degrees of freedom*.[37,38]   This t distribution replaces the standardized normal distribution of $(z - \zeta)/\sigma_z$ used to compute confidence limits for ζ when σ_z is known (Sec. 5-6).   Measured values of $\bar{z}$ are, then, associated with symmetrical confidence limits

$$
\zeta_1(\bar{z}) = \bar{z} - t_{1-\alpha/2} \frac{S_z}{\sqrt{N}} \qquad \zeta_2(\bar{z}) = \bar{z} + t_{1-\alpha/2} \frac{S_z}{\sqrt{N}}
\tag{5-43}
$$

for ζ, where the tabulated fractile $t_{1-\alpha/2}$ is defined by the confidence coefficient

$$1 - \alpha = \text{Prob}\left[|\bar{z} - \zeta| \leq |t|_{1-\alpha}\frac{S_z}{\sqrt{N}}\right] = \text{Prob}\left[|\bar{z} - \zeta| \leq t_{1-\alpha/2}\frac{S_z}{\sqrt{N}}\right] \quad (5\text{-}44)$$

The t distribution is more spread out than the standardized normal distribution (u distribution), so that Eq. (43) defines wider confidence intervals than Eq. (39) (Fig. 5-5). This reduction in precision simply accounts for the fact that our confidence-interval width is now determined by the *measured* quantity S_z, which is itself subject to statistical fluctuations. As $m = N - 1 \to \infty$, S_z fluctuates less and less: t is asymptotically normal, and it is usually reasonable to replace t fractiles by u fractiles for $m > 30$.[37,38]

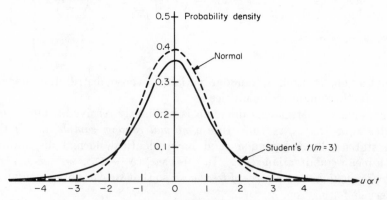

FIG. 5-5. Student's t distribution compared to the standardized normal distribution. (*From G. A. Korn and T. M. Korn, Mathematical Handbook for Scientists and Engineers, McGraw-Hill, New York, 1961.*)

In practice, confidence intervals based on Student's t distribution are commonly employed even if the subsample estimates $z_1, z_2, \ldots, z_N$ are statistically independent and have identical probability distributions which are only *approximately* normal.[37] This is frequently true if z is a subsample average $\bar{f}$ of n statistically independent similar measurements f_k or ^kf, as in the important case of repetitive-computer Monte-Carlo simulation (Sec. 8-4).

An even more favorable situation results if the measurements f_k or ^kf are themselves statistically independent and have identical approximately normal distributions (e.g., Monte-Carlo simulation of approximately Gaussian random processes). In this case, there is no need to take subsample averages. Given, say, an approximately normal random sample $(^1f, {}^2f, \ldots, {}^nf)$ with sample variance

$$S_f{}^2 = \frac{n}{n-1}\overline{(f - \bar{f})^2} = \frac{1}{n-1}\sum_{k=1}^{n} {}^kf^2 - \frac{n}{n-1}\bar{f}^2 \quad (5\text{-}45)$$

the statistic

$$\frac{z - \zeta}{S_f/\sqrt{n}} = \frac{\bar{f} - E\{f\}}{(\bar{f} - \bar{f})^{2^{1/2}}/\sqrt{n - 1}} \tag{5-46}$$

is approximately distributed like Student's t with $n - 1$ degrees of freedom; the approximation usually improves with increasing sample size n[46] and is exact if the ^kf are normally distributed. The t distribution yields symmetrical confidence limits

$$\zeta_1(\bar{f}) = \bar{f} - t_{1-\alpha/2}\frac{S_f}{\sqrt{n}} \qquad \zeta_2(\bar{f}) = \bar{f} + t_{1-\alpha/2}\frac{S_f}{\sqrt{n}} \tag{5-47}$$

where $t_{1-\alpha/2}$ can be replaced with $u_{1-\alpha/2}$ for $n > 30$.

We may, if we wish, compute the sample variance (45) concurrently with the sample average $\bar{f}$ for successive values of n and stop data taking and computation manually or automatically when

$$\frac{S_f{}^2}{n} \leq \left(\frac{e_1}{t_{1-\alpha/2}}\right)^2 \tag{5-48}$$

where e_1 is a desired confidence-interval half-width (see also Sec. 8-3).

Under conditions similar to those governing the application of the t distribution, it is also possible to derive confidence intervals based on the sample *range*

$$r_f = \max_{k=1,2,\ldots,n} (^kf) - \min_{k=1,2,\ldots,n} (^kf) \tag{5-49}$$

instead of the sample variance $S_f{}^2$.[46,47] The sample range is easier to compute than the sample variance but is a less efficient estimate of the ensemble dispersion, so that a given confidence-interval width will require larger sample sizes. Var $\{r_f\}$ also decreases much less rapidly with the sample size n than Var $\{S_f\}$;[37] for $n > 20$, it is, then, preferable to derive confidence intervals based on the *average range* obtained from subsamples comprising 5 to 10 observations each.[46,47]

MEASUREMENT (ESTIMATION) OF CORRELATION FUNCTIONS

5-8. Introduction. Continuous Correlators and Time-delay Implementation. *Correlators* produce estimates of ensemble correlation functions

$$R_{xy}(t_1,t_2) = E\{x(t_1)y(t_2)\} \qquad (t_2 = t_1 + \tau) \tag{5-50}$$

from given samples or records of input functions $x(t)$, $y(t)$. Correlators are of the greatest practical importance. They are used, in particular,

1. To test for statistical dependence between two random functions (presence of common spectral components), or between a random input and a known function (cross-correlation detection).[3,4]
2. To estimate (measure) d-c and periodic components of a signal; and to estimate system frequency response and impulse response

in the presence of noise, without interrupting normal system operation (Sec. 7-11). Correlation functions also serve as system-optimization criteria.[39]

3. To predict mean-square delay errors in control systems (Sec. 1-3).

The basic *continuous* (*all-analog*) *correlator* of Fig. 5-6a works with stationary inputs $x(t)$, $y(t)$ and averages $x(t - \tau)y(t)$. At low signal frequencies, the time delay can be obtained with a curve-follower-equipped double-carriage servo table (Fig. 3-2). More frequently, one employs continuous correlation with tape-recorded data, which permit

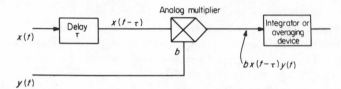

FIG. 5-6a. Basic analog correlator.

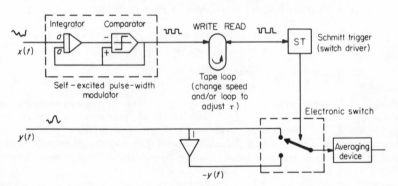

FIG. 5-6b. An analog correlator employing pulse-width modulation for both magnetic-recorder time delay and multiplication. Analog-computer time-division multipliers can be used to produce pulse-width modulation.

convenient time-delay implementation through playback-head displacement.[40] The delayed function $x(t - \tau)$ can also be produced through recording (or rerecording) of $x(t)$ on a tape loop or magnetic drum whose speed is adjusted in accordance with the desired time delay τ.[40] In many communication systems, $x(t - \tau) = a \sin \omega(t - \tau)$ is obtained with a phase-shifting circuit, and the multiplier is a simple superheterodyne mixer. Note that correlation with an averaging time T will require observations or data records over a period of length $T + \tau_{MAX}$, where τ_{MAX} is the largest delay τ under consideration.

Direct (AM) magnetic recording will not reproduce d-c levels accurately. Telemetered data are often already given in frequency-modulated form (with an added reference-frequency channel); but where continuous data are to be recorded specifically for correlation, a pulse-width-modulation recording scheme may be preferable. Pulse-width demodulation requires only simple averaging and is insensitive to tape or drum speed, so that no reference-frequency track is required. Best of all, the pulse-width-modulated variable can multiply another voltage by simple switching in the manner of a time-division multiplier (Fig. 5-6b).[3] The pulse-width modulator in Fig. 5-6b is, in fact, an ordinary triggered (constant-frequency) or self-excited (variable-frequency) time-division-multiplier modulator. Reference 39 shows inexpensive circuits of both types and also discusses multiplier switches and output filters. Pulse repetition rates between 1 and 20 Kc are practical for magnetic recording.

Reasonably small delays (delay-frequency products ω below 5 to 10 radians) can also be produced by operational-amplifier circuits or passive networks approximating the constant-delay transfer function $e^{-\tau s}$ by a rational transfer function, such as

$$H(s) = \frac{476 - 160.5\tau s + 22.8\tau^2 s^2 - 1.48\tau^3 s^3}{476 + 309\tau s + 91.8\tau^2 s^2 + 12.1\tau^3 s^3 + \tau^4 s^4} \approx e^{-\tau s} \quad (5\text{-}51)$$

(see also Fig. 2-12).[42] Many similar time-delay approximations exist;[39] while they are usually designed for various compromises between low phase error and low transient error, Gonzalez[41] has investigated the design of lumped-parameter delay approximations specifically optimized for correlation applications with roughly known signal spectra.

To produce a table or graphical record of the desired correlation function, we must step the time delay τ through the required delay range. The stepwise variation of τ is sometimes replaced by continuous variation for plotting or display. It is clear that the rate $d\tau/dt = \lambda$ must be small. Bendat[2] studied the increase in the variance of $\langle x(t)x(t+\tau)\rangle_T$ due to continuous delay variation for the simple case of stationary Gaussian noise with $R_{xx}(\tau) = a^2 e^{-\alpha|\tau|}$. He found the variance increase to be less than $a^2\lambda^2\alpha T/3$; note that the error increases with increasing observation-time-bandwidth product αT. The effect is qualitatively similar for other types of low-pass-filtered noise.

Rational-transfer-function approximation of a time-variable delay requires caution. Many commonly used operational-amplifier circuits and networks approximate the transfer operator $e^{-(d/dt)(\tau \cdot)}$ rather than the correct time-delay operator $e^{-\tau(d/dt)}$, and the order of d/dt and $\tau(t)$ must be observed unless τ is constant. It is, however, possible to argue that the error due to interchanging the order of d/dt and $\tau(t)$ is small for the necessarily small values of $d\tau/dt = \lambda$ used in correlation measurements.[42,43]

5-9. Sampled-data Correlation. *Sampled-data correlators* (Fig. 5-7a, b) produce estimates of correlation functions

$$R_{xy}(t,\, t+\tau) = E\{x(t)y(t+\tau)\}$$

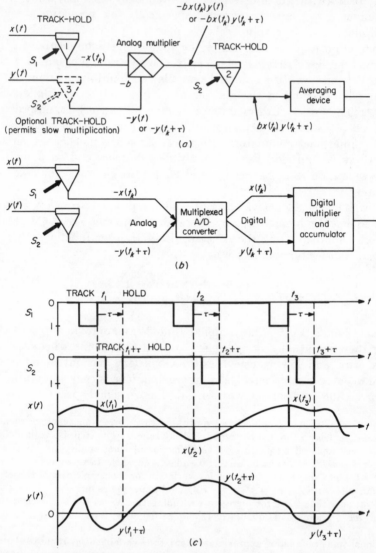

Fig. 5-7. Analog and digital sampling correlators (a), (b), and sampling-pulse timing diagram (c). Each track-hold circuit tracks when its binary control variable (S_1 or S_2) equals digital "one," and holds on digital "zero" (see also Sec. 2-13). In Fig. 5-7a, track-hold 2 *follows* the multiplier in order to ensure that the circuit can average only products $x(t_i)y(t_k + \tau)$ with $i = k$.

as finite-time sampled-data averages

$$[x(t)y(t + \tau)]_n = \frac{1}{n} \sum_{k=1}^{n} x(t_k)y(t_k + \tau) \qquad (5\text{-}52)$$

obtained by sampling the time histories of two stationary inputs $x(t)$, $x(y)$ (Fig. 5-7c). Since the simple correlators of Fig. 5-7a, b can handle

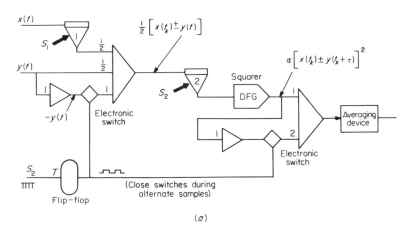

(a)

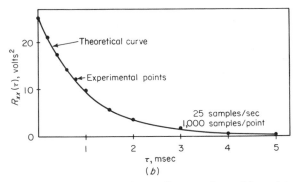

(b)

FIG. 5-8. Simplified "quarter-square" sampling correlator (a), and typical measured autocorrelation function (b). Sampling pulses S_1, S_2 are the same as in Fig. 5-7c. The same apparatus will also measure mean-square delay errors.

only one pair of samples $x(t_1)$, $y(t_1 + \tau)$ at a time, each time interval $t_{k+1} - t_k = \Delta t$ between samples must exceed the desired delay τ, so that we shall waste much of our data unless repetitive data-record play-back is possible (see also Sec. 5-9).

The analog multiplier in the sampling correlator of Fig. 5-7a can be replaced by a simple diode-function-generator squaring circuit (Sec. 2-3) if we alternately produce voltages proportional to $[x(t_k) + y(t_k + \tau)]^2$

and $-[x(t_k) - y(t_k + \tau)]^2$ and average over $2n$ samples, since

$$E\{xy\} = \tfrac{1}{4}[E\{(x + y)^2\} - E\{(x - y)^2\}] \tag{5-53}$$

("quarter-square" correlator, Fig. 5-8).[21,22]

The apparatus of Figs. 5-7a, b and 5-8 can just as well be employed to sample each of n successive pairs of records $^k x(t)$, $^k y(t)$ obtained in separate experiments or Monte-Carlo-type computer runs (Sec. 4-2) to produce sample averages

$$\overline{x(t_1)y(t_1 + \tau)} = \frac{1}{n}\sum_{k=1}^{n} {}^k x(t_1)\,{}^k y(t_1 + \tau) \tag{5-54}$$

The latter method constitutes the only practical scheme for estimating correlation functions of nonstationary as well as stationary processes.

5-10. Some Special Data-handling Techniques.   Figure 5-9a illustrates the use of recirculating function-storage circuits in a correlator. Complete data records of $x(t)$ and $y(t)$ are stored on two function-storage

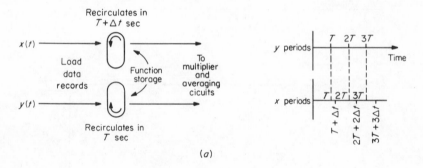

(a)

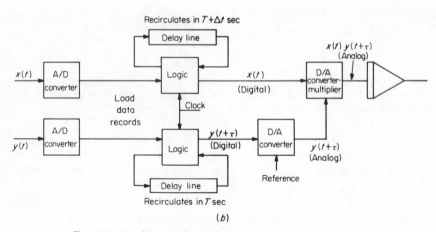

(b)

Fig. 5-9. Special function-delay techniques for correlation.

units (e.g., magnetic-tape loops) whose delay times differ by one sampling period Δt. As $x(t)$ and $y(t)$ recirculate, $y(t)$ is automatically delayed by successive integral multiples of Δt, so that the correlation estimate is computed for successive delays $\tau = k\,\Delta t(k = 0,1,2,\ldots)$. Note that the playback for computation and display can be faster or slower than the data-acquisition rate.

Figure 5-9b shows a similar correlator employing magnetostrictive delay lines for digital function storage. With a 10-msec delay line capable of storing 1,000 10-bit words, only fast 10-msec data records could be stored during a single delay period. With slower sampling rates, we can, however, store successive samples, one by one, during successive delay periods or successive multiples of a delay period. Suitable readout timing permits us to read all samples during one delay period for fast computation and display, but slow readout (one sample per m delay periods) is also possible. Delay-line storage is especially attractive if it is possible to employ coarse quantization using relatively few (4 to 8) bits per sample (Chap. 6). Note also that a digital-to-analog converter is used to implement fast multiplication in Fig. 5-9b.

5-11. Effects of Statistical Fluctuations and Correlator-input Noise. (a) **General Relations.** The variances of continuous and sampled-data correlation-function estimates like $\langle x(t)y(t + \tau)\rangle_T$, $\langle x(t)y(t + \tau)\rangle_{\mathrm{EWP}}$, $[x(t)y(t + \tau)]_n$ for jointly stationary $x(t)$, $y(t)$ are given by the corresponding expressions (8), (9), and (32). Unfortunately, each variance depends on

$$E\{f(0)f(\lambda)\} = E\{x(t)x(t + \lambda)y(t + \tau)y(t + \tau + \lambda]\} \qquad (5\text{-}55)$$

and this fourth-order moment of the joint distribution of $x(t)$ and $y(t)$ is hardly ever known. In the special case of jointly Gaussian and stationary signals $x(t)$, $y(t)$ with zero mean values, we have[2]

$$E\{f(0)f(\lambda)\} = R_{xx}(\lambda)R_{yy}(\lambda) + R_{xy}{}^2(\tau) + R_{xy}(\tau + \lambda)R_{xy}(\tau - \lambda) \qquad (5\text{-}56)$$

but even this involves the unknown correlation function $R_{xy}(\tau)$ itself and hence yields useful information only in simple special cases.

For stationary Gaussian $x(t)$, it can be shown that[50]

$$\mathrm{Var}\ \{\langle x(t)x(t + \tau)\rangle_T\} \leq \frac{4}{T} \int_0^\infty R_{xx}{}^2(\lambda)\, d\lambda \qquad (|\tau| < T)$$

In general, it will be necessary to make repeated independent estimates $z_1, z_2, \ldots, z_N$ of $R_{xy}(\tau)$ or $R_{xy}(t, t + \tau)$ and to obtain confidence limits by the methods of Sec. 5-7. These methods apply, in particular, also to Monte-Carlo-type estimation of $R_{xy}(t_1, t_2)$ in terms of the sample average $\overline{x(t_1)y(t_2)}$.

(b) **Simple Gaussian Signals.** To illustrate the dependence of the autocorrelation-function estimate

$$\langle x(t)x(t+\tau)\rangle_T = \frac{1}{T}\int_0^T x(\lambda)x(\lambda+\tau)\,d\lambda \tag{5-57}$$

on signal bandwidth and delay, we shall restrict ourselves to stationary Gaussian $x(t)$ with

$$R_{xx}(\tau) = a^2 e^{-\alpha|\tau|} + [E\{x\}]^2 \tag{5-58}$$

(see also Sec. 5-2). We substitute Eq. (58) into Eq. (56) with $x = y$ and employ Eq. (8) to find

$$\text{Var}\{\langle x(t)x(t+\tau)\rangle_T\} = \frac{a^4}{2(\alpha T)^2}\{2\alpha T - 1 + 2e^{-2\alpha T} + [(2\alpha\tau + 1)(2\alpha T - 1)$$
$$- 2(\alpha\tau)^2]e^{-2\alpha\tau}\} \quad (T > \tau \ge 0) \tag{5-59}$$

For $\tau = 0$, this agrees with Eq. (15). For observation times T large compared to the reciprocal signal bandwidth, we have

$$\frac{a^4}{\alpha T} \le \text{Var}\{\langle x(t)x(t+\tau)\rangle_T\} \le 2\frac{a^4}{\alpha T} \quad (|\tau| \le T) \tag{5-60}$$

(within 1 per cent for $\alpha T \ge 10^4$).

For the more general case of a stationary Gaussian signal $x(t)$ with

$$R_{xx}(\tau) = a^2 e^{-\alpha|\tau|}\cos\omega_1\tau + [E\{x\}]^2 \tag{5-61}$$

one similarly obtains

$$\text{Var}\{\langle x(t)x(t+\tau)\rangle_T\} \le 2\frac{a^4}{\alpha T} \quad (\alpha T \ge 10^4, |\tau| \le T) \tag{5-62}$$

as derived by Bendat,[2] who also calculated confidence limits for $R_{xx}(\tau)$ by assuming the estimate (56) to be approximately normally distributed with the variance computed as above.

(c) **Random-phase Periodic Signals.** For the random-phase sinusoid $x(t) = a \sin(\omega t + \alpha)$ (Sec. 1-9), we have

$$R_{xx}(\tau) = \frac{a^2}{2}\cos\omega\tau \tag{5-63}$$

and[13]

$$\text{Var}\{\langle x(t)x(t+\tau)\rangle_T\} = \frac{a^4}{8}\left(\frac{\sin\omega T}{\omega T}\right)^2 \le \frac{a^4}{8(\omega T)^2} \tag{5-64}$$

Note that the variance (64) is independent of τ and equals *zero* for $T = \pi/\omega$, $2\pi/\omega$, ... More generally, for every random-phase periodic process $x(t)$ with period T_0 (Sec. 1-10), $\text{Var}\{\langle x(t)x(t+\tau)\rangle_T\} = 0$ whenever $T = T_0, 2T_0, \ldots$.

(d) *Correlator errors due to spurious noise inputs* $n_1(t)$ $n_2(t)$ added to the respective stationary cross-correlator inputs $x(t)$, $y(t)$ are related to the effect of statistical fluctuations. For if, as is often the case, n_1, n_2 are stationary and

$$R_{n_1 n_2}(\tau) \equiv R_{n_1 y}(\tau) \equiv R_{x n_2}(\tau) \equiv 0$$

then

$$R_{x+n_1,y+n_2}(\tau) = R_{xy}(\tau) + R_{n_1 y}(\tau) + R_{x n_2}(\tau) + R_{n_1 n_2}(\tau) = R_{xy}(\tau)$$

i.e., the noise effects would be "correlated out" by an *ideal* correlator. Actual correlation estimates obtained by averaging $x(t)y(t + \tau)$ are still unbiased estimates of $R_{xy}(\tau)$, and the noise affects only the statistical fluctuations of the correlator output. This fact is, indeed, the practical reason for employing cross-correlators to estimate amplitudes, Fourier components, etc., of signals corrupted by uncorrelated noise or other signals (see also Secs. 4-5, 7-9, and 7-11). The empirical sample-size determination methods of Sec. 5-7 are again useful. Input and output signal-to-noise ratios of correlation detectors for periodic signals are further discussed in refs. 3 and 4.

In *autocorrelation* measurements with additive noise, $R_{x+n,x+n}(\tau)$ does contain an error term $R_{nn}(\tau)$. Bendat[2] treats the special case of auto-correlation estimation with signal and noise autocorrelation functions of the type (58) in detail.

AMPLITUDE-DISTRIBUTION MEASUREMENTS

5-12. Probability Estimates. Practical Slicer Circuits. To estimate (measure) the probability Prob $[a < x(t_1) \leq b]$ that a random-signal sample $x(t_1)$ falls into the class interval $a < x \leq b$, we generate the function

$$f[x(t)] = \begin{cases} 1 & [a < x(t) \leq b] \\ 0 & \text{otherwise} \end{cases}$$

$$\text{with } E\{f[x(t)]\} = \text{Prob } [a < x(t) \leq b] \quad (5\text{-}65)$$

Sample averages or, if $x(t)$ is stationary, finite-time averages of $f[x(t)]$ serve as estimates of Prob $[a < x(t) \leq b]$. While continuous averaging is readily possible, the digital nature (0 or 1) of $f[x(t)]$ makes it especially convenient to compute the sampled-data averages

$$[f]_n = \frac{1}{n} \sum_{k=1}^{n} f[x(t_k)] \qquad \bar{f} = \frac{1}{n} \sum_{k=1}^{n} f[^k x(t_1)] \qquad (5\text{-}66)$$

by simple counting of 1's (Fig. 5-10).

As an important special case, a simple analog comparator (Sec. 2-12) with input $x(t) - X$ produces the output

$$f[x(t)] = \begin{cases} 1 & [x(t) \leq X] \\ 0 & \text{otherwise} \end{cases} \qquad (5\text{-}67)$$

which, when suitably averaged, yields estimates of the *cumulative distribution function* $P(X,t) \equiv \text{Prob } [x(t) \leq X]$. An array of such comparators can estimate 10 to 100 values $P(X_1,t)$, $P(X_2,t)$, . . . of the

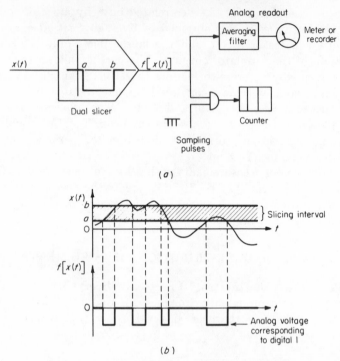

FIG. 5-10. Basic probability-estimation scheme (a), and waveforms (b).

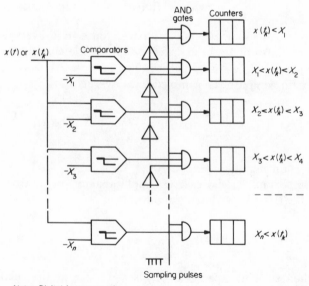

FIG. 5-11. A comparator-array amplitude-distribution analyzer.

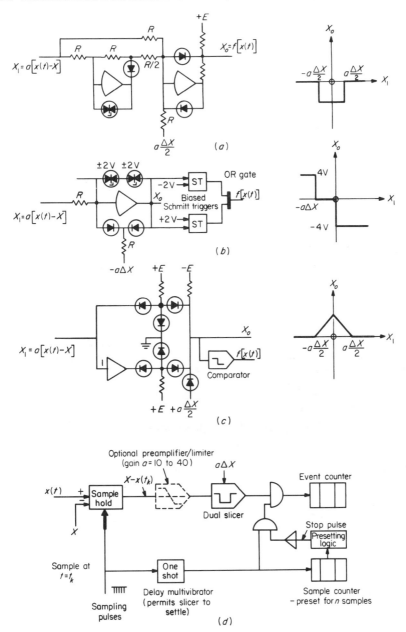

Note: Digital I corresponds to −6 V

FIG. 5-12. Dual-slicer circuits (a), (b), (c), and a complete dual-slicer amplitude-distribution analyzer (d). The circuit of Fig. 5-12a can be set up on existing analog computers and furnishes analog as well as digital output; the hybrid circuit of Fig. 5-12b is as accurate, less expensive, and faster. Dual-slicer circuits are also useful for go–no-go testing.

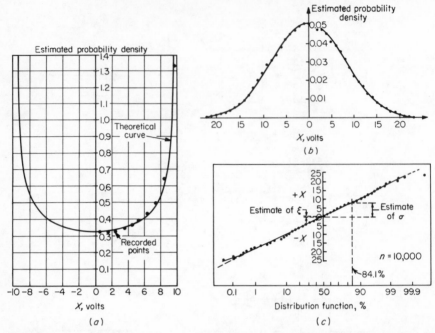

FIG. 5-13a, b, c. Probability-density estimates for a ±10-volt sinusoidal waveform (a), and Gaussian noise (b) obtained with the circuits of Fig. 5-12a and d, and cumulative distribution of Gaussian noise (c).   (*University of Arizona.*)

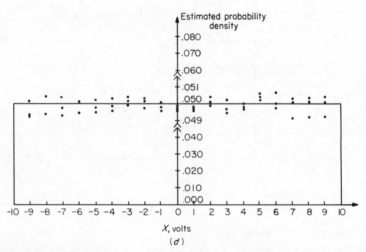

FIG. 5-13d. Probability-density estimates for a ±10-volt triangular waveform (uniform distribution), with $n = 1,000$ samples/point, $\Delta X = 1$ volt. Statistical fluctuations are seen to be within 0.001 or 2 per cent of the nominal value $p(0) = 0.050$, in good agreement with Eq. (78).   (*University of Arizona, data from ref. 29.*)

distribution function from each set of data; and the addition of simple digital logic circuits produces simultaneous estimates of a set of class-interval probabilities Prob $[X_k < x(t) \leq X_{k+1}]$ (Fig. 5-11). The class intervals may or may not be of uniform length. Comparator-array amplitude-distribution analyzers are widely used in nuclear physics to analyze scintillation-detector output pulses and often have elaborate provisions for storage, display, and printout of the estimated distributions.

In hybrid-computer random-process studies, it is usually sufficient to estimate one class-interval probability at a time; in fact, we may want to estimate only a single probability, such as a hit probability or detection probability (Secs. 4-4 and 4-5). Figure 5-12a, b, c shows *dual-slicer*

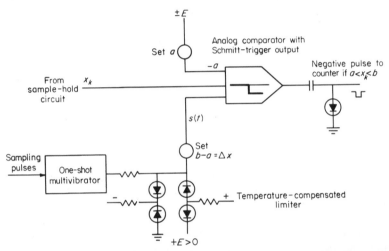

FIG. 5-14. A sampled-data amplitude-distribution analyzer requiring only a single comparator. x_k is a sample value $x(t_k)$ or $^k x(t_1)$ of $x(t)$ or $^k x(t)$. $s(t)$ is a pulse waveform accurately limited to rise from 0 to $b - a = \Delta x$ once per sampling period. A comparator step occurs and is counted if and only if $a < x_k < b$. (*University of Arizona, ref. 36.*)

circuits producing functions $f[x(t)]$ of the desired form (65). The resolution of such slicer circuits is of the order of hundredths of a volt at d-c and tenths of a volt at 1 Kc.[24–30, 36] The optional resolution-increasing preamplifier included in the complete amplitude-distribution analyzer illustrated in Fig. 5-12d improves resolution at low frequencies. In case of sampled-data measurements, a sample-hold circuit should precede the slicer, so that the latter can work with the relatively slow sample-hold output. Figure 5-13 represents typical results (see also Sec. 5-13).

Figure 5-14 shows a somewhat different amplitude-distribution analyzer system suitable for sampled-data analysis and Monte-Carlo-type studies.[36] The circuits of Fig. 5-15 combine slicer and gate to pass r-f pulses when $X - \Delta x/2 < x(t) < X + \Delta x/2$.[25]

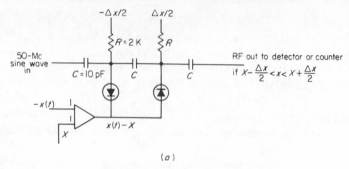

(a)

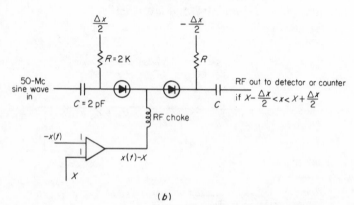

(b)

Fig. 5-15. Two switching circuits combining slicer and gate (ref. 25). RC must be small compared to the sine-wave period.

5-13. Measurement of Probability Density.

The circuits of Fig. 5-12 permit the use of class intervals as narrow as 50 mV for estimating values of the probability density $p(X,t)$ from

$$\left.\begin{aligned} p(X,t) &\approx \frac{1}{\Delta x} \operatorname{Prob}\left[X - \frac{\Delta x}{2} < x(t) \leq X + \frac{\Delta x}{2} \right] \\ p(X,t) &\approx \frac{1}{\Delta x} \operatorname{Prob}\left[X - \Delta x < x(t) \leq X \right] \end{aligned}\right\} \quad (5\text{-}68)$$

or

Figure 5-13 shows examples of practical results.

If $x(t)$ is stationary, and $p(X,t_1)\Delta x = p(X)\Delta x$ is estimated by continuous analog averaging of the slicer output, then the triangular slicer characteristic developed in Fig. 5-12c will yield more accurate probability-density estimates, since it emphasizes contributions near the class-interval center.[28] It is possible to vary X slowly and to plot our estimated $p(X)$ vs. X curve directly with a servo table (xy plotter), whose mechanical inertia may make an averaging filter unnecessary.

In the novel probability-density analyzer of Fig. 5-16,[36] a ramp/comparator voltage-to-time converter (Sec. 5-4) produces a sharp pulse $\beta(x_k + E)$ sec after each periodic sample $x^k = x(t_k)$ or $x_k = {}^kx(t_1)$ is read, and this pulse is recorded on a magnetostrictive delay line which recirculates once per sampling period. After a sufficiently large number n of samples, the pulse density on the line will be proportional to $p(x)$, with x represented by time (delay along the line). The pulses are detected by simple averaging and yield a voltage vs. time oscilloscope display or permanent record.

Proper use of a recirculating delay line requires pulse regeneration with clock-gated logic, so that pulses can occur only at, say, 0.5-μsec clock intervals. Our pulse-position modulation, then, involves quantization. Since two or more samples x_k might produce pulses during the same time interval, we must provide digital logic which senses this fact and records the extra pulse one time interval later.

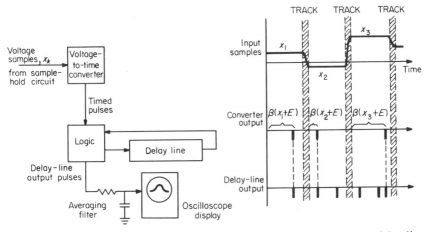

FIG. 5-16. A hybrid analog-digital probability-density analyzer employing delay-line storage to permit oscilloscope display of the probability-density curve. (*Contributed by R. Maybach, University of Arizona.*)

5-14. Statistical Fluctuations of Probability Estimates and Probability-density Estimates. (a) Correlated Samples.

Prediction of Var $\{\langle f \rangle_T\}$, Var $\{\langle f \rangle_{\text{EWP}}\}$, or Var $\{[f]_n\}$ from Eqs. (8), (9), or (32) requires knowledge of $E\{f(0)f(\lambda)\} = \text{Prob } [a < x(t) < b, \ a < x(t + \lambda) < b]$ which is, in general, difficult or impossible to obtain. The method of Sec. 5-7 applies.

Special cases of stationary Gaussian random processes have been investigated in more detail. If, in particular,

$$p(x) = \frac{1}{\sqrt{2\pi}\,\sigma}\, e^{-x^2/2\sigma^2} \qquad R_{xx}(\tau) = \sigma^2 e^{-\alpha\tau} \qquad (5\text{-}69)$$

and $\alpha T \gg 1$, then the variance of our estimate $\langle f \rangle_T$ for Prob $[x(t) \le X]$ is approximately[34]

$$\text{Var } \{\langle f \rangle_T\} \approx \frac{2\sigma p(x)}{\sqrt{2\pi}\,\alpha T} \frac{1}{1 + X^2/\sigma^2} \qquad (\alpha T \gg 1, \ X < 5\sigma) \qquad (5\text{-}70)$$

but σ is, again, rarely known. More interesting, perhaps, is the corresponding vari-

ance of the probability-density estimate obtained with an approximately triangular*
slicer characteristic (Fig. 5-12c), which is given within about 10 per cent by[28]

$$\text{Var } \{\langle f \rangle_T\} \approx p^2(x) \frac{\log_e 4}{\alpha T} \qquad [\alpha T \gg 1, (\Delta x)^2 \ll \sigma^2] \tag{5-71}$$

for, in this case, the per cent rms error ϵ_{RMS} is, approximately, independent of the
unknown variance σ^2:

$$\epsilon_{\text{RMS}} \approx 100 \sqrt{\frac{\log_e 4}{\alpha T}} \qquad [\alpha T \gg 1, (\Delta x)^2 \ll \sigma^2] \tag{5-72}$$

(b) Independent Samples. In many important applications, we
average n *statistically independent* samples $f[x(t_k)]$ of a stationary process,
or n independent samples $^k f = f[^k x(t_1)]$ from a Monte-Carlo simulation.
In this case, $nz = n[f]_n$ or $nz = n\bar{f}$ is a *binomial* random variable, i.e.,

$$\text{Prob } [nz = m] = \binom{n}{m} P^m (1 - P)^{n-m} \qquad (m = 0,1, \ldots ,n) \tag{5-73}$$

with
$$\left. \begin{array}{l} E \{nz\} = n \text{ Prob } [a < x(t_1) < b] = nP \\ \text{Var } \{nz\} = nP(1 - P) \end{array} \right\} \tag{5-74}$$

We can, therefore, employ tables of the binomial distribution to calculate
confidence intervals for our estimate z (Appendix), and

$$E\{z\} = \text{Prob } [a < x(t_1) < b] = P \qquad \text{Var } \{z\} = \frac{P(1 - P)}{n} \tag{5-75}$$

z is asymptotically normal with the parameters (75); approximations
based on the normal distribution are usually reasonable if $nP(1 - P) \geq 9$.[38]

In accordance with Eq. (74), the *rms error* due to statistical fluctuations of our probability estimate is

$$e_{\text{RMS}} = \sqrt{\text{Var } \{\bar{f}\}} \text{ (or } \sqrt{\text{Var } \{[f]_n\}}) = \sqrt{\frac{P(1 - P)}{n}} \tag{5-76}$$

and the corresponding *per cent rms error* is

$$\epsilon_{\text{RMS}} = 100 \frac{\sqrt{\text{Var } \{\bar{f}\}}}{E\{f\}} \left(\text{or } 100 \frac{\sqrt{\text{Var } \{[f]_n\}}}{E\{f\}} \right) = 100 \sqrt{\frac{1 - P}{nP}} \tag{5-77}$$

In the case of probability-density estimation with a small slicer interval
Δx, the "probability element" $\Delta P \approx p(X,t_1) \Delta x$ is small, and the rms
error of our estimate for $p(X,t_1) \approx \Delta P/\Delta x$ is given by

$$\left. \begin{array}{l} e_{\text{RMS}} \approx \frac{1}{\Delta x} \sqrt{\frac{\Delta P}{n}} \approx \sqrt{\frac{p(X)}{n \, \Delta x}} \\ \epsilon_{\text{RMS}} = \frac{e_{\text{RMS}}}{p(X)} \approx 100 \sqrt{\frac{1}{np(X) \, \Delta x}} \end{array} \right\} \tag{5-78}$$

---

* Equations (71) and (72) are actually computed for a slicer characteristic shaped
like a normal error curve of dispersion Δx, which is not too different from the characteristic obtained in Fig. 5-12c with some diode-breakpoint rounding.

For a constant sample size n, both e_{RMS} and ϵ_{RMS} increase as the slicer interval Δx is decreased. Note, however, that probability-density-estimate fluctuations may tend to average out when we fit a set of such estimates with a smooth $p(X)$ vs. X curve.

It is interesting to compare the rms errors (78) of dual-slicer probability-density estimates with those of probability-density estimates obtained by approximate differentiation of an estimated cumulative distribution function $P(X) = \text{Prob} [x \leq X]$. The simplest formula is

$$p(X) = \frac{\partial P(X)}{\partial X} \approx \frac{1}{\Delta x} [P(X + \Delta x) - P(X)] \qquad (5\text{-}79)$$

It is reasonable to consider measured estimates of $P(X)$ and $P(X + \Delta x)$ as statistically independent and, for small Δx, as of approximately equal variance $P(X)[1 - P(X)]/n$. The rms errors of probability-density estimates based on Eq. (79) are then

$$\left.\begin{aligned} e_{RMS} &\approx \frac{1}{\Delta x} \sqrt{\frac{2P(X)[1 - P(X)]}{n}} \\ \epsilon_{RMS} &\approx \frac{100}{p(X,t_1)\,\Delta x} \sqrt{\frac{2P(X)[1 - P(X)]}{n}} \end{aligned}\right\} \qquad (5\text{-}80)$$

For small Δx, this can be much worse than (78), even though estimates of $P(X)$ and $P(X + \Delta x)$ may be more accurate than dual-slicer estimates of $p(x)$. Interestingly enough, a more elaborate approximate-differentiation formula, like

$$p(X) = \frac{\partial P(X)}{\partial X} \approx \frac{1}{2\Delta x} [-3P(X) + 4P(X + \Delta x) - P(X + 2\Delta x)]$$

causes still worse rms errors [$\sqrt{13/4}$ times as large as (80)], since even larger fluctuating quantities are subtracted to form a small difference.

5-15. Joint-probability Estimates. Studies of hit probabilities, target vulnerability, radar target acquisition, and diversity reception require us to estimate the probability $P(t_1,t_2) = \text{Prob} [x(t_1),y(t_2) \text{ in } D]$ of finding a pair of random variables $x(t_1)$, $y(t_2)$ in a specified domain D of the xy plane. A primitive but fairly practical solution of this problem[46] applies sample values of $x(t_1)$ and $y(t_2)$ as horizontal and vertical deflection voltages to a cathode-ray oscilloscope fitted with an opaque mask cut out in the shape of the desired region D. A photocell facing the cathode-ray-tube screen is then illuminated if and only if (x,y) is in D and produces

$$f[x(t_1),y(t_2)] = \begin{cases} 1 & [x(t_1),y(t_2) \text{ in } D] \\ 0 & \text{otherwise} \end{cases} \text{ with } E\{f\} = P \qquad (5\text{-}81)$$

Such a two-dimensional comparator can be replaced by various combinations of comparators, slicers, and logic circuits (Fig. 5-17). It is, in particular, a simple matter to estimate a complete set of values of the two-dimensional cumulative distribution function

$$P[X_1,t_1;Y_2,t_2] = \text{Prob} [x(t_1) \leq X_1, y(t_2) \leq Y_2]$$

Note also that the boundaries of many regions in two or more dimensions can be defined by inequalities on a single function of two or more

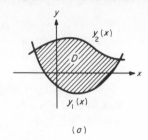

(a)

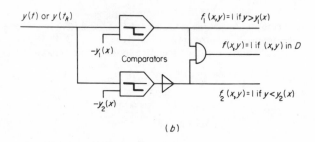

(b)

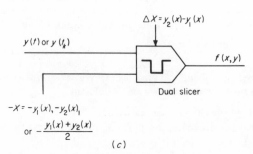

(c)

FIG. 5-17. Definition of a random event described by two random variables (a), and slicer circuits yielding joint-probability estimates (b, c).

variables, e.g.,

$$f(x,y) = x^2 + y^2 - r^2 < 0 \qquad f(x,y,z) = ax^2 + by^2 + cz^2 - d < 0$$

Violation of such inequalities can be sensed by a single analog comparator with input f.

REFERENCES AND BIBLIOGRAPHY

Measurement of Averages and Correlation Functions

1. Davenport, W. B., and W. L. Root: *Introduction to Random Signals and Noise*, McGraw-Hill, New York, 1958.
2. Bendat, J. S.: *Principles and Applications of Random-noise Theory*, Wiley, New York, 1958.
3. Lee, Y. W.: *Statistical Theory of Communication*, Wiley, New York, 1960.
4. Middleton, D.: *An Introduction to Statistical Communication Theory*, McGraw-Hill, New York, 1960.

5. Davenport, W. B., R. A. Johnson, and D. Middleton: Statistical Errors in Measurements on Random Functions, *J. Appl. Phys.*, April, 1952.
6. Otterman, J.: Computation of Exponentially-mapped-past Statistical Variables, *IRE Trans. PGAC*, January, 1960; see also Fano, R. M. *J. Acoust. Soc.*, September, 1950.
7. Meyer-Brötz, G.: Die Messung von Kenngrössen Stochastischer Progresse mit dem electronischen Analogrechner, *Elektron. Rechenanlagen*, 4: 103 (1962).
8. Rubin, A. I.: Continuous Data Analysis with Analog Computers Using Statistical and Regression Techniques, *IRETEC*, March, 1963.
9. Diamantides, N. D.: Analog Technique Derives Correlation Functions, *Electronics*, Apr. 13, 1962.
10. Bell, H., and V. C. Rideout: A High-speed Correlator, *IRETEC*, June, 1954.
11. McFadden, J. A.: The Correlation Function of a Sine Wave Plus Noise After Extreme Clipping, *IRE Trans. PGIT*, June, 1956.
12. Widrow, B.: A Study of Rough Amplitude Quantization by Means of Nyquist Sampling Theory, *IRE Trans. PGCT*, December, 1956.
13. Kaiser, J. F., and R. K. Angell: New Techniques and Equipment for Correlation Computation, *Tech. Mem.* 7668-TM-2, MIT Servomechanisms Laboratory, December, 1957.
14. Becker, C. L., and J. V. Wait: Two-level Correlation on an Analog Computer, *IRETEC*, December, 1961.
15. Ekre, H.: Polarity-coincidence Correlation Detection of a Weak Noise Source, *IEEE Trans. PGIT*, January, 1963.
16. Bussgang, J. J.: Crosscorrelation Functions of Amplitude-distorted Gaussian Signals, *MIT Research Lab. Electronics Rept.* 216, Cambridge, Mass., 1952.
17. Rosenheck, B. M.: Detecting Signals by Polarity Coincidence, *Electronics*, Jan. 29, 1960.
18. Cooper, R.: Crosscorrelation with Binary Signals, *Memo.*, Electrical Engineering Department, Purdue University, 1962.
19. Keast, D. N.: An Analog System for the Analysis of Random-data Signals up to 10 Kc, *IRE Trans. PGI*, September, 1962.
20. Ross, C. W., and K. W. Goff: An Experimental Correlation Analyzer for Measuring System Dynamics, *Memo.*, Leeds and Northrup, Inc., 1961.
21. Conant, B. K.: A Hybrid Analog-digital Statistics Computer, *ACL Memo 45*, Electrical Engineering Department, University of Arizona, 1964.
22. Maybach, R.: Hybrid Analog-digital Measurement of Sample Averages and Correlation Functions, *ACL Memo 85*, Electrical Engineering Department, University of Arizona, 1964.
23. Janac, K.: A Direct Determination of Correlation Functions for Generators of Random Processes, *Proc. 3d AICA Conf.*, Opatija, Yugoslavia, 1961; Presses Académiques Européennes, Brussels, 1962.

Amplitude-distribution Analyzers

24. Zoll, D. J.: Simple Plotter Analyzes Radar Noise Rapidly, *Electronics*, Mar. 14, 1958.
25. White, H. E.: An Analog Probability-density Analyzer, *MIT Research Lab. Electronics Rept.* 326, April, 1957.
26. Bickart, T. A.: Amplitude Slicer, *Electronics*, Feb. 27, 1959.
27. Caldwell, W. F., G. A. Korn, and G. R. Peterson: A Precision Amplitude-distribution Analyzer, *IRETEC*, June, 1960.
28. Waters, W. M.: Estimation of the Probability-density Function, *Memo.* RL/60/IMA-13, Johns Hopkins University, Baltimore, Md., August, 1960.

29. Brubaker, T. A., and G. A. Korn: Accurate Amplitude-distribution Analyzer Combines Analog and Digital Logic, *Rev. Sci. Instr.*, March, 1961.
30. Korn, G. A.: Control Applications for New Deadspace Limiter, *Control Eng.*, March, 1962.
31. Wolf, A. A., and J. H. Dietz: A Method of Measurement and Display of Probability Functions of Ergodic Random Processes by Orthogonal-series Synthesis, *Proc. IRE*, September, 1962.
32. Ratz, A. G.: An Amplitude-probability-density Analyzer for Vibration and Acoustic Studies, *Bull.* 0-55, Ortholog Division, Gulton Industries, Inc., Trenton, N.J., 1963.
33. Broch, J. T.: Automatic Recording of Amplitude-density Curves, *Tech. Rev.* 4, Bruel and Kjaer Instruments, Inc., Cleveland, Ohio, 1959.
34. Baburin, V. M., et al.: Calculation of Distribution Functions for Random Processes from Experimental Results, *Automatika i Telemekhanika*, May/November, 1962.
35. Bendat, J. S.: Statistical Errors in Peak Probability Distribution Measurements and Structural Fatigue Damage Predictions, *Rept.* MAC-306-01, Measurement Analysis Corp., Santa Monica, Calif., 1963.
36. Maybach, R.: New Techniques for Measuring Probability and Probability Density, *ACL Memo* 97, Electrical Engineering Department, University of Arizona, 1964.

Miscellaneous

37. Cramér, H.: *Mathematical Methods of Statistics*, Princeton University Press, Princeton, N.J., 1951.
38. Korn, G. A., and T. M. Korn: *Mathematical Handbook for Scientists and Engineers*, McGraw-Hill, New York, 1961.
39. ———: *Electronic Analog and Hybrid Computers*, McGraw-Hill, New York, 1964.
40. Rideout, V. C.: Random-process Studies, in Huskey, H. D., and G. A. Korn, *Computer Handbook*, McGraw-Hill, New York, 1962.
41. Gonzalez, E.: Mathematical Determination of the Approximate Autocorrelation Function, *IEEETEC*, August, 1965.
42. King, W. J., and V. C. Rideout: Improved Transport-delay Circuits for Analog-computer Use, *Proc. 3d AICA Conf.*, Opatija, Yugoslavia, 1961; Presses Académiques Européennes, Brussels, 1962.
43. Vichnevetsky, R.: Analog-computer Simulation of a Time-dependent Delay, *Ann. AICA*, April, 1964.
44. Tomovič, R.: Hysteresis Correction of Amplitude Comparators, *Ann. AICA*, June, 1959.
45. Jespers, P., et al.: A New Method to Compute Correlation Functions, *Intern. Symposium on Information Theory*, Liège, Belgium, 1962; *IRE Trans. PGIT*, September, 1962.
46. Levine, L.: *Methods for Solving Engineering Problems Using Analog Computers*, McGraw-Hill, New York, 1964.
47. Hald, A.: *Statistical Theory with Engineering Applications*, Wiley, New York, 1952.
48. Grenander, U., and M. Rosenblatt: *Statistical Analysis of Stationary Time Series*, Wiley, New York, 1957.
49. Fox, H. L.: The Measurement of Probability Density, *J. Acoust. Soc. Am.*, June, 1961.
50. Laning, J. H., and R. H. Battin: *Random Processes in Automatic Control*, McGraw-Hill, New York, 1956.

CHAPTER **6**

STATISTICAL MEASUREMENTS
WITH QUANTIZED DATA

STATISTICAL EFFECTS OF QUANTIZATION

6-1. Introduction. Digital data processing necessarily involves quantization (roundoff, grouping) of input data samples. The range of each random variable, say x, is subdivided into *class intervals*

$$i\,\Delta x - \frac{\Delta x}{2} < x \le i\,\Delta x + \frac{\Delta x}{2} \qquad (i = 0, \pm 1, \pm 2, \ldots)$$

of equal width Δx. The quantization operation replaces each value of x by the nearest class-interval center $i\,\Delta x$ (Fig. 6-1a). The quantizer output x_Q can be regarded as the sum of the input x and a roundoff error

$$n_Q = x_Q - x \qquad (6\text{-}1)$$

$n_Q = n_Q(t)$ is referred to as *quantization noise*, although the "noise" n_Q is definitely (not just stochastically) determined if x is known (Fig. 6-1b). If statistics, such as averages or correlation estimates, are computed from quantized data, the roundoff will increase estimate variances and may also affect (bias) the mean of the estimate. For an important class of random processes, however, theoretical study yields the highly practical result that *the biasing effects of quantization average out approximately or can be approximately predicted and corrected even with surprisingly coarse quantization.* A quantitative hold on this phenomenon will permit us to realize the most remarkable savings in analog-to-digital conversion and digital data transmission and storage. Computation of 13-bit estimates of mean values, mean squares, and correlation functions will rarely require conversion, transmission, and/or storage of over 8 bits,

131

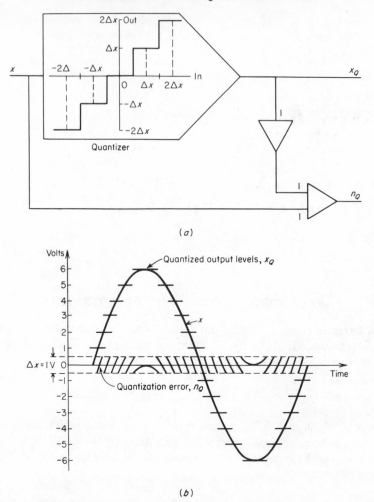

FIG. 6-1. Demonstration of amplitude quantization (a), and quantizer input, output, and quantization noise for sinusoidal input (b).

and 4 bits or less is often sufficient. Digital computation of 13-bit estimates will then require 13-bit output, but at most 8-bit inputs.

The statistical theory of amplitude quantization, due essentially to B. Widrow,[1,16–18] will be reviewed in Secs. 6-8 to 6-12. We will, however, begin by simply stating the principal results (Secs. 6-3 and 6-4) and then demonstrate their practical application (Secs. 6-4 to 6-7) before we present any theoretical derivation.

6-2. Characteristic Functions. For all random variables u,v (continuous, discrete, or otherwise), we can introduce *characteristic functions*

$$\chi_u{}^{(q)} = E\{e^{jqu}\} \qquad \chi_{u,v}(q_1,q_2) = E\{e^{j(q_1u+q_2v)}\} \qquad (6\text{-}2)$$

Each characteristic function uniquely defines the corresponding probability distribution.[2] Series expansion of the exponential yields

$$\left.\begin{aligned}
\chi_u(q_1) &= 1 + jqE\{u\} - \tfrac{1}{2}q^2E\{u^2\} \cdots \\
\chi_{u,v}(q_1,q_2) &= 1 + jq_1E\{u\} + jq_2E\{v\} - \tfrac{1}{2}q_1{}^2E\{u^2\} \\
&\quad - \tfrac{1}{2}q_2{}^2E\{v^2\} - q_1q_2E\{uv\} + \cdots
\end{aligned}\right\} \quad (6\text{-}3)$$

for all real q, q_1, q_2 whenever the expected values (moments) on the right exist. It follows that $\chi_u(0) = \chi_{u,v}(0,0) = 1$, and

$$E\{u^m\} = j^{-m}\frac{d^m\chi_u}{d^mq}\bigg]_{q=0} \qquad E\{u^mv^n\} = j^{-(m+n)}\frac{\partial^{m+n}\chi_{u,v}}{\partial^mq_1\partial^nq_2}\bigg]_{q_1=q_2=0} \quad (6\text{-}4)$$

If u and v are statistically independent random variables, then

$$\chi_{u,v}(q_1,q_2) = \chi_u(q_1)\chi_v(q_2) \qquad \chi_{u+v}(q) = \chi_u(q)\chi_v(q) \quad (6\text{-}5)$$

Conversely, the first relation implies statistical independence, but the second one does not necessarily do so.

6-3. The Quantizing Theorems and Sheppard's Corrections. We now state the principal results of the statistical theory of amplitude quantization,[1,16-18] reserving the proofs for Secs. 6-8 and 6-9.

1. If the probability density $p(x)$ of our input x is "band-limited" so that its characteristic function $\chi_x(q) \equiv E\{e^{jqx}\}$ vanishes for $|q| \geq 2\pi/\Delta x - \epsilon$ ($\epsilon > 0$), then every existing mean value (moment) $E\{x^m\}$ ($m = 1,2, \ldots$) is completely determined by moments of the quantizer output x_Q, and the first-order probability distribution of the quantization noise n_Q is uniform between $-\Delta x/2$ and $\Delta x/2$.

2. If the joint probability density $p(x,y)$ of two input variables x, y is "band-limited" so that the joint characteristic function $\chi_{x,y}(q_1,q_2)$ $E\{e^{j(q_1x+q_2y)}\}$ is zero for $|q_1| \geq 2\pi/\Delta x - \epsilon$, $q_2 \geq 2\tau/\Delta y - \epsilon$ ($\epsilon > 0$), then every existing moment $E\{x^my^n\}$ ($m,n = 1,2, \ldots$) is completely determined by joint moments of the quantizer outputs x_Q, y_Q; and quantization noise samples $n_{Qx} = x_Q - x$, $n_{Qy} = y_Q - y$ are uniformly distributed and statistically independent.

More specifically, we shall prove in Sec. 6-9 that the conditions of theorem 1 imply

$$\left.\begin{aligned}
E\{x\} &= E\{x_Q\} \\
E\{x^2\} &= E\{x_Q{}^2\} - \tfrac{1}{12}(\Delta x)^2 \\
E\{x^4\} &= E\{x_Q{}^4\} - \tfrac{1}{2}(\Delta x)^2E\{x_Q{}^2\} + O[(\Delta x)^4]
\end{aligned}\right\} \quad (6\text{-}6)$$

and hence

$$\text{Var}\{x_Q\} = \text{Var}\{x\} + \tfrac{1}{12}(\Delta x)^2$$
$$\text{Var}\{x_Q{}^2\} = \text{Var}\{x^2\} + \tfrac{1}{3}(\Delta x)^2E\{x^2\} + O[(\Delta x)^4] \quad (6\text{-}7)$$

whenever the expected values in question exist. Relations of this type have been known for many years as *Sheppard's corrections for grouped data;*[3] Widrow's theory furnishes a more general and rigorous justification for these formulas.

Similarly, the conditions of theorem 2 imply

$$E\{xy\} = E\{x_Q y_Q\} \qquad (x \not\equiv y) \tag{6-8}$$

and hence, if we let $x = x(t_1)$ and $y = x(t_2)$ or $y(t_2)$,

$$R_{xx}(t_1,t_2) = \begin{cases} E\{x_Q^2(t_1)\} - \frac{1}{12}(\Delta x)^2 & (t_1 = t_2) \\ R_{x_Q x_Q}(t_1,t_2) & (t_1 \not= t_2) \end{cases} \tag{6-9}$$

$$R_{xy}(t_1,t_2) = R_{x_Q y_Q}(t_1,t_2) \qquad (x \not\equiv y) \tag{6-10}$$

Finally,

3. If the probability distribution of x is "band-limited" so that $\chi_x(q) = 0$ for $|q| \geq \pi/\Delta x$, then the probability distribution of x is *completely determined* by that of the quantizer output x_Q. An analogous theorem holds for the joint distribution of two quantizer inputs (Sec. 6-9).

HYBRID ANALOG-DIGITAL MEASUREMENTS EMPLOYING COARSE QUANTIZATION

6-4. Gaussian or Approximately Gaussian Data. If the appropriate quantizing theorems apply, Eqs. (6) to (10) indicate that the effects

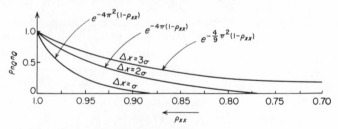

FIG. 6-2. Normalized autocorrelation function of quantization noise, $\rho_{n_Q n_Q} \approx \rho_{x_Q x_Q} - \rho_{xx}$ vs. ρ_{xx} for stationary Gaussian $x(t)$, where

$$\rho_{uu}(\tau) = \frac{R_{uu}(\tau) - [E\{u\}]^2}{E\{u^2\} - [E\{u\}]^2}$$

(Based on ref. 1.)

of even relatively coarse quantization on *statistics* are either negligible or easily corrected. Actually, real random data cannot possibly satisfy the conditions of Sec. 6-3 *exactly*, since physical signals are necessarily bounded; for continuous $x(t)$, moreover, statistical independence of $n_Q(t_1)$, $n_Q(t_2)$ for arbitrarily small $\tau = t_2 - t_1$ would imply infinite signal power.[1,16] Nevertheless, many real signals satisfy the quantizing theorems so nearly that excellent approximations result, and the errors of such approximations can be neatly predicted by the relations of Sec. 6-9.

For the important case of *Gaussian data*, Table 6-1 and Fig. 6-2 summarize the most important results and indicate that *quantization* errors in measurements of $E\{x\}$, $E\{x^2\}$, *and* $R_{xx}(\tau)$ *for Gaussian processes are either negligible or easily corrected even with class intervals Δx as large as 3σ.*

6-5. Simplified Correlators. Hybrid analog-digital techniques involving coarse quantization are especially fruitful for correlation measurements, for we may be able to replace relatively expensive analog-delay and multiplier circuits by simple digital circuits. With Gaussian (or approximately Gaussian) signals, three-bit-plus-sign conversion and delay circuits can feed a simple digital or hybrid multiplier/accumulator to produce excellent correlation estimates in many practical applications.[1,4,5,17,20-26]

Even one-bit correlators, which merely average sign $x(t_1)$ sign $y(t_2)$ with the simplest of digital circuitry (Fig. 6-3a), can be very useful. *For Gaussian data with zero mean*, in particular, the one-bit correlation function is simply related to the true correlation function $R_{xy}(t_1,t_2)$:[6]

$$E\{\text{sign } x(t_1) \text{ sign } y(t_2)\} = \frac{2}{\pi} \arcsin \frac{R_{xy}(t_1,t_2)}{\sqrt{E\{x^2(t_1)\}E\{y^2(t_2)\}}} \quad (6\text{-}11)$$

Similar formulas have been derived for autocorrelation and cross-correlation of known signals with additive Gaussian noise.[1,4,7-11,23] One-bit correlators are especially inexpensive and reliable, since they require only comparators and digital circuitry. One-bit correlators can replace true correlators in many testing, detection, and process-measurement applications: Widrow,[1] for instance, applied one-bit correlation to recorded radar returns from the planet Venus and obtained practically unequivocal detection in over 40 db of noise.

As a somewhat less radical measure, we can correlate $x_Q(t_1)$ with $y(t_2)$; i.e., we quantize only one of the two correlator input signals. This still permits digital delay, and multiplication is conveniently accomplished with a simple D/A converter whose reference input is replaced by $y(t_2)$. The simplest correlators of this type employ one-bit quantization of $x(t_1)$, i.e., they average $y(t_2)$ sign $x(t_1)$; this permits hybrid multiplication by a simple analog switch (Fig. 6-3b). *For Gaussian signals with zero mean*, the resulting estimates are simply proportional to true correlation estimates:[11,17]

$$E\{y(t_2) \text{ sign } x(t_1)\} = \frac{E\{|x(t_1)|\}}{\sqrt{E\{x^2(t_1)\}}} \frac{R_{xy}(t_1,t_2)}{\sqrt{E\{x^2(t_1)\}}}$$

$$= \sqrt{\frac{2}{\pi}} \frac{R_{xy}(t_1,t_2)}{\sqrt{E\{x^2(t_1)\}}} \quad (6\text{-}12)$$

In particular, for any Gaussian x with zero mean,

$$E\{x \text{ sign } x\} = E\{|x|\} = \sqrt{\frac{2}{\pi}} \sqrt{E\{x^2\}} \quad (6\text{-}13)$$

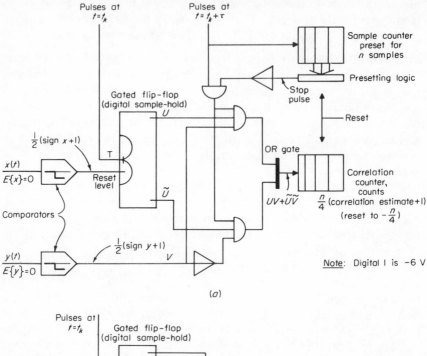

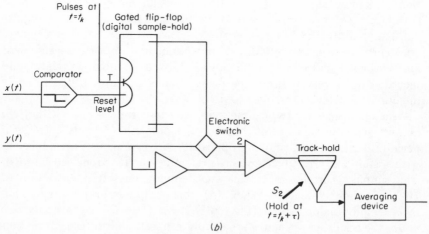

Fig. 6-3. Approximate correlation employing one-bit quantization of both x and y (a), and of x alone (b).

which permits us to measure the mean square of a Gaussian signal by its mean absolute value, which is usually easier to compute.

6-6. Use of Dither.[1,12,24]   Given any random variables s_x which satisfies the first or second quantizing theorem of Sec. 6-3, the same holds for the sum $x + s_x$ of s_x and every random variable x statistically independent of s_x, since

$$\chi_{x+s_x}(q) = \chi_x(q)\chi_{s_x}(q) \tag{6-14}$$

(Sec. 6-2).   Even if s_x satisfies

$$\chi_{s_x}(q) = 0 \qquad \left(|q| \geq \frac{2\pi}{\Delta x}\right) \qquad (6\text{-}15)$$

only approximately, $x + s_x$ will also satisfy the quantizing theorem approximately.

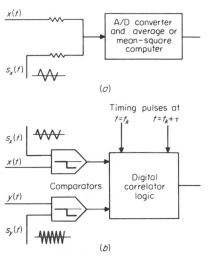

(a)

(b)

FIG. 6-4a, b. Hybrid analog-digital averaging circuit with dither (a), and one-bit correlator with dither (b).

We can, therefore, greatly extend the applicability of coarse-quantization estimates by adding *dither* or *interpolation variables* s_x, s_y to practically arbitrary input data x and/or y.   Figure 6-4a shows the use of dither for coarse-quantization estimation of $E\{x\}$.   The dither input s_x must

1. Satisfy the condition (15) (for the given class-interval size Δx) to a sufficiently good approximation.
2. Be statistically independent of x.
3. Have zero mean so as not to bias our estimate, i.e.,

$$E\{x + s_x\} = E\{x\}$$

4. Contain no spectral components lower in frequency than the most significant signal components; dither frequencies as high as our apparatus will handle will favor our filtering operations.

Speaking in terms of voltage measurements, $s_x = s_x(t)$ can be a noise voltage or an independent periodic voltage added to the data input $x(t)$.   In the latter case,

5. Periodic-dither frequencies must be either incommensurable with the sampling frequency, or they may be cleverly synchronized with the sampling rate so as to generate a "typical" pseudo-random sample of dither over the averaging period (Fig. 6-4c).[22,24]

To approximate the condition (15), s_x must range at least between $-\Delta x/2$ and $\Delta x/2$. The approximation will, generally speaking, improve with larger dither voltages, but the mean-square dither also increases estimate variances (Sec. 6-7). Triangle-wave or sawtooth dither, which is uniformly distributed over its amplitude range, is convenient. For a

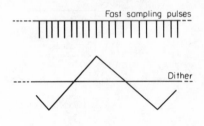

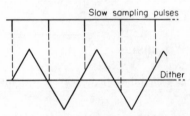

FIG. 6-4c. Synchronization of periodic dither and sampling pulses for fast sampling (approximating continuous averaging) and for slow sampling. The averaging period should equal a (large) integral number of dither periods. Sawtooth waves and staircase waveforms derived from digital counters can replace the triangle-wave dither.

peak-to-peak triangle or sawtooth amplitude equal to one class-interval width x it is shown in Sec. 6-13 that

$$E\{(x + s_x)_Q\} = E\{x\} \qquad (6\text{-}16)$$

holds *exactly*, even through the triangle wave satisfies the quantizing theorem only approximately. We can interpret the effect of the dither intuitively as a sort of statistical interpolation which distributes $x + s_x$ more evenly over the discrete sample values of $(x + s_x)_Q$.

For correlation, dither voltages s_x and s_y are added to the respective correlator inputs x and y. s_x and s_y must have zero mean and must be mutually uncorrelated and statistically independent of x and y. For triangle waves s_x, s_y with zero mean, peak-to-peak amplitudes Δx, Δy, and different frequencies,

$$E\{(x + s_x)_Q(y + s_y)_Q\} = E\{xy\} \qquad (6\text{-}17)$$

(see also Sec. 6-13).

Figure 6-4b illustrates the special case of *one-bit correlation with dither*. For signals x,y both ranging between $-a$ and a, one-bit quantization groups data into two class intervals centered at $-a/2$ and $a/2$, and the class-interval width is $\Delta x = \Delta y = a$. This requires a peak-to-peak amplitude $2a$ for triangle-wave dither. Since the new variables $x + s_x$, $y + s_y$ range between $-2a$ and $2a$, their one-bit quantization corresponds to class-interval centers at $-a$ and a, so that

$$\left. \begin{aligned} (x + s_x)_Q &= a \text{ sign } (x + s_x) \\ (y + s_y)_Q &= a \text{ sign } (y + s_y) \end{aligned} \right\} \tag{6-18}$$

The analysis outlined in Sec. 6-13 shows that

$$E\{\text{sign } (x + s_x) \text{ sign } (y + s_y)\} = \frac{1}{a^2} E\{xy\} \tag{6-19}$$

Although the addition of appropriate zero-mean dither will not *bias* our estimates, it can affect estimate *variances*. To minimize variance increases due to dither, we favor the use of periodic dither and

1. Employ as high dither frequencies as practical.
2. Compute finite-time averages over an integral number of dither periods (this implies the use of harmonically related dither frequencies in correlators).
3. Generate "representative" dither samples in the manner of Fig. 6-4c.

6-7. Effect of Quantization on Statistical Fluctuations. When quantized samples of $x_Q(t)$ are used to compute sampled-data estimates of $E\{x(t_1)\}$, viz.,

$$\overline{x_Q(t_1)} = \frac{1}{n} \sum_{k=1}^{n} {}^k x_Q(t_1) \tag{6-20a}$$

(sample average over n independent experiments) or

$$[x_Q]_n = \frac{1}{n} \sum_{k=1}^{n} x_Q(k \, \Delta t) \tag{6-20b}$$

(sampled-data time average for a stationary process), the estimate variances are given by[2]

$$\left. \begin{aligned} \text{Var } \{\overline{x_Q(t_1)}\} &= \frac{1}{n} \text{Var } \{x_Q(t_1)\} \\ \text{Var } \{[x_Q]_n\} = \frac{1}{n} \text{Var } \{x_Q\} & \\ + \frac{2}{n} \sum_{k=1}^{n-1} \left(1 - \frac{k}{n} \right) \{R_{x_Q x_Q}(k \, \Delta t) &- [E\{x_Q\}]^2\} \end{aligned} \right\} \tag{6-21}$$

Equations (6) to (10), Table 6-1, and Fig. 6-2 indicate that these variances will not differ too badly from the corresponding expressions for unquantized data as long as the quantizing theorems hold approximately. In particular, we have in this case

$$\text{Var } \{\overline{x_Q}\} = \frac{1}{n} \text{Var } \{x_Q\} \approx \text{Var } \{\bar{x}\} + \frac{1}{12} \frac{(\Delta x)^2}{n} \qquad (6\text{-}22)$$

Similarly, correlation-estimate variances[2] are not seriously increased by quantization if appropriate second-order and fourth-order joint distributions of the correlator inputs x, y are "band-limited."

**Table 6-1. Errors Resulting from Application of
Eqs. (6) and (7) to Gaussian Processes***

Δx	$\sigma = \sqrt{\text{Var } \{x\}}$	2σ	3σ
$\max \|E\{x_Q\} - E\{x\}\|$ if $E\{x\} \neq 0$	$8.3 \times 10^{-10} \Delta x$	$2.3 \times 10^{-3} \Delta x$	$3.5 \times 10^{-2} \Delta x$
$\text{Var } \{x_Q\} - \text{Var } \{x\}$ $- \frac{(\Delta x)^2}{12}$ $(E\{x\} = 0)$	$-1.1 \times 10^{-8} \sigma^2$	$-3.1 \times 10^{-2} \sigma^2$	$-0.54 \sigma^2$
$E\{n_Q{}^2\} - \frac{(\Delta x)^2}{12}$ $(E\{x\} = 0)$	$-2.6 \times 10^{-10} (\Delta x)^2$	$-7.2 \times 10^{-4} (\Delta x)^2$	$-1.1 \times 10^{-2} (\Delta x)^2$

* Data from ref. 1.

If we employ dither (Sec. 6-6) for coarse-quantization measurements of $E\{x\}$, the dither variance Var $\{s_x\}$ will, approximately,* simply add to the quantization-noise variance $(\Delta x)^2/12$. For triangle-wave dither s_x of peak-to-peak amplitude Δx, Var $\{s_x\} = (\Delta x)^2/12$, and

$$\text{Var } \{(x + s_x)_Q\} \leq \text{Var } \{x\} + \tfrac{1}{6}(\Delta x)^2 \qquad (6\text{-}23)$$

For *one-bit correlation* without dither (Sec. 6-5) we cannot usually apply the quantizing theorem, but we know that the square of the digital multiplier output sign x sign y in Fig. 6-3a is necessarily always 1. Hence

$$\text{Var } \{\text{sign } x \text{ sign } y\} = E\{[\text{sign } x \text{ sign } y]^2\} - [E\{\text{sign } x \text{ sign } y\}]^2$$
$$= 1 - [E\{\text{sign } x \text{ sign } y\}]^2 \qquad (6\text{-}24)$$

where we can substitute the expression (11) when x and y are Gaussian signals with zero mean.

If we have no a priori knowledge about x and y other than their range $-a$ to a, one-bit correlation will require dither, say triangle-wave dither

* The exact variance can be computed from Eq. (35) with the aid of the relation (4).

with peak-to-peak amplitude $2a$ (Sec. 6-6). The square of the digital-multiplier output is always 1; recalling Eq. (16), we find

$$E\{[(x + s_x)_Q(y + s_y)_Q]^2\} = a^4 E\{\text{sign } (x + s_x) \text{ sign } (y + s_y)\} = a^4$$

It follows that

$$\text{Var }\{(x + s_x)_Q(y + s_y)_Q\} = a^4 - [E\{xy\}]^2 \qquad (6\text{-}25)$$

if these quantities exist, no matter how large or small Var $\{xy\}$ is. The possibly very high variance (25) expresses the information loss in one-bit correlation and is the price of equipment simplicity. The resulting estimate variances might turn out to be impractically large for reasonable sample sizes or observation times. In particular, for the independent-sample estimate $\overline{a^2 \text{ sign } (x + s_x) \text{ sign } (y + s_y)}$, we find

$$\text{Var }\{\overline{a^2 \text{ sign } (x + s_x) \text{ sign } (y + s_y)}\} = \frac{a^4 - [E\{xy\}]^2}{n} \qquad (6\text{-}26)$$

Smit,[26] on the other hand, studied the polarity-coincidence estimates $\overline{\text{sign } x(t) \text{ sign } x(t + \tau)}$ and $\sin \overline{[(\pi/2) \text{ sign } x(t) \text{ sign } x(t + \tau)]}$ for the normalized autocorrelation function $E\{x(t)x(t + \tau)\}/E\{x^2(t)\}$ of Gaussian signals experimentally. Using *closely spaced* (correlated) samples and no dither, he found that the dispersion of the polarity-coincidence estimate was rarely over 150 per cent of the dispersion measured for the conventional estimate $\overline{x(t)x(t + \tau)}/\overline{x^2(t)}$; this was readily overcome through an increase in the sample size. The difference between the percentage errors of the polarity-coincidence and conventional estimates was even smaller. Fluctuation errors of polarity-coincidence correlation estimates surely deserve more theoretical and experimental study.

THEORETICAL JUSTIFICATION

6-8. Probability Distribution of Quantized Variables. Referring back to Sec. 6-1 and Fig. 6-1, we consider a continuous random input $x = x(t)$ with first-order probability density $p(x)$ at some sampling time $t = t_1$. The corresponding quantizer output

$$x_Q = x + n_Q = i \, \Delta x \qquad \left(i \, \Delta x - \frac{\Delta x}{2} < x \leq i \, \Delta x + \frac{\Delta x}{2}; \right.$$

$$\left. i = 0, \pm 1, \pm 2, \ldots \right) \qquad (6\text{-}27)$$

is a discrete random variable, but we can represent its distribution by a (symbolic) probability density

$$p_Q(x_Q) = \sum_{i = -\infty}^{\infty} \delta(x_Q - i \, \Delta x) \int_{i \, \Delta x - \Delta x/2}^{i \, \Delta x + \Delta x/2} p(x) \, dx \qquad (6\text{-}28)$$

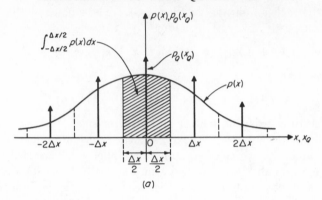

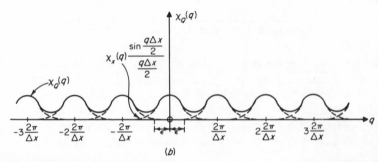

Fig. 6-5. Probability distribution of a quantizer output (a), and formation of the quantizer-output characteristic function (b).

i.e., by "comb" of impulse functions concentrating the probabilities Prob $[i \, \Delta x - (\Delta x/2) < x \le i \, \Delta x + (\Delta x/2)]$ at the class-interval centers $i \, \Delta x$ (Fig. 6-5a). We rewrite the expression (28) as

$$p_Q(x_Q) = \sum_{i=-\infty}^{\infty} c_i \delta(x_Q - i \, \Delta x) \qquad (6\text{-}29a)$$

with $c_i = \int_{i\,\Delta x - \Delta x/2}^{i\,\Delta x + \Delta x/2} p(x) \, dx = \int_{-\infty}^{\infty} p(\lambda - i \, \Delta x) \, \text{rect} \, \frac{\lambda}{\Delta x} \, d\lambda$

$$(i = 0, \pm 1, \pm 2, \, . \, . \, .) \qquad (6\text{-}29b)$$

where each coefficient appears as a convolution of $p(x)$ and the "rectangle function"

$$\text{rect} \, \frac{x}{\Delta x} = \begin{cases} 1 & \left(|x| < \dfrac{\Delta x}{2}\right) \\ 0 & \left(|x| > \dfrac{\Delta x}{2}\right) \end{cases} \qquad (6\text{-}30)$$

Similarly, for a pair of random variables x, y with joint probability density $p(x,y)$, we can represent the joint distribution of the quantizer outputs x_Q, y_Q by the symbolic density

$$p_Q(x_Q,y_Q) = \sum_{i=-\infty}^{\infty} \sum_{k=-\infty}^{\infty} c_{ik}\, \delta(x_Q - i\, \Delta x)\delta(y_Q - k\, \Delta y) \quad (6\text{-}31a)$$

with $\quad c_{ik} = \int_{-\infty}^{\infty} \int_{-\infty}^{\infty} p(x - i\, \Delta x, y - k\, \Delta y)\, \text{rect}\, \frac{x}{\Delta x}\, \text{rect}\, \frac{y}{\Delta y}\, dx\, dy$

$$(i,k = 0, \pm 1, \pm 2, \ldots) \quad (6\text{-}31b)$$

6-9. Proof of the Quantizing Theorems.   We recall

$$\int_{-\infty}^{\infty} e^{jqx}\, \delta(x - i\, \Delta x)\, dx = e^{jiq\, \Delta x}$$

to find the characteristic function (Sec. 6-2) of the quantizer output x_Q, viz.,

$$\chi_Q(q) = \int_{-\infty}^{\infty} e^{jqx_Q} p_Q(x_Q)\, dx_Q = \int_{-\infty}^{\infty} e^{jqx_Q} \sum_{i=-\infty}^{\infty} c_i\, \delta(x_Q - i\, \Delta x)\, dx_Q$$

$$= \sum_{i=-\infty}^{\infty} c_i e^{jiq} e^{jiq\, \Delta x} \quad (6\text{-}32)$$

This is a Fourier series representing a periodic function with period $2\pi/\Delta x$. Since $2\pi p(\lambda - i\, \Delta x)$ is the Fourier transform of $e^{-jiq\, \Delta x}\chi(q)$, and $2\pi\, \text{rect}\, \lambda/\Delta x$ is the Fourier transform of $\Delta x \sin (q\, \Delta x/2)/(q\, \Delta x/2)$, we can use Borel's convolution theorem[3] to transform the convolution integrals (29b) into products, so that

$$\chi_Q(q) = \frac{\Delta x}{2\pi} \sum_{i=-\infty}^{\infty} e^{jiq\, \Delta x} \int_{-\infty}^{\infty} e^{-ji\mu\, \Delta x}\chi_x(\mu)\, \frac{\sin (\mu\, \Delta x/2)}{\mu\, \Delta x/2}\, d\mu$$

$$= \frac{\Delta x}{2\pi} \int_{-\infty}^{\infty} \sum_{i=-\infty}^{\infty} e^{ji\, \Delta x(q-\mu)}\, \chi_x(\mu)\, \frac{\sin (\mu\, \Delta x/2)}{\mu\, \Delta x/2}\, d\mu \quad (6\text{-}33)$$

with suitable convergence implied by the integrability of $p(x)$.[2]   Under the integral sign it is safe to employ the symbolic Fourier-series relation

$$\frac{\Delta x}{2\pi} \sum_{i=-\infty}^{\infty} e^{jiq\, \Delta x} = \sum_{k=-\infty}^{\infty} \delta\left(q - k\, \frac{2\pi}{\Delta x}\right) \quad (6\text{-}34)$$

It follows that our Fourier series (32) or (33) represents the periodic function

$$\chi_Q(q) = \sum_{i=-\infty}^{\infty} \chi_x\left(q - i\, \frac{2\pi}{\Delta x}\right) \frac{\sin\, [q - i(2\pi/\Delta x)](\Delta x/2)}{[q - i(2\pi/\Delta x)](\Delta x/2)} \quad (6\text{-}35)$$

obtained through superposition of similar terms displaced by successive multiples of $2\pi/\Delta x$.

If now $\chi_x(q) = 0$ for $|q| \geq 2\pi/\Delta x - \epsilon$ ($\epsilon > 0$), then adjacent replicas of $\chi_x(q) \sin (q\, \Delta x/2)(q\, \Delta x/2)$ in Fig. 6-5b do not overlap in the interval $-\epsilon < q < \epsilon$, so that

$$\chi_Q(q) = \chi_x(q) \frac{\sin (q\, \Delta x/2)}{q\, \Delta x/2} \qquad (|q| < \epsilon) \qquad (6\text{-}36)$$

Differentiation of Eq. (36) relates every existing derivative of $\chi_x(q)$ at $q = 0$ uniquely to derivatives of $\chi_Q(q)$ at $q = 0$. Remembering Eq. (4), *we can recover every existing expected value (moment)* $E\{x^m\}$ $(m = 1, 2, \ldots)$ *from the quantizer-output distribution if the first-order probability distribution of the input* x *is "band-limited" so that* $\chi_x(q) = 0$ *for* $|q| \geq 2\pi/\Delta x - \epsilon$ $(\epsilon > 0)$. More specifically, differentiation of Eq. (36) at $q = 0$ yields the important relations (6).

For $\epsilon \geq \pi/\Delta x$, there is no overlap at all in Fig. 6-5b, and $\chi_Q(q)$ defines $\chi_x(q)$ uniquely: *the first-order probability distribution of the input* x *is completely determined by that of the quantizer output* x_Q *if* $\chi_x(q) = 0$ *for* $|q| \geq \pi/\Delta x$. This theorem is similar to (but not identical with) the well-known sampling theorem[3] for band-limited time functions.

Precisely analogous reasoning produces similar results for the joint distributions of two random variables x, y and of two corresponding quantizer outputs x_Q, y_Q. If $\chi_{x,y}(q_1, q_2) = 0$ for $|q_1| \geq 2\pi/\Delta x - \epsilon$, $|q_2| \geq 2\pi/\Delta y - \epsilon$ $(\epsilon > 0)$, then

$$\chi_Q(q_1, q_2) = \chi_{x,y}(q_1, q_2) \frac{\sin (q_1\, \Delta x/2)}{q_1\, \Delta x/2} \frac{\sin (q_2\, \Delta y/2)}{q_2\, \Delta y/2} \qquad (|q_1|, |q_2| < \epsilon) \quad (6\text{-}37)$$

Differentiation at $q_1 = q_2 = 0$ yields Eq. (8) and similar relations for higher-order moments. Finally, $\chi_{x,y}(q_1, q_2)$ and hence the joint second-order distribution of x and y is completely determined by that of x_Q and y_Q if $\chi_{x,y}(q_1, q_2) = 0$ for $|q_1| \geq \pi/\Delta x$, $|q_2| \geq \pi/\Delta y$.

6-10. Properties of Quantization Noise. If x is in the ith class interval, the first-order probability density of the quantization noise $n_Q = x_Q - x$ is $p_x(n_Q - i\, \Delta x)$ rect $n_Q/\Delta x$. Thus,

$$p_{n_Q}(n_Q) = \sum_{i=-\infty}^{\infty} p_x(n_Q - i\, \Delta x) \text{ rect } \frac{n_Q}{\Delta x} \qquad (6\text{-}38)$$

The characteristic function $\chi_{n_Q}(q)$ is $1/2\pi$ times the inverse Fourier transform of $p_{n_Q}(n_Q)$. We recall that $2\pi p_x(n_Q - i\, \Delta x)$ is the Fourier transform of $e^{-jiq\,\Delta x}\chi_x(q)$, and that 2π rect $n_Q/\Delta x$ is the Fourier transform of $\Delta x \sin (q\, \Delta x/2)/(q\, \Delta x/2)$. We again apply Borel's convolution theorem, this time to make transform products into convolutions:

$$\chi_{n_Q}(q) = \frac{\Delta x}{2\pi} \sum_{i=-\infty}^{\infty} \int_{-\infty}^{\infty} e^{-ji\lambda\,\Delta x}\chi_x(\lambda) \frac{\sin (q-\lambda)(\Delta x/2)}{(q-\lambda)(\Delta x/2)}\, d\lambda$$

$$= \frac{\Delta x}{2\pi} \int_{-\infty}^{\infty} \sum_{i=-\infty}^{\infty} e^{-ji\lambda\,\Delta x}\chi_x(\lambda) \frac{\sin (q-\lambda)(\Delta x/2)}{(q-\lambda)(\Delta x/2)}\, d\lambda$$

We once again employ the relation (34) and find

$$\chi_{n_Q}(q) = \sum_{k=-\infty}^{\infty} \chi_x\left(k\,\frac{2\pi}{\Delta x}\right)\frac{\sin\,[q - k(2\pi/\Delta x)](\Delta x/2)}{[q - k(2\pi/\Delta x)](\Delta x/2)} \tag{6-39}$$

If the distribution of our input signal x is "band-limited" so that $\chi_x(q) = 0$ for $|q| \geq 2\pi/\Delta x$, then

$$\left.\begin{array}{ll} \chi_{n_Q}(q) = \dfrac{\sin\,(q\,\Delta x/2)}{q\,\Delta x/2} & p_{n_Q}(n_Q) = \dfrac{1}{\Delta x}\,\text{rect}\,\dfrac{n_Q}{\Delta x} \\[3mm] E\{n_Q\} = 0 & \text{Var}\,\{n_Q\} = E\{n_Q{}^2\} = \tfrac{1}{12}\,(\Delta x)^2 \end{array}\right\} \tag{6-40}$$

i.e., the quantization noise is uniformly distributed between $-\Delta x/2$ *and* $\Delta x/2$.

Precisely analogous reasoning yields the joint distribution of quantization-noise samples $n_{Qx} = x_Q - x$, $n_{Qy} = y_Q - y$. We find

$$\chi_{n_{Qx},n_{Qy}}(q_1,q_2) = \sum_{i=-\infty}^{\infty}\sum_{k=-\infty}^{\infty} \chi_{x,y}\left(i\,\frac{2\pi}{\Delta x}, k\,\frac{2\pi}{\Delta y}\right)$$
$$\frac{\sin\,[q_1 - i(2\pi/\Delta x)](\Delta x/2)}{[q_1 - i(2\pi/\Delta x)](\Delta x/2)}\,\frac{\sin\,[q_2 - k(2\pi/\Delta y)(\Delta y/2)}{[q_2 - k(2\pi/\Delta y)](\Delta y/2)} \tag{6-41}$$

If $\chi_{x,y}(q_1,q_2) = 0$ for $|q_1| \geq 2\pi/\Delta x$, $|q_2| \geq 2\pi/\Delta y$, then

$$\left.\begin{array}{c} \chi_{n_{Qx},n_{Qy}}(q_1,q_2) = \dfrac{\sin\,(q_1\,\Delta x/2)}{q_1\Delta x/2}\,\dfrac{\sin\,(q_2\,\Delta y/2)}{q_2\,\Delta y/2} \\[3mm] p_{n_{Qx},n_{Qy}}(n_{Qx},n_{Qy}) = \dfrac{1}{\Delta x\,\Delta y}\,\text{rect}\,\dfrac{n_{Qx}}{\Delta x}\,\text{rect}\,\dfrac{n_{Qy}}{\Delta y} \\[3mm] E\{n_{Qx}n_{Qy}\} = 0 \end{array}\right\} \tag{6-42}$$

i.e., the quantization-noise samples n_{Qx} and n_{Qy} are uniformly distributed and statistically independent, even though x and y may not be independent.

When the first quantizing theorem of Sec. 6-3 holds, then Eqs. (6) and (40) imply

$$\begin{aligned} R_{xn_Q}(t_1,t_1) &= E\{x(t_1)n_Q(t_1)\} \\ &= \tfrac{1}{2}[\text{Var}\,\{x_Q(t_1)\} - \text{Var}\,\{x(t_1)\} - \text{Var}\,\{n_Q(t_1)\}] = 0 \end{aligned} \tag{6-43}$$

It can also be shown[1] that $|R_{xn_Q}(t_1,t_2)|$ must be zero for all $\tau = t_2 - t_1$; hence quantization noise and input are uncorrelated (n_Q is, of course, *not* statistically independent of x but, indeed, completely determined when x is given). For Gaussian data with $\Delta x < 3\sigma$, the expression (43) is not zero but can be calculated with the aid of Table 6-1; R_{xn_Q} is still small.

6-11. Quantization of Gaussian Variables.[1]   (a) For Gaussian data

$$p(x) = \frac{1}{\sqrt{2\pi}\,\sigma}\,e^{-\frac{1}{2}(x-\xi/\sigma)^2} \qquad \chi_x(q) = e^{-\frac{1}{2}\sigma^2q^2-j\xi q} \tag{6-44}$$

Substitution of the Gaussian characteristic function $\chi_x(q)$ into Eq. (35) yields $\chi_Q(q)$. If $\xi = E\{x\} = 0$ (Gaussian data with zero mean), then $p_Q(x)$ is, like $p(x)$, an even function, and

$$E\{x_Q{}^m\} = E\{x^m\} = 0 \qquad (m = 1,3,5, \ldots) \tag{6-45}$$

In this case $\chi_Q(q)$, too, is an even real function, which looks like Fig. 6-5b; for $\Delta x \leq 3\sigma$, only the terms corresponding to $i = 0$, $i = \pm 1$ in Eq. (35) contribute appreciably to the derivatives of $\chi_Q(q)$ at $q = 0$. Specifically, the contribution of the $i = \pm 1$ terms to the derivative at $q = 0$ is[1]

$$E\{x_Q{}^2\} - E\{x^2\} - \tfrac{1}{12}(\Delta x)^2 = -2\sigma^2 \left[2 + \frac{1}{2\pi^2}\left(\frac{\Delta x}{\sigma}\right)^2 \right] e^{-2\pi^2(\sigma/\Delta x)^2} \tag{6-46}$$

which was used in the computation of Table 6-1. Using Eq. (39), we similarly compute

$$E\{n_Q{}^2\} - \tfrac{1}{12}(\Delta x)^2 = \frac{(\Delta x)^2}{\pi^2} e^{-2\pi^2(\sigma/\Delta x)^2} \tag{6-47}$$

(b) For $\xi = E\{x\} \neq 0$, differentiation of Eq. (35) yields, in accordance with Eq. (4),

$$E\{x_Q\} - E\{x\} = \frac{\Delta x}{\pi} e^{-2\pi^2(\sigma/\Delta x)^2} \sin \frac{2\pi\xi}{\Delta x} \tag{6-48}$$

if we neglect all terms other than those with $i = 0$, $i = \pm 1$. Note that the correction varies sinusoidally with ξ.

(c) For stationary Gaussian data with zero means, the joint distribution of $x_1 = x(t_1)$, $x_2(t_2)$ is described by

$$p(x_1,x_2) = \frac{1}{2\pi\sigma^2 \sqrt{1-\rho^2}} \exp \left\{ -\frac{1}{2\sigma^2(1-\rho^2)}(x_1{}^2 - 2\rho x_1 x_2 + x_2{}^2) \right\} \tag{6-49}$$

$$\chi_{x_1,x_2}(q_1,q_2) = \exp \left\{ -\frac{\sigma^2}{2}(q_1{}^2 + 2\rho q_1 q_2 + q_2{}^2) \right\} \tag{6-50}$$

where ρ is the correlation coefficient $E\{x_1 x_2\}/\sigma^2 = R_{xx}(t_2 - t_1)/\sigma^2$. Equation (35) yields $\chi_Q(q_1,q_2)$, and differentiation in accordance with Eq. (4) produces the approximate values of $E\{x_{1Q}x_{2Q}\}$ used in Fig. 6-3.

Note that similar calculations can be carried out for non-Gaussian data as well, as long as the requisite characteristic functions are known and decay reasonably quickly as $|q|$ increases.

6-12. Shifted Class Intervals, Simplified Correlators, and Unequal Class Intervals. Watts[17] has extended Widrow's theory to the case of quantization by class intervals shifted with respect to those in Fig. 6-1, i.e.,

$$a_1 + i\,\Delta x - \frac{\Delta x}{2} < x \le a_1 + i\,\Delta x + \frac{\Delta x}{2}$$

$$(i = 0, \pm 1, \pm 2, \ldots)$$

$$a_2 + k\,\Delta y - \frac{\Delta y}{2} < y \le a_2 + k\,\Delta y + \frac{\Delta y}{2}$$

$$(k = 0, \pm 1, \pm 2, \ldots)$$

$$(6\text{-}51)$$

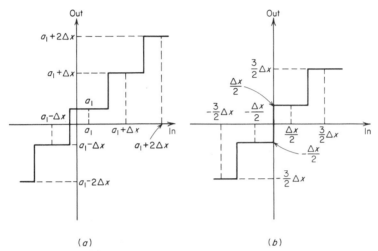

(a) (b)

Fig. 6-6. Quantization with shifted class intervals (a), and the special case $a = \Delta x/2$ (b).

(Fig. 6-6).   A derivation analogous to that of Sec. 6-9 yields

$$\chi_Q(q) = \sum_{i=-\infty}^{\infty} e^{2\pi j i \frac{a_1}{\Delta x}} \chi_x\left(q - i\frac{2\pi}{\Delta x}\right) \frac{\sin\left[q - i(2\pi/\Delta x)\right](\Delta x/2)}{[q - i(2\pi/\Delta x)](\Delta x/2)} \quad (6\text{-}52)$$

$$\chi_Q(q_1, q_2) = \sum_{i=-\infty}^{\infty} \sum_{k=-\infty}^{\infty} e^{2\pi j\left(i\frac{a_1}{\Delta x} + k\frac{a_2}{\Delta y}\right)} \chi_{x,y}\left(q_1 - i\frac{2\pi}{\Delta x}, q_2 - k\frac{2\pi}{\Delta y}\right)$$

$$\frac{\sin\left[q_1 - i(2\pi/\Delta x)\right](\Delta x/2)}{[q_1 - i(2\pi/\Delta x)](\Delta x/2)} \frac{\sin\left[q_2 - k(2\pi/\Delta y)\right](\Delta y/2)}{[q_2 - k(2\pi/\Delta y)](\Delta y/2)} \quad (6\text{-}53)$$

These expressions reduce to Eqs. (35) and (37) for $a_1 = a_2 = 0$; the general formulas can be useful where analog-to-digital converters are expressly designed for specific ranges of random variables.   A more important application is the one-bit quantization employed in the simplified correlators of Sec. 6-5.   For the one-bit correlator of Fig. 6-3a,

$$a_1 = \frac{\Delta x}{2} = a_2 = \frac{\Delta y}{2} = \frac{a}{2} \quad (6\text{-}54)$$

if both x and y are assumed to range between $-a$ and a, so that Eq. (53) becomes

$$
\chi_Q(q_1,q_2) = \sum_{i=-\infty}^{\infty} \sum_{k=-\infty}^{\infty} (-1)^{i+k} \chi_{x,y}\left(q_1 - \frac{i\pi}{a}, q_2 - \frac{k\pi}{a}\right)
$$
$$
\frac{\sin\left[(a/2)q_1 - i\pi\right]}{(a/2)q_1 - i\pi} \frac{\sin\left[(a/2)q_2 - k\pi\right]}{(a/2)q_2 - k\pi} \quad (6\text{-}55)
$$

If x alone is quantized, Eq. (53) is replaced by

$$
\chi_Q(q_1,q_2) = \sum_{i=-\infty}^{\infty} e^{2\pi j i \frac{a_1}{\Delta x}} \chi_{x,y}\left(q_1 - i\frac{2\pi}{\Delta x}, q_2\right) \frac{\sin\left[q_1 - i(2\pi/\Delta x)\right](\Delta x/2)}{\left[q_1 - i(2\pi/\Delta x)\right](\Delta x/2)}
$$
$$
(6\text{-}56)
$$

where we again substitute $a_1 = \Delta x/2$ for one-bit quantization, as in Fig. 6-3b. The results of Sec. 6-5 follow by differentiation of Eqs. (55) and (56) in accordance with the relation (4).

Further improvements in the quality of coarse-quantization estimates might result from the use of suitably selected *unequal* class intervals. Such techniques, explored in a different context in refs. 27 to 30, bear further investigation in connection with statistical measurements. Unequal-interval quantization would seem to apply mainly to specialized applications affording a good deal of a priori knowledge of signal distributions.

6-13. Quantization of Signal Plus Dither.   Let x be an input signal which may or may not satisfy a quantizing theorem. We add a dither variable s_x uniformly distributed between $-b$ and b to x (Fig. 6-4a), so that

$$
p_{s_x}(s_x) = \begin{cases} \dfrac{1}{2b} & (|s_x| < b) \\ 0 & (|s_x| > b) \end{cases} \qquad \chi_{s_x}(q) = \frac{\sin bq}{bq} \qquad (6\text{-}57)
$$

Let $s_x = s_x(t)$ be statistically independent of $x(t)$ (random-phase triangle wave whose frequency is not commensurable with that of any periodic component of x). Then, in accordance with Eq. (14),

$$
\chi_{x+s_x}(q) = \chi_x(q)\chi_{s_x}(q) = \chi_x(q)\frac{\sin bq}{bq} \qquad (6\text{-}58)
$$

and Eq. (52) yields the characteristic function of the quantizer output in Fig. 6-4a

$$
\chi_{(x+s_x)Q}(q) = \sum_{i=-\infty}^{\infty} e^{2\pi j i \frac{a_1}{\Delta x}} \chi_x\left(q - i\frac{2\pi}{\Delta x}\right)
$$
$$
\frac{\sin b[q - i(2\pi/\Delta x)]}{b[q - i(2\pi/\Delta x)]} \frac{\sin\left[q - i(2\pi/\Delta x)\right](\Delta x/2)}{\left[q - i(2\pi/\Delta x)\right](\Delta x/2)} \quad (6\text{-}59)
$$

If we choose the dither amplitude b so that

$$b = \frac{\Delta x}{2} \tag{6-60}$$

then

$$
\begin{aligned}
\chi_{(x+s_x)Q}(q) &= \sum_{i=-\infty}^{\infty} e^{2\pi j i \frac{a_1}{\Delta x}} \chi_x \left(q - i \frac{2\pi}{\Delta x} \right) \left\{ \frac{\sin\,[q - i(2\pi/\Delta x)](\Delta x/2)}{[q - i(2\pi/\Delta x)](\Delta x/2)} \right\}^2 \\
&= \sum_{i=-\infty}^{\infty} e^{2\pi j i \frac{a_1}{\Delta x}} \chi_x \left(q - i \frac{2\pi}{\Delta x} \right) \frac{1 - \cos\,(q\,\Delta x)}{(q\,\Delta x - 2\pi i)^2} \tag{6-61}
\end{aligned}
$$

For $a_1 = 0$ or $a_1 = \Delta x/2$ (see also Sec. 6-12), differentiation of Eq. (61) at $q = 0$ in accordance with Eq. (4) produces the *exact* result

$$E\{(x + s_x)_Q\} = E\{x\} \tag{6-62}$$

even though the distribution of $x + s_x$ is only approximately "band-limited." Quite similarly, we can add uncorrelated dither samples s_x, s_y (samples of triangle waveforms with different frequencies and amplitudes $\Delta x/2$, $\Delta y/2$) to the input signals x, y of a correlator and find

$$E\{(x + s_x)_Q(y + s_y)_Q\} = E\{xy\} \tag{6-63}$$

(see also Fig. 6-4b).

REFERENCES AND BIBLIOGRAPHY

1. Widrow, B.: A Study of Rough Amplitude Quantization by Means of Nyquist Sampling Theory *IRE Trans. PGCT*, December, 1956, see also *Tech. Rept.* 2103-1, Stanford Electronics Laboratories, Stanford, Calif., 1960.
2. Davenport, W. B., and W. L. Root: *Introduction to Random Signals and Noise*, McGraw-Hill, New York, 1958.
3. Korn, G. A., and T. M. Korn: *Mathematical Handbook for Scientists and Engineers*, McGraw-Hill, New York, 1961.
4. Kaiser, J. F., and R. K. Angell: New Techniques and Equipment for Correlation Computation, *MIT Servomechanisms Lab., Tech. Memo.* 7668-TM-2, December, 1957.
5. Maybach, R.: Hybrid Analog-digital Measurement of Sample Averages and Correlation Functions, *ACL Memo* 85, Electrical Engineering Department, University of Arizona, 1964.
6. McFadden, J. A.: The Correlation Function of a Sine Wave Plus Noise After Extreme Clipping, *IRE Trans. PGIT*, June, 1956.
7. Becker, C. L., and J. V. Wait: Two-level Correlation on an Analog Computer, *IRETEC*, December, 1961.
8. Ekre, H.: Polarity-coincidence Correlation Detection of a Weak Noise Source, *IEEE Trans. PGIT*, January, 1963.
9. Cooper, R.: Crosscorrelation with Binary Signals, *Memo.*, Electrical Engineering Department, Purdue University, 1962.
10. Rosenheck, B. M.: Detecting Signals by Polarity Coincidence, *Electronics*, Jan. 29, 1960.
11. Bussgang, J. J.: Crosscorrelation Functions of Amplitude-distorted Gaussian Signals, *MIT RLE Rept.* 216, 1952.

12. Jespers, P., et al.: A New Method to Compute Correlation Functions, *Intern. Symposium on Information Theory*, Liege, Belgium, 1962; see *IRE Trans. PGIT*, September, 1962.
13. Van Vleck, J. H.: The Spectrum of Clipped Noise, *Rept.* 51, Radio Research Laboratory, Harvard University, 1943.
14. Bennett, W. R.: Spectra of Quantized Signals, *Bell System Tech. J.*, July, 1948.
15. Bohn, E. V.: A Continuously Acting Adaptive Analog Computer for Determining the Impulse Response of Control Systems with Gaussian Signals, *Trans. Eng. Inst. Canada*, **5**(3), (1961).
16. Kosyakin, A. A.: The Statistical Theory of Amplitude Quantization, *Automatika i Telemekhanika*, June, 1961.
17. Watts, D. G.: A General Theory of Amplitude Quantization with Applications to Correlation Determination, *1EE Monograph* 481 M, November, 1961.
18. Bonnet, G.: Sur la Statistique du Second Ordre des Signaux Aleatoires Quantifies, *Compt. Rend.*, **225**: 825 (1962).
19. Furman, G. C.: Improving the Quantization of Random Signals by Dithering, *Rept.*, Rand Corp., Santa Monica, Calif., May, 1963.
20. Veltman, B. P. Th., and H. Kwakernaak: Theorie und Technik der Polaritätskorrelation für die dynamische Analyse niederfrequenter Signale und Systeme, *Regelungstechnik*, September, 1961.
21. Veltman, B. P. Th., and A. vanden Bos: On the Applicability of the Relay- and Polarity- coincidence Correlator in Automatic Control, *Proc. IFAC Conf.*, Basel, 1963.
22. Veltman, B. P. Th.: Unpublished communication (1964). References 23 to 26 are background material (in Dutch) for refs. 20 to 22.
23. Vanden Bos, A.: Calculation of Correlation Functions by the Polarity-coincidence Method, *Research Rept.*, Department of Technical Physics, Technical University Delft, Netherlands, October, 1962.
24. Van Bemmel, J. H.: Calculation and Measurement of Correlation Functions with the Aid of Dither, *Research Rept.*, Department of Technical Physics, Technical University Delft, Netherlands, October, 1963.
25. Van Loon, D.: Properties of Quantized Statistical Signals, *Research Rept.*, Department of Technical Physics., Technical University Delft, Netherlands, October, 1963.
26. Smit, H. J. P.: Dispersion of Autocorrelation Estimates, Thesis, Department of Technical Physics, Technical University Delft, Netherlands, 1963.
27. Max, J.: Quantizing for Minimum Distortion, *IRE Trans. PGIT*, March, 1960.
28. Bruce, J. D.: Optimum Quantization for a General Error Criterion, *MIT Quarterly Progress Rept.* 69, April, 1963.
29. Bluestein, L. I., and R. J. Schwarz: Optimum Zero-memory Filters *IRE Trans. PGIT*, October, 1962.
30. Bluestein, L. I.: Asymptotically Optimum Quantizers and Optimum Analog to Digital Converters for Continuous Signals, *IEEE Trans. PGIT*, July, 1964.
31. McFadden, J. A.: The Fourth Product Moment of Infinitely Clipped Noise, *IRE Trans. PGIT*, December, 1958.
32. Walli, C. R.: Quantizing and Sampling Errors in Hybrid Computation, *Proc. Fall Joint Computer Conf.*, 1964.
33. Korn, G. A.: Statistical Measurements with Quantized Data, *Simulation*, April, 1965.

CHAPTER 7

MEASUREMENT OF SPECTRAL DENSITIES, FOURIER COMPONENTS, AND SYSTEM RESPONSE

MEASUREMENT OF SPECTRAL DENSITIES AND FOURIER ANALYSIS

7-1. Introduction and Survey. The estimation of spectral-density values

$$\begin{aligned}
\Phi_{xx}(\omega_F) &= \int_{-\infty}^{\infty} R_{xx}(\tau)e^{-j\omega_F\tau}\,d\tau = 2\int_{0}^{\infty} R_{xx}(\tau)\cos\omega_F\tau\,d\tau \\
\Phi_{xy}(\omega_F) &= \int_{-\infty}^{\infty} R_{xy}(\tau)e^{-j\omega_F\tau}\,d\tau \\
&= \int_{-\infty}^{\infty} R_{xy}(\tau)\cos\omega_F\tau\,d\tau - j\int_{-\infty}^{\infty} R_{xy}(\tau)\sin\omega_F\tau\,d\tau
\end{aligned} \right\} \quad (7\text{-}1)$$

(Sec. 1-7) from actual stationary-process data is necessarily an indirect operation whose correct interpretation requires caution. A number of rather different measurement situations arise in practice.

(a) Spectral-density Estimation with Analog Filters. Filter-type analog spectrum analyzers estimate, say, the power spectral density $\Phi_{xx}(\omega)$ of a stationary input $x(t)$ by the mean output of narrowband filters (see also Sec. 7-2). Referring to Fig. 7-1,

$$E\{z^2\} = \int_{-\infty}^{\infty} |H_F(j\omega)|^2\Phi_{xx}(\omega)\,\frac{d\omega}{2\pi} = \int_{-\infty}^{\infty} a_F(\omega)\Phi_{xx}(\omega)\,\frac{d\omega}{2\pi}$$
$$\approx (2a\,\Delta f)\Phi_{xx}(\omega_F) \quad \text{with} \quad a_F(\omega) = |H_F(j\omega)|^2 \quad (7\text{-}2)$$

(see also Sec. 1-7). The quantity $2a\,\Delta f$ can be obtained through calibration with a white-noise input of known spectral density;[10,17] a is defined if Δf is taken to be the equivalent filter bandwidth introduced in Sec. 7-3.*   Note that *the use of Eq.* (2) *implies essentially steady-state conditions at the filter output in Fig.* 7-1, *even if we employ finite-time averaging. Hence, Eq.* (2) *applies only if our analog input or data record* $x(t)$ *is available for a time long compared to all filter time constants* (and hence to $1/\Delta f$).

If the filter input in Fig. 7-1 is switched from zero to $x(t)$ for a finite data run of T sec, then $E\{z^2\}$ and $R_{xx}(\tau)$ are related by the Wiener-Lee relations (1-24) for a time-variable linear operator.   If we employ simple integrator averaging for T' sec,[1]

$$\left.\begin{array}{l} E\{\langle z^2 \rangle_{T'}\} \;=\; \displaystyle\int_{-\infty}^{\infty} a_F(\omega)\Phi_{xx}(\omega)\,\frac{d\omega}{2\pi} \;\approx\; (2a\,\Delta f)\Phi_{xx}(\omega_F) \\[4mm] \text{with}\qquad a_F(\omega) \;=\; \dfrac{T^2}{T'}\displaystyle\int_{-\infty}^{\infty} |H_F(j\Omega)|^2\,\mathrm{sinc}^2\,\frac{T(\omega-\Omega)}{2\pi}\,\frac{d\Omega}{2\pi} \end{array}\right\} \quad (7\text{-}3)$$

where the integration time T' must be large compared to the run time T.†   Equation (2) is merely an approximation to Eq. (3) lor large values of T.   As before, we can

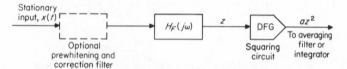

FIG. 7-1. Analog power-spectrum estimation with a filter.

find $2a\,\Delta f$ through calibration with a known noise input; the nature of $a_F(\omega)$ does not permit resolution of frequencies farther apart than $1/T$ even if T' is infinite.

Repetitive playback of a data record (tape loop) of length T for filter-type spectrum analysis is often convenient but also produces a statistical steady-state condition *only* if one run of the record is sufficiently long.   Otherwise, the resolution produced is essentially that of Eq. (3).[1]

(b) Computation of Spectral Densities from Correlation Functions.   *For data runs too short to produce steady-state filter output*, it is often preferable to employ *Fourier transformation of correlation-function estimates* in accordance with the Wiener-Khinchine relations (1), usually by digital computation (Sec. 7-3).

(c) General Remarks.   Prewhitening and Correction Filters. We shall see in Sec. 7-3 that the correlation method of spectral analysis produces, like the filter technique, biased estimates whose mean values are always *weighted averages of the true spectral density over frequency.* Thus, every estimate $F(\omega_F)$ of $\Phi_{xx}(\omega_F)\cdot$ const, whether it is obtained with

---

* $a = 1$ for an ideal rectangular filter with $|H_F(j\omega)|^2 = \mathrm{rect}\left(\dfrac{\omega-\omega_F}{2\pi\,\Delta f}\right)$, $\omega_F \geq \pi\,\Delta f$.

† $\mathrm{sinc}\,\lambda \equiv \dfrac{\sin\pi\lambda}{\pi\lambda}$.

a filter or by correlation, will be clustered about a mean value of the form

$$E\{F(\omega_F)\} = \int_{-\infty}^{\infty} a_F(\omega)\Phi_{xx}(\omega)\, \frac{d\omega}{2\pi} \approx (2a\,\Delta f)\Phi_{xx}(\omega_F) \qquad (7\text{-}4)$$

For good frequency resolution, the "weight function" $a_F(\omega)$, like $|H_F(j\omega)|^2$ in Eq. (2), must differ appreciably from zero only over a small frequency interval containing $\omega = \omega_F$ and must be positive over most of this interval. Note that a spectrum analyzer calibrated with white noise will always produce low estimates of spectral-density peaks narrow compared to the passband.[17]

If the shape of $\Phi_{xx}(\omega)$ is roughly known a priori, we can design a *prewhitening filter* to make the bandpass-filter input spectrum more nearly constant over the passband, so that scaling is improved, and Eq. (4) gives a better approximation to $\Phi_{xx}(\omega_F)$; the effect of the prewhitening filter must be divided out of the final result. Prewhitening is needed especially with narrowband analyzers having secondary passbands ("side lobes"), which might enhance spectral peaks outside the main passband. *The correction calculation can also include corrections for frequency-response limitations of measurement-system transducers.*[23]

If we are interested in the low-frequency end of a spectrum, it will pay to subtract the mean from all input data in order to avoid the effects of a delta spike at zero frequency.[1] We will assume that this has been done wherever necessary.

(d) Sampled-data Measurements: The Aliasing Problem. If analog data $x(t)$ are sampled periodically every Δt sec (sampling rate $\omega_S/2\pi = 1/\Delta t$ cps), the samples $x(k\,\Delta t)$ $(k = 0,\pm1,\pm2,\,\ldots)$ of the sinusoid

$$x(t) \equiv \cos[\omega t - 2(\omega_S - \omega)\,\Delta t] \qquad \left(\omega < \omega_S = \frac{2\pi}{\Delta t}\right) \qquad (7\text{-}5)$$

are *exactly duplicated* by the samples $x(k\,\Delta t)$ of

$$x(t) \equiv \cos[(2\omega_S - \omega)t + 2(\omega_S - \omega)\,\Delta t] \qquad (7\text{-}6)$$

(Fig. 7-2a). There exists, moreover, an infinite set of other sinusoids, with circular frequencies $2\omega_S + \omega$, $4\omega_S \pm \omega$, $\ldots$, whose samples $x(k\,\Delta t)$ also exactly duplicate those of (5) and (6). It follows that, with sampled-data measurements, spectral components with circular frequencies $2\omega_S \pm \omega$, $4\omega_S \pm \omega$, $\ldots$ will be superimposed on the spectral density measured at ω radians/sec and cause *aliasing or folding errors* in the measured results. Periodic sampling effectively transforms the data process $x(t)$ with power spectral density $\Phi_{xx}(\omega)$ into the impulse sequence $x(t)\sum_{k=-\infty}^{\infty}\delta(t - k\,\Delta t)$, whose power spectral density is

$$\Phi_{xx}'(\omega) = \sum_{k=-\infty}^{\infty}\Phi_{xx}(\omega + k\omega_S) \qquad (7\text{-}7)$$

(Fig. 7-2b). Sampled-data measurements will estimate the *aliased* spectral density (7) instead of the desired spectral density $\Phi_{xx}(\omega)$.

An inspection of Fig. 7-2b indicates that a *sampling rate* $\omega_S/2\pi = 1/\Delta t$ *exceeding all significant signal frequencies by a factor of two* will, in principle, eliminate errors due to aliasing. This assumes, however, that there is no significant high-frequency noise mixed with our data. The expense of a high sampling rate used merely to prevent aliasing is objectionable if we

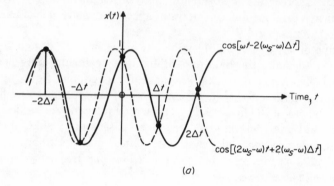

(a)

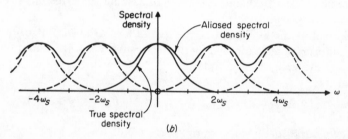

(b)

Fig. 7-2. Aliasing for two sine waves sampled at $\omega_S/2\pi = 1/\Delta t$ samples per second (a), and aliased power spectrum (b). $\pm\omega_S/2\pi$, $\pm 3\omega_S/2\pi$, . . . are "folding frequencies."

are interested only in low-frequency portions of $\Phi_{xx}(\omega)$. Whenever possible, we shall want to remove data frequency components above the *folding frequency* $1/2\Delta t$ cps (Fig. 7-2b) with the aid of a suitable steep-sided low-pass filter *ahead of the sampler.*

Another possibility arises if we know a priori that our spectral density has prominent peaks, which would cause very objectionable aliasing errors. It is then possible to select a sampling rate ω_S for each value of ω_F such that aliasing due to the prominent peaks, at least, does not occur near $\omega = \omega_F$.

7-2. Filter-type Analog Spectral Analyzers.   (a) Power-spectrum Analyzers.   In analog *power-spectrum analyzers* (Fig. 7-1), operational-amplifier filters (Sec. 2-10, Fig. 7-3) permit sharp filtering ($Q > 100$) from a few Kc down to subaudio frequencies, and high-Q LC filters serve at higher frequencies. Playback of recorded data in the subaudio-frequency range (e.g., control-system or geophysical data) can be speeded

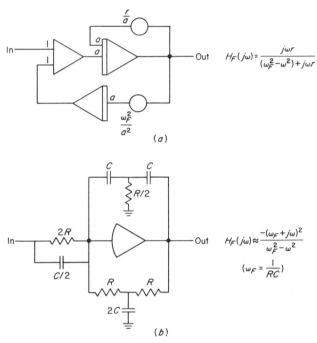

$$H_F(j\omega) = \frac{j\omega r}{(\omega_F^2 - \omega^2) + j\omega r}$$

(a)

$$H_F(j\omega) \approx \frac{-(\omega_F + j\omega)^2}{\omega_F^2 - \omega^2}$$

$$(\omega_F = \frac{1}{RC})$$

(b)

FIG. 7-3. Operational-amplifier bandpass filters.   Staggered filters can be cascaded to approximate rectangular bandpass characteristics.

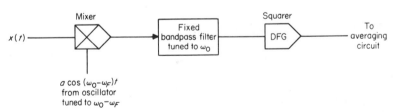

FIG. 7-4. Heterodyne power-spectrum analyzer.   Note that heterodyning makes the effective filter bandwidth Δf proportional to ω_F.   Prewhitening filter is not shown.

up for faster data processing and to permit the use of high-Q LC filters. The filter frequency $\omega_F/2\pi$ is changed either directly or (more frequently) by heterodyning (Fig. 7-4).   Spectrum analyzers are most frequently built as special-purpose computers; ref. 23, however, shows a complete heterodyne power-spectrum analyzer setup patched on a general-purpose analog computer.

(b) Cross-spectrum Analyzers. For measurement purposes, the (generally complex) cross-spectral density

$$\Phi_{xy}(\omega) = \int_{-\infty}^{\infty} R_{xy}(\tau)e^{-j\omega\tau}\, d\tau = \text{Re}\,\Phi_{xy}(\omega) + j\,\text{Im}\,\Phi_{xy}(\omega)$$

of two stationary random variables $x(t)$, $y(t)$ (Sec. 1-7) is represented in terms of its real and imaginary parts (sometimes known as co-spectral

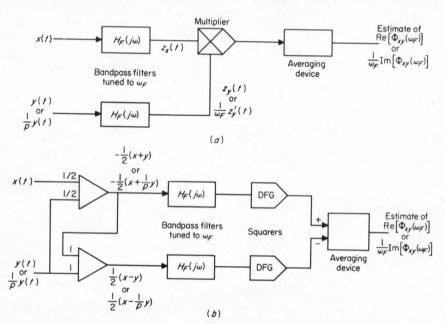

Fig. 7-5. Cross-spectrum analyzers. No prewhitening filters are shown.

density and quadrature spectral density), with

$$\left.\begin{array}{l} |\Phi_{xy}(\omega)| = \sqrt{(\text{Re}\,\Phi_{xy})^2 + (\text{Im}\,\Phi_{xy})^2} \\ \arg \Phi_{xy}(\omega) = \arctan (\text{Im}\,\Phi_{xy}/\text{Re}\,\Phi_{xy}) \end{array}\right\} \qquad (7\text{-}8)$$

For sufficiently long stationary data records, filter-type cross-spectrum analyzers implement the relations

$$\left.\begin{array}{l} E\{z_x(t)z_y(t)\} \approx (2a\,\Delta f)\,\text{Re}\,\Phi_{xy}(\omega_F) \\ E\{z_x(t)z_y'(t)\} \approx (2a\,\Delta f)\,\text{Im}\,\Phi_{xy}(\omega_F) \\ a = |H_F(j\omega_F)|^2 \end{array}\right\} \qquad (7\text{-}9)$$

where $z_x(t)$, $z_y(t)$ are outputs of filters with frequency-response functions $H_F(j\omega)$, and $z_y'(t)$ is the output of a filter with frequency response $\omega_F H_F(j\omega)/j\omega$ (Fig. 7-5a). Alternatively, we can employ two power-spectrum analyzers to determine the cross-spectral density from

$$\text{Re } \Phi_{xy}(\omega_F) = \tfrac{1}{4}[\Phi_{x+y,x+y}(\omega_F) - \Phi_{x-y,x-y}(\omega_F)]$$

$$\text{Im } \Phi_{xy}(\omega_F)$$

$$= \frac{\omega_F}{4}\,[\Phi_{x+\frac{1}{p}y,\,x+\frac{1}{p}y}(\omega_F) - \Phi_{x-\frac{1}{p}y,\,x-\frac{1}{p}y}(\omega_F)] \qquad \left(p \equiv \frac{d}{dt}\right) \Bigg\} \qquad (7\text{-}10)$$

in the manner of Fig. 7-5b.[12,14] In heterodyne-type spectral analyzers, the 90-deg phase shift expressed by multiplication with $1/j$ or $1/p$ in Fig. 7-5a and b is often more conveniently implemented through heterodyning with two local oscillators having equal frequencies and 90-deg phase difference (Fig. 7-6).[12,14,17]

Note that identical prewhitening, anti-alias, or correction filters (Sec. 7-1) in the x and y channels of a cross-spectrum analyzer will cause

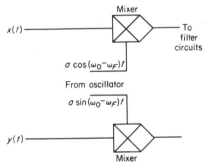

FIG. 7-6. Method for obtaining 90-deg phase shift in heterodyne cross-spectrum analyzers.

identical phase distortion in both channels, so that the measured *phase* spectrum remains unaffected.

Cross-spectrum analyzers are useful especially for determining the frequency-response function $H_{\text{SYSTEM}}(j\omega)$ of a linear time-invariant system with stationary input $x(t)$ and output $y(t)$ from the relation

$$H_{\text{SYSTEM}}(j\omega) = \frac{\Phi_{xy}(\omega)}{\Phi_{xx}(\omega)} \qquad (7\text{-}11)$$

(c) **Dynamic-range Requirements.** For Gaussian data with zero mean, the *dynamic range* of a spectrum-analyzer squaring circuit or multiplier should accommodate inputs up to about four times the corresponding input rms values (Sec. 5-5). The analyzer rms noise level at the squarer input should be less than one-third of the lowest rms signal level to keep the error within 11 per cent for the lowest spectral densities. It follows that a spectral-density range of, say, 100:1 requires a squarer-input dynamic range (rms noise level to maximum) of at least

$$20 \log_{10} 4 + 20 \log_{10} 3 + 20 \log_{10} 100 \approx 62 \text{ db}$$

Most commercially available spectral analyzers have squarer-input dynamic ranges of only about 30 db, so that they cannot be too accurate.[17] Squaring accuracies better than 0.5 per cent of half-scale are, while quite feasible, rare in practice. For Gaussian data, it is, however, possible to measure mean-square filter output in terms of mean absolute output (Sec. 6-5), which is more favorable from a dynamic-range point of view. It is also possible to employ manual or automatic rescaling for different frequency ranges as well as prewhitening to increase the accuracy.[17]

(d) **Digital Filtering.** Digital computation of spectral densities is most frequently based on Fourier transformation of correlation-function estimates. This method, however, requires prior computation of a considerable number of estimated correlation-function values, *even if we are interested in only a few values of the spectral-density function.* In such a case, it may be preferable to simulate the filtering/squaring operation of the analog spectral analyzer in Fig. 7-1 digitally. We can, say, average the squares of digitally computed quantities

$$z_i = \sum_{k=-n}^{m} h_k x[(i-k)\,\Delta t] \qquad (i = 0, \pm 1, \pm 2, \ldots) \tag{7-12}$$

which approximate values of a continuous weighting-function integral. The weighting coefficients h_k are chosen so as to implement a suitable bandpass response $H_F(j\omega)$ if we substitute

$$x(i\,\Delta t) = e^{j\omega i\,\Delta t} \qquad z_i = H_F(j\omega)e^{j\omega i\,\Delta t} \tag{7-13}$$

in Eq. (12). For finite data records, this procedure will produce an estimate of the form (3); in the course of our digital computation, however, we can at once design the weighting coefficients h_k so as to yield a favorable

$$a_F(\omega) = \left(\frac{T^2}{T'}\right) \int_{-\infty}^{\infty} |H_F(j\omega)|^2 \operatorname{sinc}^2 \left[\frac{T(\omega - \Omega)}{2\pi}\right] \frac{d\Omega}{2\pi}$$

in Eq. (3). In effect, this will involve (digital) multiplication of $x(t)$ by a "data-window" function $w(t)$ similar to the lag windows (16), (17) in Sec. 7-3, together with digital filtering. A complete digital-computer program is discussed in ref. 7.

7-3. Computation of Spectral-density Estimates from Correlation-function Estimates.   (a) General Theory.

Given an unbiased estimate $\hat{R}_{xy}(\tau)$ [e.g., $\langle x(t)y(t+\tau)\rangle_T$, Sec. 5-8] of $R_{xy}(\tau)$, substitution of $\hat{R}_{xy}(\tau)$ for $R_{xy}(\tau)$ in Eq. (1) should yield a corresponding unbiased estimate of $\Phi_{xy}(\omega_F)$. Unfortunately, we do not know $\hat{R}_{xy}(\tau)$ for absolute delays $|\tau|$ greater than some finite value $\tau_1 \leq T$, since correlation-function estimates cannot be computed for $|\tau| > T$ and will have acceptable variances only for substantially smaller absolute delays (perhaps $|\tau| < 0.1T$, Sec. 5-11).

Fourier transformation of the "truncated" correlation-function estimate

$$\hat{R}_{xx}(\tau) \operatorname{rect}\left(\frac{\tau}{2\tau_1}\right) = \begin{cases} \hat{R}_{xx}(\tau) & (|\tau| < \tau_1) \\ 0 & (|\tau| > \tau_1) \end{cases}$$

yields the spectral-density estimate

$$F(\omega_F) = \int_{-\infty}^{\infty} \hat{R}_{xx}(\tau) \operatorname{rect}\left(\frac{\tau}{2\tau_1}\right) e^{-j\omega_F \tau}\, d\tau \tag{7-14}$$

whose expected value is

$$E\{F(\omega_F)\} = \int_{-\infty}^{\infty} R_{xx}(\tau) \, \text{rect}\left(\frac{\tau}{2\tau_1}\right) e^{-j\omega_F \tau} \, d\tau$$

$$= \int_{-\infty}^{\infty} 2\tau_1 \, \text{sinc}\left[\frac{\tau_1}{\pi}(\omega - \omega_F)\right] \Phi_{xx}(\omega) \frac{d\omega}{2\pi}$$

since multiplication by the "window function" rect $(\tau/2\tau_1)$ in the time domain corresponds to convolution with $2\tau_1 \, \text{sinc}(\omega\tau_1/\pi) = 2\tau_1 \sin \omega\tau_1/\omega\tau_1$ in the frequency domain. *The mean of our estimate is a weighted average of $\Phi_{xx}(\omega)$ over frequency,*

$$E\{F(\omega_F)\} = \int_{-\infty}^{\infty} a_F(\omega)\Phi_{xx}(\omega) \frac{d\omega}{2\pi} \approx (2a \, \Delta f)\Phi_{xx}(\omega_F) \left.\right\}$$

with
$$a_F(\omega) = 2\tau_1 \, \text{sinc}\left[\frac{\tau_1}{\pi}(\omega - \omega_F)\right] \qquad (7\text{-}15)$$

just as in the case of filter-type spectrum estimation. The "weight" function $a_F(\omega)$ becomes more sharply peaked near $\omega = \omega_F$ for larger values of τ_1 (which implies larger observation times T). Unlike $|H_F(j\omega)|^2$ in Eq. (2), however, $a_F(\omega)$ has *negative* as well as positive values. Because of the negative "side lobes" of $a_F(\omega)$ (Fig. 7-7a), our estimate (14) can be negative if $\Phi_{xx}(\omega_F)$ is a smaller value next to a large peak of $\Phi_{xx}(\omega)$. Our estimate is, then, not only biased (this is more or less true for all spectral-density estimates), but rather uncomfortably so.

To improve this situation, we substitute a "window function" (lag window) which decays more smoothly toward zero at $\tau = 0$ and $\tau = T$ for the "abrupt" window rect $(\tau/2\tau_1)$. The resulting weight function $a_F(\omega)$ is thus given a large positive "main lobe" near $\omega = \omega_F$ and as small negative and positive "side lobes" as possible without making the main lobe too flat and wide. In particular, Fourier transformation of

$$\hat{R}_{xx}(\tau)w(\tau) = \hat{R}_{xx}(\tau)\left(a_0 + 2a_1 \cos \frac{\pi\tau}{\tau_1}\right) \text{rect}\left(\frac{\tau}{2\tau_1}\right) \qquad (7\text{-}16)$$

with $a_0 = 0.5 \qquad a_1 = 0.25 \qquad$ (HANNING WINDOW) $\qquad (7\text{-}17)$
and $a_0 = 0.54 \qquad a_1 = 0.23 \qquad$ (HAMMING WINDOW) $\qquad (7\text{-}18)$

yield estimate mean values

$$\int_{-\infty}^{\infty} a_F(\omega)\Phi_{xx}(\omega) \frac{d\omega}{2\pi} \approx (2a \, \Delta f)\Phi_{xx}(\omega_F) \qquad (7\text{-}19)$$

with the weight functions

$$a_F(\omega) = 2a_0\tau_1 \, \text{sinc} \frac{\tau_1}{\pi}(\omega - \omega_F) + 2a_1\tau_1 \, \text{sinc}\left[\frac{\tau_1}{\pi}(\omega - \omega_F) + 1\right]$$

$$+ 2a_1\tau_1 \, \text{sinc}\left[\frac{\tau_1}{\pi}(\omega - \omega_F) - 1\right] \qquad (7\text{-}20)$$

These weight functions are reasonably selective (Sec. 7-3) and have only relatively small negative excursions (Fig. 7-7b).[1] The necessary computations are usually carried out digitally (Sec. 7-3b).

(b) **Sampled-data Estimates.**[1,12,16,22] For digital data processing, we will, after due precautions against aliasing errors (Sec. 7-1d), calculate

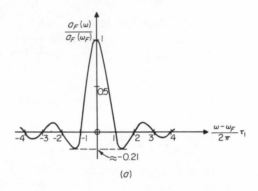

(a)

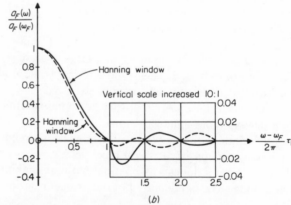

(b)

Fig. 7-7. The analyzer power-response function $a_F(\omega)$ vs. $\omega - \omega_F$ for the simple rectangular lag window (a), and Hamming and Hanning windows (b). The two principal side lobes of the Hamming window are only about one-third as high as those for the Hanning window, but the amplitudes of subsequent side lobes fall off less rapidly. (*Data from ref. 1.*)

a modified approximate Fourier transform of a sampled-data correlation-function estimate, say

$$R_h = R_{-h} = [x(t)x(t + h\,\Delta t)]_n = \frac{1}{n}\sum_{i=1}^{n} x(i\,\Delta t)x(i\,\Delta t + h\,\Delta t)$$

$$(h = 0,1,2, \ldots ,N) \quad (7\text{-}21)$$

where $N\,\Delta t = \tau_1$ is again the maximum lag for which we can estimate the correlation function. It will be fair to assume $E\{x\} = 0$ (Sec. 7-1c).

R_h is an unbiased estimate of $R_{xx}(h \, \Delta t)$ (Sec. 5-9). We approximate the Wiener-Khinchine relation (1) in the form

$$
\left.
\begin{aligned}
\Phi_{xx}(\omega_F) &= \int_{-\infty}^{\infty} R_{xx}(\tau)e^{-j\omega_f \tau} \, d\tau \approx \sum_{h=-N}^{N} R_h e^{-jhk \, \Delta\omega \, \Delta t} \, \Delta t \\
&= \left(R_0 + 2 \sum_{h=1}^{N} R_h \cos \frac{2\pi hk}{2N+1} \right) \Delta t = F(k \, \Delta\omega)
\end{aligned}
\right\}
$$

$$
\text{with} \quad N \, \Delta t = \tau_1 \qquad \Delta\omega = \frac{2\pi}{(2N+1) \, \Delta t} \qquad \omega_F = k \, \Delta\omega
$$

$$(k = 1, \ldots, N) \quad (7\text{-}22)$$

The expected value of our estimate becomes

$$
\begin{aligned}
E\{F(\omega_F)\} &= \sum_{h=-N}^{N} R_{xx}(h \, \Delta t)e^{-j\omega_F h \, \Delta t} \, \Delta t = \Delta t \sum_{h=-N}^{N} \int_{-\infty}^{\infty} \Phi_{xx}(\omega)e^{j(\omega-\omega_F)h \, \Delta t} \frac{d\omega}{2\pi} \\
&= \int_{-\infty}^{\infty} \Phi_{xx}(\omega) \left[\sum_{h=-N}^{N} e^{j(\omega-\omega_F)h \, \Delta t} \, \Delta t \right] \frac{d\omega}{2\pi} = \int_{-\infty}^{\infty} a_F(\omega)\Phi_{xx}(\omega) \frac{d\omega}{2\pi}
\end{aligned} \quad (7\text{-}23)
$$

$$
\text{with} \qquad a_F(\omega) = 2\pi \, \Delta t \, \frac{\sin (2N+1)(\omega - \omega_F)(\Delta t/2)}{\sin (\omega - \omega_F)(\Delta t/2)} \qquad (7\text{-}24)
$$

The expected value (23) of our sampled-data estimate is, again, a weighted average of $\Phi_{xx}(\omega)$ similar to (15); once again, we must reduce the rather large negative side lobes of $a_F(\omega)$ (similar to Fig. 7-7a) through multiplication of $\hat{R}_{xx}(h \, \Delta t) = R_h$ by a suitable lag-window function $w(h \, \Delta t)$. An equivalent but more convenient operation is to employ an appropriately weighted average of several values of $F(\omega)$ near $\omega = \omega_F$ as a new (smoothed) estimate.[1,12] In particular, the new estimates given by

$$
\left.
\begin{aligned}
F'(0) &= a_0 F(0) + 2a_1 F(\Delta\omega) \\
F'(k \, \Delta\omega) &= a_0 F(k \, \Delta\omega) + a_1 F[(k+1) \, \Delta\omega] + a_1 F[(k-1) \, \Delta\omega] \\
&\qquad\qquad (k = 1, 2, \ldots, N)
\end{aligned}
\right\} \quad (7\text{-}25)
$$

$$
\text{with} \qquad\qquad \Delta\omega = \frac{2\pi}{(2N+1)\Delta t} \approx 2\pi \, \Delta f \qquad (7\text{-}26)
$$

correspond to the use of window functions analogous to (16), (17) if[1]

$$
\begin{aligned}
a_0 &= 0.5 & a_1 &= 0.25 & (\text{``ALIASED'' HANNING WINDOW}) & \quad (7\text{-}27) \\
a_0 &= 0.54 & a_1 &= 0.23 & (\text{``ALIASED'' HAMMING WINDOW}) & \quad (7\text{-}28)
\end{aligned}
$$

If we take expected values in Eq. (26) and use Eq. (24), we find

$$
E\{F'(k \, \Delta\omega)\} = \int_{-\infty}^{\infty} a_F'(k \, \Delta\omega)\Phi_{xx}(\omega) \frac{d\omega}{2\pi} \qquad (7\text{-}29)
$$

where the new weight function $a_F'(\omega)$ has a more favorable shape similar to Fig. 7-7b.

The windows defined by Eqs. (27) and (28) are called "aliased" windows, because estimates $F(\omega_F)$, $F'(\omega_F)$ based on sampled data R_h will necessarily contain the aliasing errors discussed in Sec. 7-1d. Equation (29) for the "aliased" Hanning and Hamming windows is, in fact, identical with Eq. (19) for unaliased Hanning and Hamming windows if $\Phi_{xx}(\omega)$ is replaced by the aliased spectral density (7) in Eq. (19),[1] or if $\Phi_{xx}(\omega) = 0$ for $|\omega| > \pi/\Delta t$.

Analogous sampled-data estimates $F'(k\,\Delta\omega)$, $G'(k\,\Delta\omega)$ for the respective real and imaginary parts of a cross-power spectral density $\Phi_{xy}(\omega)$ may be obtained from [1,12,16]

$$
\left.
\begin{aligned}
R_k &= [x(t)y(t + k\,\Delta t)]_n = \frac{1}{n}\sum_{i=1}^{n} x(i\,\Delta t)y(i\,\Delta t + k\,\Delta t) \\
&\hspace{4cm} (k = 0, \pm 1, \pm 2, \ldots, \pm N) \\
F(k\,\Delta\omega) &= \left[R_0 + \sum_{h=1}^{N} (R_{-h} + R_h)\cos hk\,\Delta\omega\,\Delta t \right]\Delta t \\
G(k\,\Delta\omega) &= \left[\sum_{h=1}^{N} (R_{-h} - R_h)\sin hk\,\Delta\omega\,\Delta t \right]\Delta t \\
F'(0) &= a_0 F(0) + 2a_1 F(\Delta\omega) \\
G'(0) &= 0 \\
F'(k\,\Delta\omega) &= a_0 F(k\,\Delta\omega) + a_1 F[(k+1)\Delta\omega] + a_1 F[(k-1)\Delta\omega] \\
G'(k\,\Delta\omega) &= a_0 G(k\,\Delta\omega) + a_1 G[(k+1)\Delta\omega] + a_1 G[(k-1)\Delta\omega] \\
&\hspace{4cm} (k = 1, 2, \ldots, N)
\end{aligned}
\right\}
\quad (7\text{-}30)
$$

7-4. Estimate Variance vs. Frequency Resolution. Distribution of Power-spectral-density Estimates.

Unfortunately, *the variance of each spectral-density estimate will increase as we improve the frequency resolution.* For *Gaussian or approximately Gaussian data* of "effective record length"

$$
T_E = \begin{cases} T & \text{(FILTER-TYPE ANALYSIS)} \\ T - \tau_1/3 & \text{(CORRELATION ANALYSIS WITH SMOOTH WINDOWS)} \end{cases}
$$

it can be shown[1] that for each spectral-density estimate $F(\omega_F)$ whose mean value has the form (4)

$$
\text{Var}\,\{F(\omega_F)\} \approx \frac{1}{T_E}\int_{-\infty}^{\infty} [a_F(\omega)\Phi_{xx}(\omega)]^2\,\frac{d\omega}{2\pi} \qquad (7\text{-}31)
$$

provided that $\Phi_{xx}(\omega)$ *changes only negligibly over* $\frac{1}{2}T_E$ *cps to either side of the analyzer frequency* $\omega_F/2\pi$ (this excludes very sharp peaks). Note that the quantity

$$
\frac{\left[\int_{-\infty}^{\infty} a_F(\omega)\Phi_{xx}(\omega)(d\omega/2\pi) \right]^2}{\int_{-\infty}^{\infty} [a_F(\omega)\Phi_{xx}(\omega)]^2(d\omega/2\pi)} = \frac{[E\{F(\omega_F)\}]^2}{\int_{-\infty}^{\infty} [a_F(\omega)\Phi_{xx}(\omega)]^2(d\omega/2\pi)} = \Delta f
$$

$$
(\omega_F > \pi\,\Delta f) \quad (7\text{-}32)
$$

measures the analyzer frequency resolution for flat-spectrum noise. Δf (in cps) is, in fact, the bandwidth of an ideal spectrum analyzer with

$$a_F(\omega) = \operatorname{rect} \frac{\omega - \omega_F}{2\pi \, \Delta f} = \begin{cases} 1 & (|\omega - \omega_F| < \pi \, \Delta f) \\ 0 & \text{otherwise} \end{cases} \qquad (\omega_F > \pi \, \Delta f)$$

and will be called the analyzer *equivalent bandwidth*.   Reference to Eqs. (2), (3), (15), (19), and (23) shows that $\Delta f > \tfrac{1}{2}T_E$; this expresses a *fundamental limitation* on the frequency resolution obtainable for a given observation time,* rather than a deficiency of a particular measuring scheme.

Subject to our earlier assumptions, we have, then

$$\operatorname{Var} \left\{ \frac{F(\omega_F)}{2a \, \Delta f} \right\} \approx \frac{\Phi_{xx}{}^2(\omega)}{T_E \, \Delta f} \qquad \epsilon_{\text{rms}} = 100 \, \frac{\sqrt{\operatorname{Var} \{F(\omega_F)\}}}{E\{F(\omega_F)\}} \approx \frac{100}{\sqrt{T_E \, \Delta f}} \quad (7\text{-}33)$$

A variance increase due to increased frequency resolution can be offset by an increase in the observation time T; but this is possible only subject to possible constraints on the time and/or data records available for analysis.

Subject to the assumptions made for Eq. (31), experience indicates that $2T_E \, \Delta f \, F(\omega_F)/E\{F(\omega_F)\}$ is roughly distributed like a χ^2 distribution with

$$k = 2T_E \, \Delta f \qquad (7\text{-}34)$$

degrees of freedom.   We regard this as an empirical result; as a heuristic justification, k is the number of "independent" frequency bands of width $\tfrac{1}{2}T_E$ cps fitting into the analyzer bandwidth Δf.   Strictly speaking, the χ^2 distribution applies asymptotically as $T_E \, \Delta f \to \infty$ when the spectral density is constant over the passband.

The χ^2 distribution (Appendix) yields approximate confidence limits for our spectral-density estimates,

$$\operatorname{Prob} \left[\frac{2T_E \, \Delta f \, F(\omega_F)}{\chi_{\alpha/2}^2} < E\{F(\omega_F)\} < \frac{2T_E \, \Delta f \, F(\omega_F)}{\chi_{1-\alpha/2}^2} \right] = 1 - \alpha \quad (7\text{-}35)$$

where χ^2 has $2T_E \, \Delta f$ degrees of freedom, and $1 - \alpha$ is the desired confidence coefficient (see also Sec. 5-7).   For $2T_E \, \Delta f > 29$ or $T_E > 15/\Delta f$, we can regard the estimate distribution as normal.

Accurate determination of the equivalent bandwidth Δf requires calculations based on Eq. (34).[1]   For reasonably flat spectral densities, the Hanning and Hamming windows of Sec. 7-3 produce $\Delta f \approx 1.30/\tau_1$, but it

---

* For a single spectral-density peak involving abrupt changes within $1/2T$ cps in the analyzer passband, Eq. (31) is replaced by[1]

$$\operatorname{Var} \{F(\omega_F)\} \approx [E\{F(\omega_F)\}]^2$$

so that accurate measurement is impossible.

will be conservative to base our minimum observation time T on $\Delta f = 1/\tau_1$. We have, then,

$$\epsilon_{\text{rms}} \approx \frac{100}{\sqrt{T_E \, \Delta f}} \approx 100 \sqrt{\frac{\tau_1}{T_E}} \qquad (7\text{-}36)$$

Note that $T = n \, \Delta t$ must be *substantially* larger than $\tau_1 = N \, \Delta t$ for acceptably low ϵ_{rms}; e.g., $\epsilon_{\text{rms}} = 1$ per cent requires $n/N > 10,000$. In some applications, it is possible to reduce the estimate variance by averaging over the results of repeated experiments.

Reference 17 further discusses power-spectrum-estimate variances obtained with *EWP* averaging (*RC* averaging, Sec. 5-1). This type of averaging is used, in particular, with oscilloscope or recorder displays in many "quick-look" spectrum analyzers of the heterodyne type. The analysis methods of Sec. 5-3 apply; we present only the principal results. In most practical applications, *EWP* averaging with observation times T over three times the *EWP* time constant T_0 yields estimate variances about as large as those obtained with simple integrator averaging for $2T_0$ sec (see also Sec. 5-4). The rms error of the estimate will, however, be only about 4 per cent larger if the observation time is merely equal to the filter time constant T_0.[17]

Although it is, strictly speaking, preferable to keep the filter frequency $\omega_F/2\pi$ constant during the measurement, many practical power-spectrum analyzers sweep the heterodyne frequency slowly but continuously across the spectrum while the filter output is averaged. For reasonable accuracy, the frequency scan rate

$$R_S = \frac{(\tfrac{1}{2}\pi) \, d\omega_F}{dt}$$

for *EWP* averaging should not exceed

$$R_S = 4 \frac{\Delta f}{T_0} \quad \text{or} \quad R_S = \frac{(\Delta f)^2}{10} \qquad (7\text{-}37)$$

whichever is smaller.[17]

7-5. Time-variable Spectra. In many studies of nonstationary processes (geophysical phenomena, radio-wave propagation, speech patterns) the time-variable output of a filter-type power-spectrum analyzer with or without low-pass-filter averaging serves as a useful indicator of changes in the signal "frequency content." While such running-average spectra can be said to estimate averages over time and frequency of time-variable ensemble spectral densities,[24] most experimental studies of this type are simply descriptive. It will suffice here to say that we must again have a reciprocal relationship between frequency resolution (filter bandwidth) and time resolution (averaging time constant) to avoid analyzer-output fluctuations due to filter ringing. It follows that such time-variable frequency analysis makes sense only if the "power-spectrum" fluctuations are slow compared to the principal signal frequencies. As a useful example, Fig. 7-8 shows an analog-computer setup for continuous generation of the *EWP power spectral density*[23,25]

$$\Phi_{\text{EWP}}(t;\omega_F) = \left[\frac{1}{T_0} \int_0^\infty x(t - \zeta)e^{-\zeta/T_0} \cos \omega_F \zeta \, d\zeta \right]^2$$
$$+ \left[\frac{1}{T_0} \int_0^\infty x(t - \zeta)e^{-\zeta/T_0} \sin \omega_F \zeta \, d\zeta \right]^2 \qquad (7\text{-}38)$$

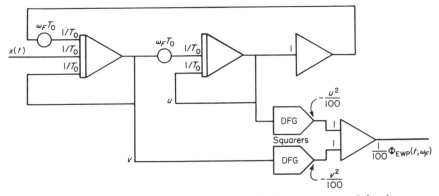

FIG. 7-8. An analyzer circuit producing the EWP power spectral density.

ANALOG-COMPUTER FOURIER ANALYSIS

7-6. Fourier Integrals.[26,28,33]   Given a suitable transient voltage $f(t)$ different from zero only for $t > 0$, the components

$$A(\omega) = \int_0^\infty f(t) \cos \omega t \, dt \qquad B(\omega) = \int_0^\infty f(t) \sin \omega t \, dt \qquad (7\text{-}39)$$

of the Fourier transform

$$F(j\omega) = \int_{-\infty}^\infty f(t) e^{-j\omega t} \, dt = A(\omega) - jB(\omega) = |F(j\omega)|e^{j\varphi(\omega)} \qquad (7\text{-}40)$$

are readily computed with analog multipliers and integrators.   Figure 7-9a illustrates a weighting-function technique, which eliminates the need for explicit multiplication by $\cos \omega t$ and $\sin \omega t$.   The simple linear-filter setup shown has two outputs with weighting functions (impulse responses, Sec. 2-10)

$$h_x(t - \lambda) = \cos \omega(t - \lambda) \qquad h_y(t - \lambda) = -\sin \omega(t - \lambda) \qquad (7\text{-}41)$$

We apply the given input $f(t)$ to this filter and obtain the output voltages

$$\left.\begin{aligned}
y(t) &= \int_0^t h_y(t - \lambda)f(\lambda) \, d\lambda \\
&= -\sin \omega t \int_0^t f(t) \cos \omega t \, dt + \cos \omega t \int_0^t f(t) \sin \omega t \, dt \\
x(t) &= -\frac{1}{\omega}\frac{dy}{dt} \\
&= \cos \omega t \int_0^t f(t) \cos \omega t \, dt + \sin \omega t \int_0^t f(t) \sin \omega t \, dt
\end{aligned}\right\} \quad (7\text{-}42)$$

If the Fourier integrals (39) exist, the functions (42) converge to

$$\left.\begin{aligned}
y_{SS}(t) &= -A(\omega) \sin \omega t + B(\omega) \cos \omega t \\
&\qquad\qquad = -|F(j\omega)| \sin [\omega t + \varphi(\omega)] \\
x_{SS}(t) &= A(\omega) \cos \omega t + B(\omega) \sin \omega t \\
&\qquad\qquad = |F(j\omega)| \cos [\omega t + \varphi(\omega)]
\end{aligned}\right\} \quad (7\text{-}43)$$

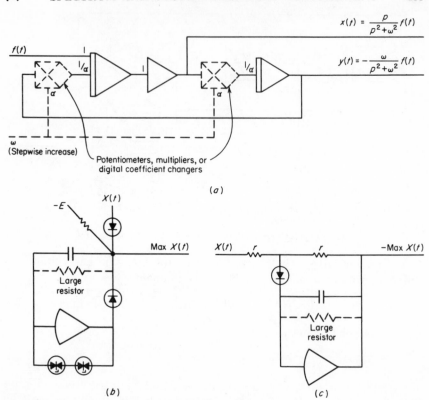

FIG. 7-9. Weighting-function technique for Fourier analysis (a), and peak-detector circuits (b).

as the transient input $f(t)$ decays; i.e., our filter exhibits sinusoidal "ringing" with amplitude and phase determined by $F(j\omega)$. We can, then, read

1. $A(\omega)$ and $B(\omega)$ by sampling $y_{SS}(t)$ and $x_{SS}(t)$, respectively, at $t = 2\pi n/\omega$, where n is an integer just large enough to yield steady-state output.
2. $|F(j\omega)|$ and $\varphi(\omega)$ by applying sample-hold outputs $A(\omega)$, $-B(\omega)$ to an inverse resolver.
3. $|F(j\omega)|$ as $[A(\omega)^2 + B(\omega)^2]^{1/2}$, or with a peak-detector circuit (Fig. 7-9b, c) applied to $x_{SS}(t)$ or $y_{SS}(t)$.

If $f(t)$ is recorded or generated in suitable form, we can produce the analyzer input $f(t)$ repetitively and step ω in small increments between runs (Fig. 7-9a).

7-7. Harmonic Analysis of Periodic Functions.[26,28,33]   To find the coefficients

$$a_k = \int_0^T f(t) \cos k\omega_0 t \, dt \qquad b_k = \int_0^T f(t) \sin k\omega_0 t \, dt \qquad (7\text{-}44)$$

in the Fourier expansion

$$f(t) = \frac{\omega_0}{2\pi} \left[\tfrac{1}{2}a_0 + \sum_{k=1}^{\infty} (a_k \cos k\omega_0 t + b_k \sin k\omega_0 t) \right] \quad (7\text{-}45)$$

of a suitable periodic function $f(t)$, we use the computer setup of Fig. 7-9a with $\omega = k\omega_0$ and sample the periodic output functions (42) at $t = 2\pi/\omega_0$.

FREQUENCY-RESPONSE MEASUREMENTS AND NYQUIST PLOTTERS

7-8. Weighting-function Method. A relatively simple way to obtain the frequency-response function $H(j\omega)$ of a stable and time-invariant computer-simulated linear system (Sec. 2-10) is with the computer setup of Fig. 7-10. Such a setup produces the impulse response $h(t)$ (Sec. 2-10),

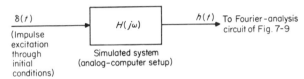

FIG. 7-10. Weighting-function method of frequency-response analysis.

and we apply the weighting-function method of Sec. 7-6 to find the real and imaginary parts of the desired frequency-response function

$$H(j\omega) = \int_{-\infty}^{\infty} h(\lambda)e^{-j\omega\lambda} \, d\lambda = A(\omega) - jB(\omega) = |H(j\omega)|e^{j\varphi(\omega)} \quad (7\text{-}46)$$

Stepwise automatic plotting of $-B(\omega)$ vs. $A(\omega)$ from sample-hold outputs yields a *Nyquist plot*, or the peak-detector output $|F(j\omega)|$ can be plotted against ω.

This weighting-function technique does not apply to frequency-response measurements on real systems; nor does it yield, for instance, the forward-gain response (output vs. error) even of simulated feedback loops, since the open-loop gain may be excessively high or exhibit instability. In such situations, we excite our system with a sinusoidal input and measure amplitude ratios and phase differences (Sec. 7-10).

7-9. Correlation Method.[32,35] The measuring system of Fig. 7-11 computes $A(\omega)$ and $B(\omega)$ by approximating

$$a^2|H(j\omega)|\langle \sin \omega t \sin [\omega t + \varphi(\omega)] \rangle = \frac{a^2}{2}|H(j\omega)| \cos \varphi(\omega) = \frac{a^2}{2} A(\omega) \; \Big\}$$

$$a^2|H(j\omega)|\langle \cos \omega t \sin [\omega t + \varphi(\omega)] \rangle = \frac{a^2}{2}|H(j\omega)| \sin \varphi(\omega) = -\frac{a^2}{2} B(\omega) \; \Big\}$$

$$(7\text{-}47)$$

and yields a direct Nyquist plot, provided that we know the input amplitude a.   While this requirement makes the correlation method less suitable for open-loop-response measurements (Fig. 7-12), it is especially well suited to closed-loop measurements on actual plants.   We employ a two-phase signal source to produce $a \sin \omega t$ and $a \cos \omega t$.   The correlators tend to discriminate against noise and harmonics in the system output; we can, in fact, perform measurements with the test input added to the normal system input.   Reasonably good results are obtained even if our sinusoidal test inputs are replaced by *square waves* with 90-deg phase

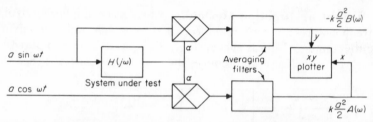

FIG. 7-11. Correlation method for closed-loop frequency-response measurement. $a \cos \omega t$ can be obtained with an adjustable phase shifter or, preferably, from a two-phase signal source.   Transducers required for many plant tests are not shown.

difference; we can then substitute simple gates for the analog multipliers in Fig. 7-11.

Although low-frequency filtering presents problems, the correlation method has been used with signal frequencies below 0.001 cps.[35]   In the case of analog-computer simulated linear systems, where noise and harmonics are no problem, and where

$$\dot{r}(t) = a\omega |H(j\omega)| \cos [\omega t + \varphi(\omega)]$$

is available, we can eliminate the need for filtering by computing

$$\left.\begin{array}{l} a^2 A(\omega) = a^2 |H(j\omega)| \cos \varphi(\omega) = a \sin \omega t r(t) + \dfrac{a}{\omega} \cos \omega t \dot{r}(t) \\[2mm] -a^2 B(\omega) = a^2 |H(j\omega)| \sin \varphi(\omega) = a \cos \omega t r(t) - \dfrac{a}{\omega} \sin \omega t \dot{r}(t) \end{array}\right\} \quad (7\text{-}48)$$

7-10. Sampling Method.[31,35]   In Fig. 7-12, two fast analog comparators mark the zero-crossing times $k\pi/\omega$ of $a \sin \omega t$ and the zero-crossing times $(2k + 1)\pi/2\omega$ of $a \cos \omega t$ $(k = 0,1,2, \ldots)$.   Memory pair 1, 2, operated by comparator 1, produces samples $e[(2k + 1)\pi/2\omega] = a$.   Electronic division yields $r(t)/a$, which is sampled to produce practically constant track-hold output voltages

$$\left.\begin{array}{l} \dfrac{1}{a}\, r\left(\dfrac{k\pi}{\omega}\right) = |H(j\omega)|\cos\varphi(\omega) = A(\omega) \\[3mm] \dfrac{1}{a}\, r\left[\dfrac{(2k+1)\pi}{2\omega}\right] = -|H(j\omega)|\sin\varphi(\omega) = -B(\omega) \end{array}\right\} \qquad (7\text{-}49)$$

for a direct Nyquist plot. Note that the amplitude a of $e(t)$ can vary with frequency, as it surely will in open-loop-response measurements with

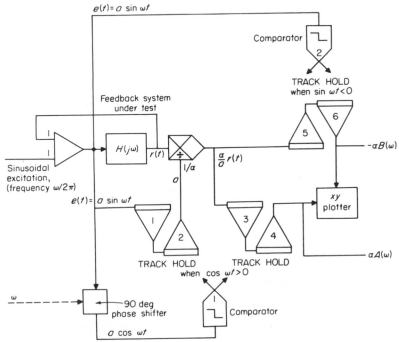

Fig. 7-12. Sampling technique for open-loop-response measurements on a computer-simulated system. The time origin is chosen so that $e(t) = a \sin \omega t$; note that a is, in general, a function of frequency.

constant sinusoidal excitation. The sampling technique is especially suitable for modern iterative differential analyzers, which can readily implement automatic frequency stepping.

$|H(j\omega)|$ and $\varphi(\omega)$ can again be obtained with an inverse resolver. We may also obtain $|H(j\omega)|$ as an amplitude ratio with two peak detectors (Fig. 7-9b, c), and $\varphi(\omega)$ with a phase-detector circuit similar to Fig. 8-14.

IMPULSE-RESPONSE MEASUREMENT THROUGH INPUT-OUTPUT CORRELATION

7-11. Correlation Method for Impulse-response Measurements.[45-54]

The impulse response $h(\lambda)$ for a linear (or approximately linear) system such as a process-control system or a nuclear reactor is frequently useful for system identification. $h(\lambda)$ may be used to indicate response amplitude, response damping, and critical frequencies directly, or it may be subjected to Fourier analysis to produce frequency-response data.   Since measurements involving actual impulse excitation are hardly ever practical, it is increasingly common practice to infer the impulse response from the system response $y(t)$ to a stationary broadband noise input $x(t)$

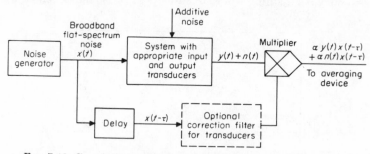

FIG. 7-13. Correlation method for impulse-response measurement.

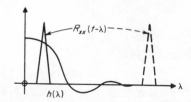

FIG. 7-14. System impulse response $h(\lambda)$, and test-signal auto-correlation function $R_{xx}(t - \lambda)$ approximating a delta function $a\delta(t - \lambda)$.   Dash lines indicate possible use of periodic test signals.

through input-output correlation with the aid of the well-known Wiener-Lee relation (1-27), i.e.,

$$R_{xy}(\tau) = \int_{-\infty}^{\infty} h(\tau - \lambda) R_{xx}(\lambda) \, d\lambda \qquad (7\text{-}50)$$

If we approximate white noise $x(t)$ with flat-spectrum noise whose bandwidth substantially exceeds that of the given system, then the noise autocorrelation function $R_{xx}(\lambda)$ in Eq. (50) is essentially replaced by an impulse function $\alpha\delta(\lambda)$ (Fig. 7-14), so that

$$R_{xy}(\tau) = \int_{-\infty}^{\infty} h(\tau - \lambda) \alpha\delta(\lambda) \, d\lambda = \alpha h(\tau) \qquad (7\text{-}51)$$

In this case, crosscorrelation yields a direct estimate of the desired system impulse response $h(\lambda)$ (Fig. 7-13).   Note, next, that such correlation measurements can usually be conveniently performed during normal system operation.   At least the *ideal* correlation function (51) is unaffected by a stationary additive signal $n(t)$ added to the system output in Fig. 7-13, and $n(t)$ may be due to normal system operation as well as to random disturbances. The noise-reducing feature of the cross-correlation method also permits us to employ such relatively small test signals $x(t)$ that normal system operation is not materially affected.

7-12. Pseudo-random-noise Techniques.[48,49,53]   As already noted in Chap. 4, a binary-noise test signal will be preferable to, say, Gaussian noise, since

1. It is easy to generate and requires only simple on-off transducers at the system input.
2. Binary signals have the most favorable ratio of mean-square input and maximum input amplitude.
3. Digital delay circuits can be used, and multiplication reduces to simple switching.

Although random telegraph signals have been successfully employed for system identification,[46] periodic pseudo-random noise (shift-register sequences, Secs. 4-9 to 4-12) are again greatly preferable, because

1. The triangular autocorrelation function of periodically sampled binary noise (Figs. 1-3 and 4-11) is an especially advantageous approximation to a true delta function.
2. The periodic nature of shift-register-sequence test signals yields especially low estimate variances if the correlator output integration is taken over an integral number of shift-register periods (see also Sec. 5-11).[48]

It is understood, of course, that the binary-noise sampling period Δt is small compared to all system time constants and oscillation periods; and that the shift-register period $(2^n - 1)\Delta t$ (Sec. 4-9) exceeds the largest delay τ of interest. Note, on the other hand, that Δt, which determines the equivalent bandwidth of the test signal, should not be smaller than, say, one-tenth to one-twentieth of the smallest time constant or natural oscillation of our system. This is dictated by the fact that the binary-noise autocorrelation function $R_{xx}(\lambda)$ (Fig. 4-11b) approximates $\alpha\delta(\lambda) = a^2 \, \Delta t \, \delta(\lambda)$; hence, the amplitude of our cross-correlation function (51) is proportional to Δt.

As an added striking advantage, *shift-register sequences permit especially elegant methods for obtaining the needed delayed sequence* $x(t - \tau)$. Poortvliet[48] utilized the shift-and-add property of maximum-length shift-register sequences (Sec. 4-9) to obtain delayed sequences $x(t - \tau)$ (Fig. 7-13) with a suitable set of modulo-2 adders (EXCLUSIVE OR circuits, Fig. 4-13a). It is, in fact, possible to obtain an entire set of delayed sequences

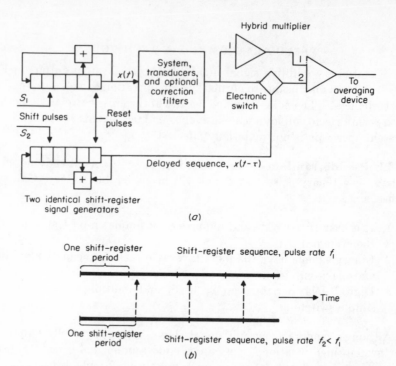

FIG. 7-15. Correlation method for impulse-response measurement with shift-register noise (a), and implementation of continuously changing delay (b).

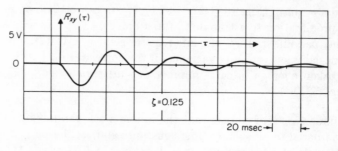

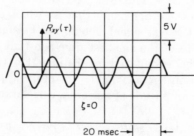

FIG. 7-16. Impulse response of damped and undamped second-order linear systems obtained by the method of Fig. 7-13 with continuously changing delay and $f_1 = 1,050$ cps, $f_2 = 1,000$ cps. Two 11-stage shift registers were used; accuracy is about 1 per cent. (*University of Arizona.*)

$x(t - \tau_1)$, $x(t - \tau_2)$, . . . simultaneously to produce correlation estimates for different values of the delay τ.

A possibly even more appealing method (Fig. 7-15a) employs two identical shift-register generators S_1, S_2 initially reset to the same pattern corresponding to $\tau = 0$. After a sufficiently large sample has been obtained, a preset counter system inhibits one shift pulse in the second shift register S_2, so that its output becomes $x(t - \Delta t)$ for the second sample. By inhibiting one shift pulse (or a number of shift pulses) after each sample, we obtain correlation estimates for x for $\tau = \Delta t$, $2\Delta t$, ... Again, if the averaging device in Fig. 7-15a is an analog low-pass filter, we can simply drive shift register S_1 with shift pulses of frequency $f_1 - \Delta f$. The delay τ between the two shift-register outputs will then vary uniformly and periodically between 0 and a complete shift-register period during successive time intervals $1/\Delta f$ (Fig. 7-15b). A recorder connected to the output of the averaging filter will, therefore, record periodic replicas of our correlation estimate as a function of delay with a repetition period $1/\Delta f$, which must be chosen to be sufficiently long for good averaging. Figure 7-16 shows two correlation estimates obtained by this convenient method, which can also be adapted to subsequent Fourier analysis by the method of Sec. 7-6.

REFERENCES AND BIBLIOGRAPHY

Measurement of Spectral Densities

1. Blackman, R. B., and J. W. Tukey: *The Measurement of Power Spectra*, Dover, New York, 1958.
2. Bates, M. R., et al.: Analog-computer Applications in Predictor Design, *IRETEC*, September, 1957.
3. Polimerou, L. G.: Spectrum Analysis of Random Noise Generators, *Communications and Electronics*, November, 1958.
4. Uberoi, M. S., and E. G. Gilbert: Technique for Measurement of Cross-spectral Density of Two Random Functions, *Rev. Sci. Instr.*, March, 1959.
5. Smith, H. W., et al.: A Power-spectrum Computer, *Rept.* 86, Electrical Engineering Research Laboratory, University of Texas, November, 1956.
6. Cooper, G., and P. Broom: Fourier Spectrum Analysis by Analog Methods, *Instruments and Control Systems*, May, 1962.
7. Welch, P. D.: A Direct Digital Method of Power-spectrum Estimation, *IBM J. Res.*, April, 1961.
8. Grand, B., et al.: Using Digital Techniques in LF Spectrum Analysis, *Electronics*, November, 1960.
9. Barton, D. W.: A Shock-spectrum Analyzer, *Rept.* 2-5323-4/77, The Boeing Co., Seattle, Wash., 1963.
10. Vichnevetsky, R.: Experimental Calibration of Bandpass Filters by the Impulse Method, *Ann. AICA*, April, 1963.
11. Chang, S. S.: On the Filter Problem of the Power-spectrum Analyzer, *Proc. IRE*, August, 1954.
12. ———: *Synthesis of Optimum Control Systems*, McGraw-Hill, New York, 1961.
13. Davis, J. C.: The Spectrum Analyzer as a Computer Element, *Electrotechnology*, May, 1963.

14. Parke, N. G.: An Analyzer for Measuring the Wiener Coherency Matrix of Two Signals, *Proc. IEEE*, June, 1963.
15. Stevens, F. R.: Multiple Filter Analysis, *Military Systems Design*, June, 1963.
16. Press, H., and J. W. Tukey: Power Spectral Methods of Analysis, and Application in Airplane Dynamics, *Bell Telephone System Monograph* 2606, 1957.
17. Bendat, J. B., and A. G. Piersol: Design Considerations and Use of Analog Power Spectral Density Analyzers, *Tech-Report* published by Minneapolis-Honeywell Regulator Company, Denver, Colo., 1964.
18. Martin, M. A.: Frequency-domain Applications to Data Processing, *IRE Trans. Space Electron. Telemetry*, March, 1959.
19. Seltzer, J. L., and D. T. McRuer: Survey of Analog Cr   spectral Analyzers, *WADC Tech. Rept.* 59-241, Wright Air Development Center, Ohio, 1959.
20. McRuer, D. T.: Autocorrelation and Spectral Density of Periodic Functions, *Tech. Mem.* 78, Systems Technology, Inc., Los Angeles, Calif., 1961.
21. ———: Computation of Spectra with Finite Run Length, *Tech. Memo.* 81, Systems Technology, Inc., Los Angeles, Calif., 1961.
22. Parzen, E.: Mathematical Considerations in the Estimation of Spectra, *Tech. Rept.* 3, Applied Mathematics and Statistics Laboratories, Stanford University, 1961.
23. Larrowe, V. L., and R. E. Crabtree: Analog Computation of Time-varying Power Spectra of Seismic Waves, *Rept.* 3708-15-T/5178-8-T, Analog Computer Laboratory, Institute of Science and Technology, University of Michigan, 1963.
24. Baghdady, E. J.: *Lectures on Communication System Theory*, McGraw-Hill, New York, 1961.
25. Otterman, J.: Exponentially-mapped-past Statistical Variables, *IRE Trans. PGAC*, January, 1960.

Fourier Analysis and Frequency-response Measurements

26. McCool, W. A.: Frequency Analysis by Electronic Analog Methods, *Project Cyclone Symposium* I, Reeves Instrument Corp., New York, March, 1951.
27. Schussler, W.: Schaltung und Messung von Ubertragunsfunktionen an einem Analogrechner, *Archiv Elek. Ubertragung*, October, 1956.
28. Teasdale, A. R.: Computing Fourier Coefficients without the Use of Multipliers, *Memo*, Temco Aircraft Corp., Dallas, Tex., 1959.
29. Paul, R. J. A., and M. H. McFadden: Measurement of Phase and Amplitude at Low Frequencies, *Electronic Eng.*, March, 1959.
30. Meyer-Brötz, G.: Anwendungen analoger Rechenelemente in der Tiefstfrequenz-Messtechnik, *Frequenz*, January, 1962.
31. Goldberg, E. A.: An Analog-computer Nyquist Plotter, *IRE Natl. Convention Record*, 1960.
32. Bekey, G. A., and L. W. Neustadt: Analog-computer Techniques for Plotting Bode and Nyquist Diagrams, *Proc. Western Joint Computer Conf.*, 1960.
33. Kovach, L. D.: Miscellaneous Techniques, in Huskey, H. D., and G. A. Korn, *Computer Handbook*, McGraw-Hill, New York, 1962.
34. Capon, J.: High-speed Fourier Analysis with Recirculating Delay-line Feedback Loops, *IRE Trans. PGI*, June, 1961.
35. Ross, C. W., and K. W. Goff: An Experimental Correlation Analyzer for Measuring System Dynamics, *Memo*, Leeds and Northrup, Inc., 1961.
36. Fuchs, A. M.: Control-system Test Equipment, *Control Eng.*, June, 1959.
37. Quarnstroom, B.: Transfer-function Determination in the Presence of Noise, *Proc. 5th Intern. Instrum. Meas. Conf.*, 1960; Academic Press, New York, 1960.
38. ———: On the Relative Merits of Methods to Measure Process Dynamics, *Acta IMECO*, Budapest, 1961.

39. Seifert, W.: Kommerzielle Frequenzgangmesseinrichtungen, *Regelungstechnik*, August, 1962.
40. Eykhoff, P.: Process-parameter Estimation, in MacMillan, R. H., et al., *Progress in Control Engineering*, vol. 2, Heywood and Co., London, 1963.
41. Hennig, T.: Testing for Plant Transfer Functions in Presence of Noise and Nonlinearity, *Control Eng.*, June and September, 1963.
42. Mesch, F.: Vergleich von Frequenzgangmessverfahren bei regellosen Störungen, *Z. Messen, Steuern, Regeln*, 7: 162 (1964).
43. Enochson, L. D.: Frequency-response Functions and Coherence Functions for Multiple-input Linear Systems, *NASA CR-32*, National Aeronautics and Space Administration, 196[...].
44. Lauber, R.: A Comparison of Fourier-analysis Methods Using an Analog Computer, *Proc. 4th AICA Conf.*, Brighton, 1964; Pressess Académiques Européennes, Brussels, 1965.

Measurement of Impulse Response by Cross-correlation

45. Lee, Y. W.: *Statistical Theory of Communication*, Wiley, New York, 1960.
46. Anderson, G. W., et al.: A Self-adjusting System, *IRE Natl. Convention Record*, 1958.
47. Sterling, J. T.: An Introduction to Pseudo-noise Codes and Correlators, *Rept.* R 62 DSD 34, General Electric Co., Syracuse, N.Y., 1962.
48. Poortvliet, D. C. J.: The Measurement of System Impulse Response by Cross-correlation with Binary Signals, *Rept.*, Technical University, Delft, Netherlands, 1962.
49. Hampton, R.: A Hybrid Analog-digital Pseudo-random-noise Generator, M.S. Thesis, University of Arizona, 1964; *Proc. Spring Joint Computer Conf.*, 1964.
50. Balcomb, J. D., et al.: A Crosscorrelation Method for Measuring the Impulse Response of Reactor Systems, *Nucl. Sci. Eng.*, October, 1961.
51. Rajagopal, V.: Determination of Reactor Transfer Functions by Statistical Correlation Methods, *Nucl. Sci. Eng.*, February, 1962.
52. Uhrig, R. E.: Measurement of Reactor Shutdown Margin by Noise Analysis, *Symposium on Reactor Kinetics and Control*, University of Arizona, March, 1963; published by Office of Technical Services, Department of Commerce, Washington, D.C., 1964.
53. Stern, T. E., and J. Valat: Highly Negative Reactivity Measurement Using Pseudo-random-source Excitation and Crosscorrelation, *Symposium on Reactor Kinetics and Control*, University of Arizona, March, 1963; published by Office of Technical Services, Department of Commerce, Washington, D.C., 1964.
54. Turin, G. L.: On the Estimation in the Presence of Noise of the Impulse Response of a Random, Linear Filter, *IRE Trans. PGIT*, March, 1957.

Miscellaneous

55. Korn, G. A., and T. M. Korn: *Electronic Analog and Hybrid Computers*, McGraw-Hill, New York, 1964.
56. Blum, M.: On Exponential Digital Filters, *J. ACM*, April, 1959.
57. Schweizer, G.: Analog Methods for Determining the Dynamics of a System with Statistical Stimuli, *Proc. 3d AICA Conf.*, Opatija, Yugoslavia, 1961; Presses Académiques Européennes, Brussels, 1962.
58. Watts, D. G.: Optimal Windows for Power-spectra Estimation, *MRC Tech. Summary Rept.* 506, Math. Research Center, University of Wisconsin, 1964.
59. Gauss, E. J.: Estimation of Power Spectral Density by Filters, *J. ACM*, January, 1964.
60. Whittlesley, J. R. B.: A Rapid Method for Digital Filtering, *Comm. ACM*, September, 1964.

CHAPTER **8**

SPECIAL TECHNIQUES
AND APPLICATIONS

INTRODUCTION

8-1. Survey. We introduced the hybrid-computer Monte-Carlo method in Chap. 4 (see especially Fig. 4-2) and discussed a few applications (Secs. 4-4 and 4-5). We subsequently turned to the design of noise generators (Secs. 4-7 to 4-12) and described statistical measurement techniques applicable to real as well as simulated experiments (Chaps. 5 to 7). We now return to scan special computing methods and applications destined to increase the importance of hybrid-computer random-process simulation. Hybrid-computer circuits really suitable for fast statistical computation are still relatively new (Sec. 8-2), promising techniques are as yet untried, and many existing results are derived from feasibility studies rather than from actual long-term computing experience. A number of interesting problems invite further theoretical and experimental research.

The 50- to 1,000-cps iteration rates of modern iterative differential analyzers can generate large statistical samples quickly, but intuitive interpretation by a human operator, as well as automatic crossplotting and optimization of statistics still places a premium on faster computation. Hence, we should like to make sample sizes as small as practical for acceptable statistical errors and confidence levels. Sample-size reduction is, of course, doubly important if computing accuracy requires slower analog and/or digital computation. Theoretical prediction of estimate variances, and thus of sample-size requirements, is practically impossible in most applications, so that we recommend following the example of classical statisticians in estimating sample variances or other measures of dispersion concurrently with estimate computation. We can, then, form

176

an idea of the confidence levels corresponding to given accuracy requirements (Sec. 5-7); we may, in fact, terminate data accumulation when a
certain confidence level is reached (*sequential estimation*, Secs. 8-3 and
8-4). An additional possibility, also derived from classical experiment-
design methods, is the reduction of estimate variances through the use of
"doctored" samples designed to represent the ideal theoretical ensemble
more accurately then a sample picked truly at random (Sec. 8-5).

**8-2. Fast Analog/Hybrid Computation. The ASTRAC II Sys-
tem.**[1-20,67] Every analog computer capable of repetitive operation (Sec.
2-4) can be adapted to statistical computations. But very high computing speed is desirable. The essential reason for ultra-fast computation is not just the sheer mass of statistical data required, but the intuitive
insight we gain by realizing the effects of system and parameter changes

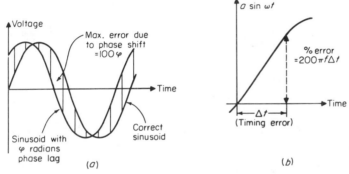

FIG. 8-1. Effects of computing-element phase errors (a) and switch-timing errors (b)
constitute the principal problems in fast analog/hybrid computation.

on statistics almost instantaneously. To simulate a dynamical system,
say a control system, one thousand times per second, we must solve 1 to
20 linear or nonlinear differential equations once every millisecond and
then reset the analog computer for the following run within 10 to 100
μsec. We shall require not only analog computing elements (summers,
integrators, multipliers, etc.) capable of operating on 1- to 100-Kc
signals with acceptable errors, but also integrator, and track-hold, and
analog-comparator timing within 50 nsec (Fig. 8-1).

To meet such specifications, the University of Arizona's ASTRAC II
iterative differential analyzer (Fig. 8-2)* employs ± 10-volt transistor
amplifiers with a unity-gain bandwidth beyond 20 Mc and extremely low
computing impedances. Summing-resistor values (Sec. 2-3) are 5K and
1K as compared to the 1M and 100K resistors employed in "slow"
analog computers. In addition, all amplifiers, multipliers, etc., are

---

* ASTRAC stands for Arizona Statistical Repetitive Analog Computer. ASTRAC
I was a vacuum-tube predecessor[1,11] of the all-solid-state ASTRAC II.

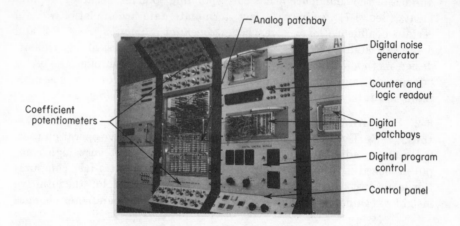

Analog patchbay

Digital noise generator

Counter and logic readout

Coefficient potentiometers

Digital patchbays

Digital program control

Control panel

FIG. 8-2. ASTRAC II console. All analog computing elements other than coefficient potentiometers plug directly into the rear of the shielded analog patchbay.

plugged directly into the rear of a shielded patchbay, while diode-function-generator networks plug into the storable problem boards. This system eliminates signal-wiring capacitances and crosstalk. Table 8-1 summarizes ASTRAC II performance, and Fig. 8-3 illustrates some of the fast computing circuits.

Table 8-1. ASTRAC II Performance Data[15,18-20]

Amplifiers:
± 10 volts, 50 mA at d-c; ± 10 volts, 30 mA to 1 Mc
D-c gain $>10^6$ (120 db) with chopper stabilization
Drift, 10 μV/deg C, <1 nA/deg C with chopper stabilization
0-db bandwidth >20 Mc, 6 db/octave rolloff
Unity-inverter phase error, 0.16 per cent (0.09 deg) at 16 Kc
Integrator phase error, 0.08 per cent (0.05 deg) at 16 Kc
Resistance ratios specified within 0.2 per cent

Integrator/Track-hold Circuits ($C = 1 \mu$F, 0.1 μF, or 0.01 μF; data for $C = 0.01 \mu$F):
Phase error in TRACK, 0.25 per cent (0.2 deg) at 10 Kc
Holding error, <0.1 per cent of half-scale in 1 msec
Switching time into HOLD or COMPUTE, <80 nsec; two circuits switch within 20 nsec of one another

Diode Quarter-square Multipliers:
Static error <0.2 per cent of half-scale
Drift, <0.7 mV/deg C
Dynamic error <0.5 per cent of half-scale at 10 Kc (0.3 deg phase error)

Analog Comparators:
Chopper-stabilized; response time <120 nsec
Static hysteresis, ± 25 mV
Drift, <25 μV/deg C

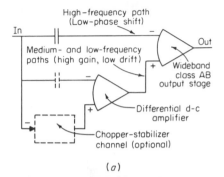

(a)

(b)

FIG. 8-3a, b. Feedforward transistor amplifier used in ASTRAC II (a), and plug-in modules (b) (see also Table 8-1). Rear connections in Fig. 8-3b carry d-c only.

ASTRAC II employs digital circuits for iteration control and statistics accumulation. Integrator and track-hold mode control, comparator outputs, analog switches, and free logic elements are terminated in a *control patchbay*. A *digital control panel* permits the operator to control repetition rate, computer-run length, readout timing, and sample sizes for statistical computations (Fig. 8-4).[10,67] A *resettable 25-bit shift-register pseudo-random-noise generator* can produce up to four digital or analog outputs and has its own small patchbay with removable patchboards. Another small patchbay controls a packaged *parameter optimizer* with a variety of optimization strategies (see also Sec. 8-15).

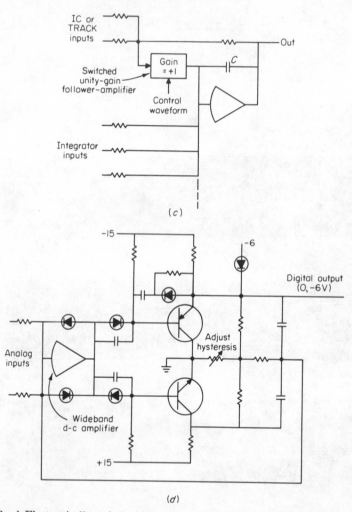

FIG. 8-3c, d. Electronically switched integrator or track-hold circuit[20] (c), and regenerative comparator with digital output[19] (d). The switched-follower output impedance in (c) is so low that no separate HOLD switch is required (see also Figs. 2-6b, 2-14, and 2-17; and Table 8-1).

ASTRAC II also has built-in analog/digital circuits for computing averages, mean squares, and probability estimates (Figs. 5-3 and 5-17b), but the ideal way to process statistical data obtained from fast analog-computer experiments is with a small stored-program digital computer in the $10,000 to $30,000 class (e.g., Digital Equipment Corporation PDP 8

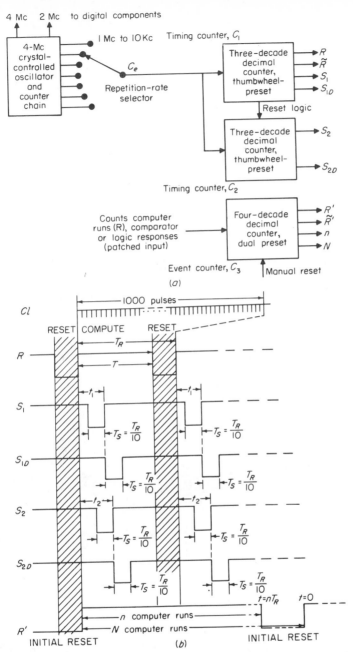

FIG. 8-4. ASTRAC II control system (a), and timing (b).   1,000 Cl pulses determine one basic RESET-COMPUTE period; the frequency of these Cl pulses determines the computing time scale and permits iteration at up to 1,000 computer runs per second. Preset decimal counters C_1, C_2 count Cl pulses to produce computer RESET pulses R and sampling pulses S_1, S_2, S_{1D}, S_{2D} at thumbwheel-selected times during each computer run. S_2 can also follow S_1 after a selected delay τ_D, or can move automatically. The dual-preset event counter C_3 counts computer runs or comparator responses to determine sample sizes and subroutine sequences.[10,67]

181

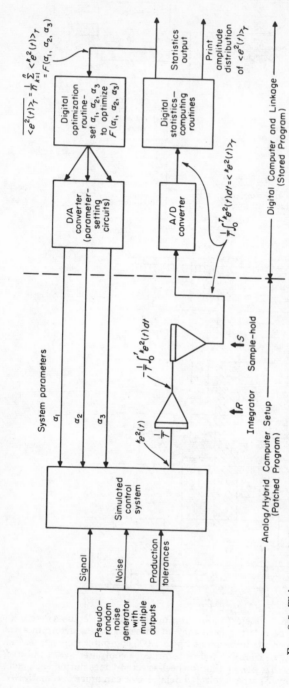

Fig. 8-5. This example illustrates the possibilities of combining an ASTRAC II-type iterative analog computer with a small stored-program digital data processor. Analog computing elements produce successive samples of the squared-error time average $\langle {}_k e^2(t) \rangle_T = \frac{1}{T} \int_0^T {}_k e^2(t) \, dt$ for a simulated control system with random input and noise. The digital computer finds successive values of the sample average $\overline{\langle {}_k e^2(t) \rangle_T} = \frac{1}{n} \sum_{k=1}^{n} \langle {}_k e^2(t) \rangle_T$ for $n = 100$ to $10{,}000$ computer runs and changes control-system parameters so as to optimize the sample average (Fig. 8-20). Note that each analog/digital and digital/analog conversion and digital-computation sequence is required only once per analog-computer run.

182

or Computer Control Corporation DDP 116), as shown in Fig. 8-5. Digital programs are conveniently stored on punched tape. Digital data processing not only yields several estimates (e.g., mean value, mean square, and amplitude distribution) from each sample, but also permits more sophisticated methods of sequential estimation (Sec. 8-3). *Since sampling, data conversion, and digital operations repeat only once or twice per analog-computer run, there are no stringent speed requirements on linkage and digital computer.* The resulting hybrid system is a much happier (and less expensive) combination than those now commonly employed for combined analog-digital simulation.

SOME SPECIAL MEASUREMENT AND SAMPLING TECHNIQUES FOR STATISTICAL SIMULATION

8-3. Confidence-interval Measurement and Sequential Estimation (see also Ref. 49). (a) **Random-sample Averages from Approximately Gaussian Data.** Consider the estimation of an ensemble average $E\{f\}$ by the sample average $\bar{f} = \dfrac{1}{n} \sum\limits_{k=1}^{n} {}^{k}f$ over a random sample $({}^{1}f, {}^{2}f, \ldots, {}^{n}f)$ obtained in n computer runs (Secs. 1-5, 4-2, and 5-4). To gauge the sample size n required for a given accuracy and confidence level (Sec. 5-6), let us assume that the random variable f is at least approximately Gaussian; if necessary, we will further approximate this condition by preaveraging (Secs. 5-7 and 8-4). For a normal (Gaussian) random sample, Eq. (5-43) defines symmetrical confidence limits $\bar{f} \pm d$ for $E\{f\}$, with

$$d = t_{1-\alpha/2} \sqrt{\frac{\overline{(f - \bar{f})^2}}{n - 1}} \qquad (n \text{ degrees of freedom}) \qquad (8\text{-}1)$$

where $t_{1-\alpha/2}$ is found from a t-distribution table for each given confidence level $1 - \alpha$. To obtain either the half-width d of a confidence interval for given α or the confidence level $1 - \alpha$ for a given acceptable error d, we must measure the sample variance $\overline{(f - \bar{f})^2}$, the sample standard deviation $\sqrt{\overline{(f - \bar{f})^2}}$ or, if this is easier, the sample mean absolute deviation $\overline{|f - \bar{f}|}$ concurrently with the sample average $\bar{f}$; note that

$$\sqrt{E\{[f - E\{f\}]^2\}} = \sqrt{\frac{\pi}{2}} E\{|f - E\{f\}|\} \qquad (8\text{-}2)$$

for normal random samples (Sec. 6-5), so that it may be permissible to employ the approximate relation

$$\sqrt{\overline{(f - \bar{f})^2}} \approx \sqrt{\frac{\pi}{2}} \, \overline{|f - \bar{f}|} \qquad (8\text{-}3)$$

for $n > 30$. Confidence-interval estimation need not be accurate, since d is usually at most a few per cent of the sample range.

For a preset sample size n, Eq. (1) permits us to compute and display either d or α from measured values of $\overline{(f - \bar{f})^2}$ or $\overline{|f - \bar{f}|}$. Figure 8-6a shows the circuit of a simple "confidence-interval meter," which may be considered as an accessory for the sample-averaging computer of Fig. 5-3. A more sophisticated approach is to compute the sample variance $\overline{(f - \bar{f})^2}$

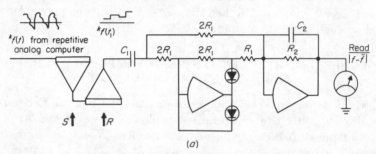

FIG. 8-6a. Analog computation of confidence-interval width for a normal-random-sample average with preset sample size n and sampling rate. The confidence-interval-meter reading is proportional to an EWP average approximating $\overline{|f - \bar{f}|}$. The time constants R_1C_1, R_2C_2 must be matched to repetition rate and sample size.

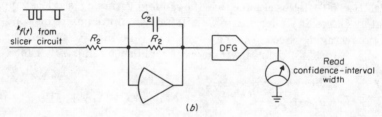

FIG. 8-6b. Analog computation of confidence-interval width for probabilities estimated from a dual-slicer output $f(t)$ (Fig. 5-12a). The confidence-interval-meter reading is proportional to a function of $<f(t)>_{EWP}$ in accordance with Fig. A-1.

for each successive value of n (or, say, for every tenth n) and to terminate data taking as soon as

$$\overline{(f - \bar{f})^2} < (n - 1)\left(\frac{d}{t_{1-\alpha/2}}\right)^2 \tag{8-4}$$

for preset values of d and α (*sequential estimation*).

Sequential estimation is most convenient with a digital statistics computer. Computation of

$$^n\bar{f} = \frac{1}{n}\sum_{k=1}^{n} {}^k f \qquad {}^n s^2 = {}^n\overline{(f - \bar{f})^2} = \frac{1}{n}\sum_{k=1}^{n} ({}^k f - {}^n\bar{f})^2 \tag{8-5}$$

can utilize the recurrence relations

$$
\left.
\begin{aligned}
{}^n\bar{f} &= {}^{n-1}\bar{f} + \frac{1}{n}\left({}^nf - {}^{n-1}\bar{f}\right) \\
{}^ns^2 &= {}^{n-1}s^2 + \frac{1}{n}\left[\left({}^nf - {}^n\bar{f}\right)^2 - {}^{n-1}s^2\right]
\end{aligned}
\right\}
\tag{8-6}
$$

Continuous analog computation of the finite-time averages

$$
\left.
\begin{aligned}
\langle f(t)\rangle_t &= \frac{1}{t}\int_0^t f(t)\,dt \\
s^2(t) &= \langle[f(t) - \langle f(t)\rangle_t]^2\rangle_t = \frac{1}{t}\int_0^t [f(t) - \langle f(t)\rangle_t]^2\,dt
\end{aligned}
\right\}
\tag{8-7}
$$

can similarly be implemented through solution of the differential equations

$$
\left.
\begin{aligned}
\frac{d}{dt}\langle f(t)\rangle_t &= \frac{1}{t}\left[f(t) - \langle f(t)\rangle_t\right] && \langle f(t)\rangle_0 = f(0) \\
\frac{d}{dt}s^2(t) &= \frac{1}{t}\left\{[f(t) - \langle f(t)\rangle_t]^2 - s^2(t)\right\} && s^2(0) = 0
\end{aligned}
\right\}
\tag{8-8}
$$

for $\langle f(t)\rangle_t$ and $s^2(t)$. Division by $t = 0$ can be achieved with a steepest-descent division loop,[67] or computation can be started at $t = t_1$ with the initial conditions $\langle f(t)\rangle_{t_1} = f(t_1)$, $s^2(t_1) = 0$; the resulting error will be small for $t_1 \ll t$.

(b) Probability Measurements. Confidence intervals for probability measurements (Secs. 5-12 to 5-15) from random samples are easily

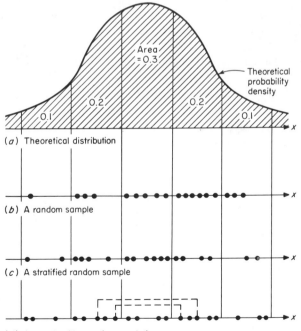

(a) Theoretical distribution

(b) A random sample

(c) A stratified random sample

(d) A sample with negative correlation

Fig. 8-7. Techniques for reducing sample variability.

derived from the binomial distribution. For given sample size n and confidence level $1 - \alpha$, the confidence-interval width for the unknown probability is a function of the estimate (statistical relative frequency) itself (Fig. A-2, Appendix). Sequential estimation of probabilities is, again, conveniently implemented with a small digital computer; Fig. 8-6b shows a simple analog confidence-interval meter suitable for use with hybrid-computer amplitude-distribution analyzers (Sec. 5-12).

8-4. Preaveraging Methods. As already noted in Sec. 5-7, confidence-interval measurements and sequential estimation based on the assumption of approximately Gaussian data become much more generally applicable if averages over a random sample ^1f, ^2f, . . . , ^nf are computed as averages over "preaverages," i.e.,

$$\bar{f} = \frac{1}{n}(^1f + {}^2f + \cdots + {}^nf)$$

$$= \frac{m}{n}\left[\frac{1}{m}(^1f + {}^2f + \cdots + {}^mf)\right.$$

$$\left. + \frac{1}{m}(^{m+1}f + {}^{m+2}f + \cdots + {}^{2m}f) + \cdots\right] \quad (8\text{-}9)$$

The set of preaverages $(1/m)(^1f + {}^2f + \cdots + {}^mf)$, $(1/m)(^{m+1}f + {}^{m+2}f + \cdots + {}^{2m}f)$, . . . very often becomes a useful approximation to a normal sample of size n/m; m between 3 and 10 has proved to be a practical choice for symmetrical distributions. Note that preaveraging in accordance with Eq. (9) will not affect the value of our sample average $\bar{f}$ but changes the sample size together with the sample variance or other dispersion measures used for confidence-level estimation.

Computation of preaverages and dispersion measures is, again, most conveniently accomplished if a stored-program digital computer is available for data processing. As an alternative, the track-hold circuits used for random-process sampling in hybrid computers can implement preaveraging in the manner of Fig. 5-2.*

* W. Giloi (private communication) has suggested that, in view of

$$\frac{E\{\overline{(z - \bar{z})^2}\}}{\frac{n}{m} - 1} = \frac{m}{n}\operatorname{Var}\{z\} = \frac{1}{n}\operatorname{Var}\{f\} = \frac{E\{\overline{(f - \bar{f})^2}\}}{n - 1}$$

confidence-interval estimation on the basis of Eq. (1) does not require actual implementation of the preaveraging operation; one merely employs $(n/m) - 1$ degrees of freedom instead of $n - 1$ degrees of freedom for the t distribution. This seems indeed justified, provided that n/m is large enough. The above relation, together with Eqs. (27.7.1) and (27.7.2) of Cramér's Mathematical Methods of Statistics (Princeton University Press, 1951), shows that the expected values of $[(z - \bar{z})^2/(n/m - 1)]^{1/2}$ and $[(f - \bar{f})^2/(n - 1)]^{1/2}$ differ by an error of the order of $(m/n)^{3/2}$, while their variances differ by a term of the order of $(m/n)^2$.

The circuit of Fig. 5-2b could also be used to produce exponentially weighted pre-averages, which could be read every m' runs without any need to reset the accumulator; but such exponentially weighted preaverages are correlated for small m' and very wasteful of data for large m'.

8-5. Variance Reduction by Special Sampling Techniques (Fig. 8-7).

In principle, every Monte-Carlo computation may be considered as the estimation of a suitable integral

$$I = \int_{-\infty}^{\infty} \int_{-\infty}^{\infty} \cdots \int_{-\infty}^{\infty} f(\lambda_1,\lambda_2, \ldots ,\lambda_N) \, dP(\lambda_1,\lambda_2, \ldots ,\lambda_N) \quad (8\text{-}10)$$

by a random-sample average

$$\overline{f(x_1,x_2, \ldots ,x_N)} = \frac{1}{n} \sum_{k=1}^{n} f(^kx_1,^kx_2, \ldots ,^kx_N) \quad (8\text{-}11)$$

where $(x_1,x_2, \ldots ,x_N)$ is a (generally multidimensional, $N > 1$) random variable with known distribution function $P(x_1,x_2, \ldots ,x_N)$; for random-process studies involving, say, a flat-spectrum noise input of bandwidth B for T sec, N can be of the order of $2BT$. For simplicity, we shall base the following discussion on Monte-Carlo estimation of the *one-dimensional* integral

$$I = \int_{-\infty}^{\infty} f(\lambda) \, dP(\lambda) \quad (8\text{-}12)$$

by

$$\overline{f(x)} = \frac{1}{n} [f(^1x) + f(^2x) + \cdots + f(^nx)] \quad (8\text{-}13)$$

although we would, most probably, employ Monte-Carlo computation in the one-dimensional case only if we required direct simulation for a partial system test, or to gain intuitive insight. Note that each calculation of $f(^kx)$ may involve solution of differential equations.

The variance of our estimate (13) of (12) on the basis of a random sample, $(^1x,^2x, \ldots ,^nx)$, is

$$\text{Var} \{\overline{f(x)}\} = \frac{1}{n} \text{Var} \{f(x)\} \quad (8\text{-}14)$$

so that the rms fluctuation decreases only as $1/\sqrt{n}$ with increasing n (Sec. 5-4). The estimate variance is due to the random fluctuation in the distribution of different samples $(^1x,^2x, \ldots ,^nx)$. We will now attempt to "doctor" the sample $(^1x,^2x, \ldots ,^nx)$ so as to reduce these fluctuations, while still preserving the relation

$$E\{\overline{f(x)}\} = E\{f(x)\} = I \quad (8\text{-}15)$$

i.e., without biasing our estimate.

(a) **Stratified Sampling.**[56] We divide the range of the random variable x into a number of suitably chosen class intervals $\xi_{j-1} < x \leq \xi_j$ and agree to fix the number n_j of otherwise independent sample values

$^kx = {}^ix_j (i = 1, 2, \ldots, n_j)$ falling into the jth class interval. Assuming a priori knowledge of the probabilities

$$P_j = \text{Prob}\,[\xi_{j-1} < x \leq \xi_j] = P(\xi_j) - P(\xi_{j-1}) \qquad (8\text{-}16)$$

associated with our class intervals (e.g., on the basis of symmetry, uniform distribution, etc.), we can employ the *stratified-sample average*

$$\overline{f(x)}_{\text{STRAT}} = \sum_j P_j \frac{1}{n_j} \Big[\sum_{i=1}^{n_j} f({}^ix_j) \Big] \qquad (8\text{-}17)$$

as an unbiased estimate of I, with

$$\text{Var}\,\{\overline{f(x)}_{\text{STRAT}}\} = \sum_j \frac{P_j{}^2}{n_j} \text{Var}\,\{f({}^ix_j)\} \qquad (8\text{-}18)$$

Note that repeated stratified samples will differ only within class intervals. The variance (18) can be smaller than the random-sample variance $\text{Var}\,\{\overline{f(x)}\}/n$ with $n = \sum_j n_j$ if a priori information permits a favorable choice of the ξ_j and n_j. In principle, it would be best to choose class intervals for equal variances

$$\text{Var}\,\{f({}^ix_j)\} = \frac{1}{P_j} \int_{\xi_{j-1}}^{\xi_j} f^2(\lambda)\,dP(\lambda) - \Big[\frac{1}{P_j} \int_{\xi_{j-1}}^{\xi_j} f(\lambda)\,dP(\lambda) \Big]^2 \qquad (8\text{-}19a)$$

and then to assign the theoretically correct number of samples to each class interval, i.e.,

$$n_j = nP_j \qquad (8\text{-}19b)$$

In this ideal case, we should have the relatively small estimate variance

$$\text{Var}\,\{\overline{f(x)}_{\text{STRAT}}\} = \frac{1}{n} \text{Var}\,\{f({}^ix_j)\} \qquad (8\text{-}20)$$

As the class intervals are decreased, the stratified-sampling techniques will produce results analogous to that of an integration formula, but ordinarily the class intervals are larger; practical applications are usually multidimensional, so that simple symmetry relations may yield favorable class intervals.

(b) Use of Correlated Samples.[55,56] If individual sample values ^kx are not statistically independent (as they would be in a true random sample), the expression (14) for our estimate variance is replaced by

$$\text{Var}\,\{\overline{f(x)}_{\text{CORREL}}\} = \frac{1}{n} \text{Var}\,\{x\} + \frac{2}{n^2} \sum_{i<k}\sum \text{Cov}\,\{^ix, {}^kx\} \qquad (8\text{-}21)$$

(see also Sec. 5-4). Judiciously introduced *negative correlation* between selected sample-value pairs ^ix, ^kx will produce negative covariance terms in Eq. (21) and may reduce the variance well below the random-sample variance Var $\{f(x)\}/n$ without biasing the estimate.

As a simple example,[56] let x be uniformly distributed between $x = 0$ and $x = 1$, and let $f(x)$ be the monotonic function $(e^x - 1)/(e - 1)$. We design our sample so that n is even, and $^2x = 1 - {}^1x$, $^4x = 1 - {}^3x$, ..., $^nx = 1 - {}^{n-1}x$, with sample values otherwise independent. Since $f(x)$ and $f(1 - x)$ are negatively correlated, we find

$$\text{Var } \{\overline{f(x)}_{\text{CORREL}}\} \approx \tfrac{1}{31} \text{ Var } \{\overline{f(x)}\}$$

so that the rms fluctuation is reduced by a factor of about 5.6. In addition, the correlated sample requires us to generate fewer random numbers. More interesting applications are, again, to multidimensional problems.[56] Note that stratified sampling, in effect, also introduces negative correlation between sample values: ^{k+1}x can no longer fall into a given class interval if ^kx has filled the latter.

(c) Use of Pseudo-random Samples. Instead of constructing and possibly recording stratified and/or correlated samples for Monte-Carlo computations, we may utilize special properties of pseudo-random-noise sequences. In particular, the shift-register states of a maximal-length shift-register generator (Sec. 4-9) with r stages correspond to the r-digit binary numbers between (and not including) 0 and $2^r - 1$, and one shift-register-sequence period produces each of these numbers exactly once. At least for low-dimensional random inputs, shift-register pseudo-random-noise generators can thus supply uniformly distributed stratified (and correlated) samples if we sample over an integral number of shift-register periods; more general distributions can be obtained with the aid of suitable function generators (Sec. 4-7). An example of the variance-reducing properties of pseudo-random noise in statistical computations was observed in the correlation experiment of Sec. 7-12. More general applications of pseudo-random-noise techniques for variance reduction await further research.

(d) Use of A Priori Information: Importance Sampling.[56] As a matter of principle, Monte-Carlo computations often can and should be simplified through judicious application of partial a priori knowledge of results. As a case in point, *importance-sampling* techniques attempt to estimate an integral (12) by a sample average $[\overline{f(y)/g(y)}]$, where y is a random variable with probability density

$$P_y(y) = g(y) \frac{dP(y)}{dy} \tag{8-22}$$

The estimate is easily seen to be unbiased. The function $g(y)$ is chosen so that

$$\text{Var } \left\{\frac{f(y)}{g(y)}\right\} = E\left\{\left[\frac{f(y)}{g(y)} - I\right]^2\right\} \tag{8-23}$$

is small, subject to the constraint $\int_{-\infty}^{\infty} p_y(y)\,dy = 1$. In particular, $g(y) = f(y)/I$ would reduce the variance (23) to zero, but this would require knowledge of the unknown quantity I. Importance sampling permits us to "concentrate" sampling near values of y of special interest, e.g., where $f(y)$ varies rapidly.

STUDIES OF REGRESSION AND PREDICTION

8-6. Simple and Multiple Regression. *Regression techniques* attempt
to approximate a stochastic relationship between two random variables
x, y by a function $y = f(x;\alpha_1,\alpha_2, \ldots)$ with parameters α_1, α_2, $\ldots$ fitted
to minimize the expected mean-square error $E\{|y - f|^2\}$ *(mean-square
regression)*, or some other measure of approximation error. The "true"
regression parameters are ensemble parameters defined by the joint probability distribution of x and y together with the error measure; *empirical*
regression methods must compute estimates a_1, a_2, $\ldots$ of the regression
parameters from an observed two-dimensional discrete sample $(x_1,y_1;x_2,y_2;$
$\ldots ;x_n,y_n)$, or from a pair of continuous data records $x(t)$, $y(t)$ observed
between $t = 0$ and $t = T$.

Classical sampled-data regression methods are treated in ref. 21. As
an example of continuous-data regression, let us fit the stochastic dependence of two given input voltages $x(t)$, $y(t)$ with an empirical linear regression formula

$$y = f(x;a_0,a_1) \equiv a_0 + a_1 x \qquad (8\text{-}24)$$

where a_0 and a_1 are made to vary slowly with time so as to keep the
EWP mean-square error

$$e^2(t) = \langle(a_0 + a_1 x - y)^2\rangle_{\text{EWP}} = \frac{1}{T_0}\int_{-\infty}^{t} e^{-\frac{t-\lambda}{T_0}}[a_0 + a_1 x(\lambda) - y(\lambda)]^2\, d\lambda$$
$$(8\text{-}25)$$

(Sec. 5-1) as small as possible. To approximate the conditions

$$\frac{\partial e^2(t)}{\partial a_0} = \frac{2}{T_0}\int_{-\infty}^{t} e^{-\frac{t-\lambda}{T_0}}[a_0 + a_1 x(\lambda) - y(\lambda)]\, d\lambda$$
$$= 2\langle(a_0 + a_1 x - y)\rangle_{\text{EWP}} = 0 \quad (8\text{-}26a)$$

$$\left.\begin{array}{l}\frac{\partial e^2(t)}{\partial a_1} = \frac{2}{T_0}\int_{-\infty}^{t} e^{-\frac{t-\lambda}{T_0}} x(\lambda)[a_0 + a_1 x(\lambda) - y(\lambda)]\, d\lambda \\ = 2\langle x(a_0 + a_1 x - y)\rangle_{\text{EWP}} = 0\end{array}\right\} \quad (8\text{-}26b)$$

required for a minimum of $e^2(t)$ with slowly varying a_0, a_1, we generate
$a_0 = a_0(t)$, $a_1 = a_1(t)$ as output voltages of integrators driven by the
respective inputs $-K\, \partial e^2/\partial a_0$, $-K\, \partial e^2/\partial a_1$, where K is a large positive
gain constant *(steepest-descent optimization, ref. 67)*. Figure 8-8 shows a
suitable analog-computer setup. Although computation will be started
at $t = 0$ instead of at $t = -\infty$, this makes no difference after a time
interval equal to, say, $4T_0$. The two voltages proportional to the expressions (26a) and (26b) are themselves produced as *EWP* averages. As

usually, the choice of the averaging time constant T_0 involves a compromise between accuracy (low estimate variances) and rapid adaptation to possible changes in the quantities being estimated. In addition, the steepest-descent gain K will be bounded by circuit-stability considerations.

Multiple regression deals similarly with functions of two or more variables. Reference 24 describes an elaborate multiple-regression study designed to fit the stochastic dependence of a variable y (yield of a chemical process) on four variables x_1, x_2, x_3, x_4 with a second-degree polynomial

$$y = f(x_1, x_2, x_3, x_4) = a_0 + \sum_{k=1}^{4} a_k x_k + \sum_{i=1}^{4} \sum_{k=1}^{4} a_{ik} x_i x_k$$

by the steepest-descent technique just outlined. In addition, the computer plotted, say, x_1 against x_2 for fixed x_3, x_4, and y. The reference also deals with the necessary scale-factor considerations.

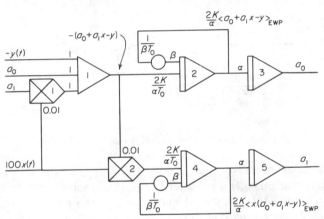

FIG. 8-8. Unscaled computer setup for a linear mean-square regression analysis using *EWP* averages. The high-gain integrators 2, 4 may need diode limiting to prevent transient overloads.

8-7. Predictor and Delay-network Evaluation.[22,27] *Prediction*, which is closely related to regression, requires estimation of future values of $f(t + \tau)$ on the basis of present and/or past values of $f(t)$. In particular, $f(t)$ may be a sample function of a stationary random process, and we attempt to predict $f(t + \tau)$ on the basis of the known or measured spectrum or autocorrelation function of $f(t)$. Again, we may be required to predict or extrapolate values of a nonstationary or deterministic random function $f(t)$ on the basis of past values or samples. Various intermediate problems exist. Even if, as is often the case, the predictor is a simple linear, time-invariant network, the weighting-function methods of Chap. 3 cannot be employed directly to evaluate the simulated predictor, since estimation of fidelity measures such as the mean-square delay error

$$\epsilon^2(t_1,t_2) = E\{[x(t_1) - y(t_2)]^2\} \qquad (t_2 = t_1 - \tau < t_1) \qquad (8\text{-}27)$$

(Sec. 1-3) necessarily requires us to store past values of $f(t)$.

Figure 8-9 illustrates the use of a tape recorder for predictor evaluation. The prediction-error output can be squared and averaged and may also be correlated with predictor-circuit parameters to produce continuous automatic optimization.

Figure 8-10 shows a track-hold scheme which, like the analogous correlation-function computer of Fig. 5-6a, is somewhat wasteful of data but is often more convenient than the tape-recorder scheme. The track-hold technique is ideally suited for studies of real or simulated predictor circuits with analog-computer simulated data. Referring to Fig. 8-10, a real or simulated predictor is fed a stationary test-signal input $x(t)$, or a sequence of random-sample functions $^kx(t)$ from an iterative-differential-analyzer

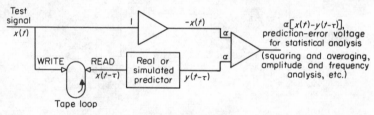

FIG. 8-9. Tape-loop method of predictor evaluation.

setup with noise-generator input (as in Fig. 4-2). Track-hold 1 samples the predictor output $y(t)$ t_1 sec after the start of each computer operating period, so that $-^ky(t_1)$ is stored and added to the predictor input $x(t)$. Track-hold 2 then samples the difference $^ky(t_1) - x(t)$ exactly $t_2 = t_1 + \tau$ sec after the start of each operating period, so that successive error samples $^kx(t_2) - ^ky(t_1)$ are presented for statistical analysis. Figure 8-10b illustrates the computer timing sequence (see also Figs. 4-2 and 8-4). Melsa and Wozny,[27] using the ASTRAC I iterative differential analyzer at the University of Arizona, tested the track-hold method of predictor evaluation on a Wiener (time-invariant) linear predictor network with stationary-noise input and on a Zadeh-Raggazini finite-time/finite-memory system,[27] both with known theoretical performance. Their results include an example of empirical predictor optimization. Computed values of predictor mean-square delay error agree with theory within about 1 per cent, an excellent result in view of the relatively low component accuracy (0.3 per cent of half-scale) of the vacuum-tube computer used.

It is easy to see that the predictor-evaluation schemes of Figs. 8-9 and 8-10 can serve equally well to study *time-delay circuits* intended to produce

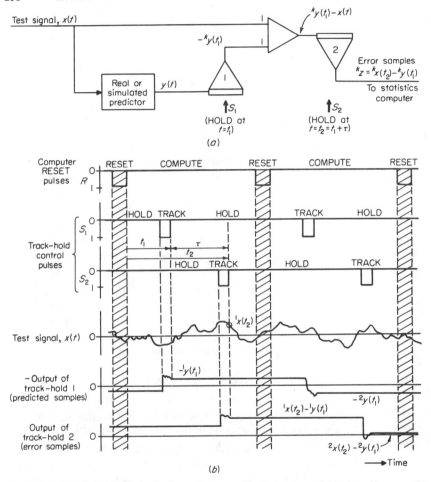

Fig. 8-10. Track-hold method of predictor evaluation (a), and timing diagram (b) (see also ref. 27).

the delayed output $f(t - \tau)$ from a given input $f(t)$.   It is only necessary to delay the input rather than the output in Figs. 8-9 and 8-10.

SIMULATION OF COMMUNICATION AND DETECTION SYSTEMS

8-8. Introduction. Time and Bandwidth Scaling.[30] The close physical analogy between electronic communication circuits and analog/ hybrid computing elements makes the latter almost ideally suited for simulation of communication and detection systems.   Slowed-down time scales permit precise studies of detector and modulator waveforms, while electronic simulation is still sufficiently fast to permit studies of communication and detection in their true statistical context with realistically large samples. As we have already seen in Sec. 4-5, detection and false-alarm probabilities or modulation-system error averages, including effects of noise, clutter, and jamming, can be measured directly. In addition, modern iterative differential analyzers can implement automatic parameter optimization of such statistics. It is fair to say that communication and detection-system simulation, although by no means as well known as control-system simulation, is one of the potentially most fruitful applications of the fast analog/hybrid computer.

With commercially available analog computers, typical time scales have been 1 cps/Kc for communications simulation and 1 cps/Mc for radar-system video waveforms, modulation envelopes, and filter bandwidths.[30] In the case of radar, events taking place in the course of a 1-μsec radar pulse could then be studied for a full second in the scale model; an i-f center frequency of 60 Mc would be represented by 60 cps, and an i-f bandwidth of 2 Mc would correspond to 2 cps. The same time-scale factor of 10^6 would represent an X-band carrier (10,000 Mc) by 10 Kc, S-band (3,000 Mc) by 3 Kc, and L-band (1,000 Mc) by 1 Kc, which is still uncomfortably fast for conventional analog computers. Fortunately, the carrier frequency as such is immaterial in many radar and communication studies, so that it can be slowed down by another factor of 10 to 1,000 without affecting results; note, however, that the *bandwidth* of carrier-frequency channels must still be scaled exactly like the i-f and video frequencies.

Much faster simulation is possible with ASTRAC II-type computers, which have typical component phase errors below 1 deg at 10 Kc and comparator-response times below 120 nsec (Sec. 8-2). Such machines permit *real-time* simulation of many audio-frequency circuits, and time scales between 10^4 and 10^2 for radar i-f and video. Separate carrier-frequency scaling will still be advisable, if permitted by the problem. ASTRAC II will, for instance, take statistics over one thousand simulated detection experiments in 1 sec, so that the investigator can evaluate the statistical effects of system-parameter changes almost instantaneously. Fast automatic parameter optimization is also possible.

8-9. Signal Generation and Modulation.[30–37] The reduced time and bandwidth scale of communication or detection simulation emphasizes the need for *frequency stability* in the audio oscillators generating simulated signals. For a time-scale factor of 10^6, simulation of a 1,000-Mc magnetron whose frequency is stable within ± 2 Mc requires an audio oscillator with ± 2 cps frequency stability.[30] Note that such stability requirements are determined by the scaling of filter bandwidths, not necessarily by carrier-frequency scaling.

Although the sine-cosine loop of Fig. 2-7d has been used for signal generation, simulated multivibrator circuits based on accurate analog

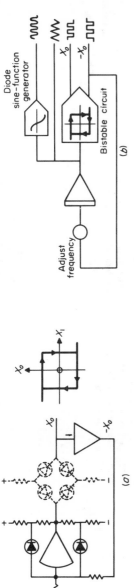

Fig. 8-11a, b. Bistable multivibrator[67] developed from a comparator with analog output $\pm E$ (a), and application to an astable-multivibrator signal generator (b) (see also Fig. 5-6b).

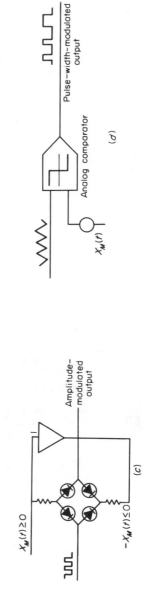

Fig. 8-11c, d. Generation of an amplitude-modulated waveform (c), and of a constant-frequency pulse-width-modulated waveform (d).

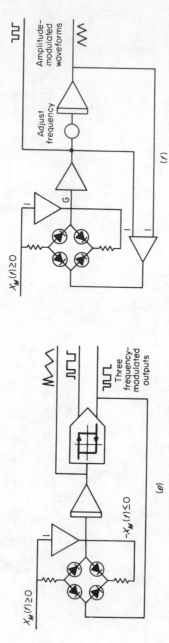

Fig. 8-11e, f. Voltage-controlled oscillator producing frequency-modulated triangular and square-wave output (e), and generation of an amplitude-modulated rectangular and triangular waveform (f). The amplifier input marked G is directly connected to the summing junction.[67]

comparators are at least as accurate and permit very convenient implementation of many different modulation schemes (Fig. 8-11). Such signal-generator circuits, used in conjunction with suitable random-noise generators (Chap. 4), permit one to simulate a wide variety of communications and detection systems in their natural environment of noise, channel delays, clutter, electronic interference, etc.

8-10. Other System Components.[30-37] **Simulation of Complete Systems.** Figure 8-12 shows two circuits for a *second-order filter* with

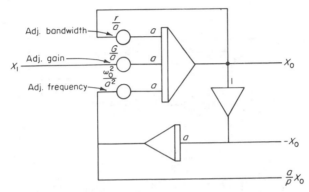

FIG. 8-12a. Analog-computer setup for a bandpass filter with frequency-response function $-j\omega G/[(\omega_0{}^2 - \omega^2) + j\omega r]$. The filter is tuned to $\omega \approx \omega_0$; the approximate filter bandwidth is defined as $r = \omega_0/Q$ (see also Fig. 7-3 and ref. 33).

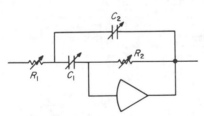

FIG. 8-12b. This adjustable operational-amplifier circuit can be used with carrier frequencies exceeding 100 Kc if suitable amplifiers are available. The frequency-response function is $-j\omega G/[(\omega_0{}^2 - \omega^2) + j\omega r]$ with $G = 1/R_1C_2$, $\omega_0{}^2 = 1/R_1R_2C_1C_2$, $r = 1/R_2C_1 + 1/R_2C_2$ (ref. 72).

adjustable Q. Such filters can be staggered and cascaded to simulate all kinds of radio-frequency and intermediate-frequency amplifiers.* A similarly wide variety of *modulators and detectors* can be simulated with the aid of patched diode circuits; Figs. 8-13, 8-14, and 8-15, respectively, show circuits simulating an *FM discriminator*, a *phase detector*, and a complete

---

* Five cascaded circuits stagger-tuned to 8.57, 9.18, 10.00, 10.88, and 11.43 Kc with the respective Q's of 10.8, 4.12, 3.33, 4.12, and 10.8 (or -3-db bandwidths of 790, 2,210, 3,000, 2,640, and 1,060 cps, respectively) yield an approximately square bandpass characteristic centered at 10 Kc and 3 Kc wide. Center frequencies and -3-db frequencies are best adjusted empirically.[72]

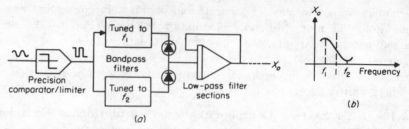

FIG. 8-13. Simulation of an FM discriminator (a), and transfer characteristic (b).

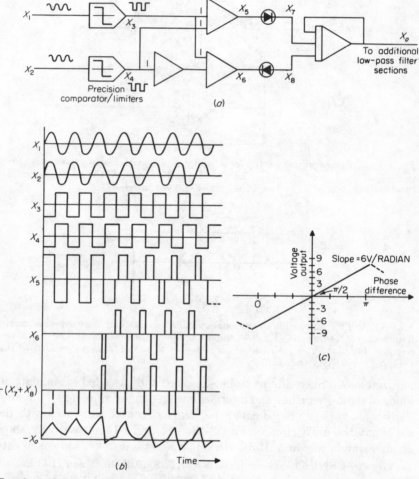

FIG. 8-14. Analog-computer representation of a phase detector (a), waveforms (b), and detector characteristic (c). (*Based on ref. 31.*)

phase-lock loop.[32]   *Heterodyne mixers* are either simply represented by electronic multipliers, or the actual voltage transfer characteristics of mixers and detectors can be accurately reproduced with diode function generators (Fig. 8-15).   Multichannel closed-loop tape recorders with selectable and/or variable tape speed are employed for applications requiring *time delays*, such as simulation of fixed or variable propagation delays and tapped delay lines for matched-filter synthesis.[30]   System simulation applies to sonar as well as to radar systems and can include all associated simulation of all servo systems, antenna drives, target dynamics, and complete guidance systems.

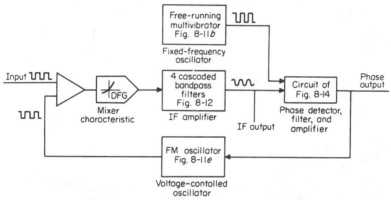

FIG. 8-15. Simulation of a phase-lock loop.   (*Based on ref. 32.*)

8-11. Simulation of Neurons and Synapses.[41]   The frequency-modulated analog multivibrator in Fig. 8-11e has been successfully employed for the simulation of sensor-type nerve cells (Fig. 8-16).   Although conventional electronic analog-computer circuits are hardly suitable for experiments requiring large numbers of artificial neurons (perceptron research), they are useful for simulation studies of the subminiature circuits used in actual neuron-simulation experiments.

SOME SYSTEM-ENGINEERING APPLICATIONS

8-12. Operations-research Applications.   An All-digital Hybrid Computer.   Monte-Carlo simulation applied to a large class of system-operation problems, including queuing problems (machine failures and service, traffic flow, production scheduling), inventory control, communication-net design, and duels (war gaming, business-management games).[46]   General-purpose stored-program digital computers are commonly employed, and programming languages specifically designed for operations simulation are available.   From a computational viewpoint, there is little need for analog computation, since the characteristics of dynamical systems involved in operations-research studies can usually be

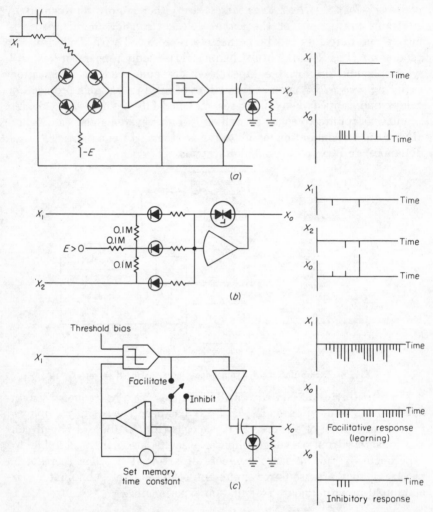

FIG. 8-16a, b, c.   (a) Sensory-neuron model.   The output-pulse frequency increases with the stimulus voltage X up to a certain saturation level.   The input filter has the transfer function $\dfrac{as + 1}{bs + 1}$, so that a step input generates a burst of output pulses which decays gradually to a steady-state pulse rate to simulate adaptation.   (b) Nonlinear summation of two simulated nerve-pulse trains.   (c) Simulated synapse with facilitative or inhibitory adaptation.

reduced to simple time delays (e.g., starting delays in traffic-flow simulation).

Some analog/hybrid simulations have been undertaken to demonstrate feasibility.[45,48]   Since there is usually no need to solve differential equations, analog computers have no significant speed advantage over digital methods.   A possible remaining advantage of analog/hybrid simulation is the opportunity for closer intuitive rapport between the experimenter and the simulated system, although this advantage may give way to new digital computers with improved display and programming consoles.

It is suggested that all-digital Monte-Carlo simulation of system operations could benefit from the combination of a small stored-program computer and a small accessory console comprising parallel logic elements (gates, flip-flops), shift-register pseudo-random-noise generators, counters, and an oscilloscope display, all linked to the digital computer through its input-output bus.   Operations-research simulation usually involves sequential logic with randomly operated gates; programming this with separate (parallel) logic elements could save a large number of serial-program instructions in the digital computer and thus permit Monte-Carlo simulation at extraordinarily high speed.   Logic elements could be programmed by patching (as in the digital expansion units of iterative differential analyzers); but it would be preferable to program all interconnections by a switching matrix controlled by a set of digital words from the digital computer.   This would then allow complete digital program storage without patching.

As an example of hybrid-computer simulation, Fig. 8-17 illustrates the analog/hybrid-computer solution of a simple inventory-control problem (see also ref. 48). Note the following features of model and computer setup:

1. The *demand rate* $r(t)$ is generated as the sum of a known *seasonal trend* $r_1(t)$ and a (stationary) *random demand rate* $r_2(t)$.   Diode D prevents $r = r_1 + r_2$ from becoming negative.[48]
2. Integrator 2 inverts and integrates $r(t)$ to produce the *inventory* $I(t)$. $I(t)$ starts with a given initial value $I(0) = I_0$ and is again brought up to I_0 whenever integrator 1 is reset ($U = 1$, *reordering*).

Our inventory-control policy consists of sampling $I(t)$ periodically at $t = t_1, t_2, \ldots$ (corresponding, for example, to weekly intervals) and reordering whenever $I(t_k)$ is below a fixed level I_1.   The problem is then to determine I_0 and I_1 so as to minimize the *inventory penalty function* $C = C_1 + C_2$.   Here, $C_1 = \int_0^T f[I(t)]\, dt$ is the *cost of maintaining the inventory* (maintenance, storage, interest, etc.), plus a *penalty* for zero or negative values of $I(t)$; for example, dC_1 may simply equal $-a\,dt$ whenever $I(t) \le 0$. C_2 is the sum of fixed *service charges* levied for each reorder.   In our simple model, orders which cannot be met are lost.   Note also that the true inventory is max $(I, 0)$, not $I(t)$ (which is allowed to become negative).

Referring again to the computer setup of Fig. 8-17, we see that

3. A comparator senses $I \le I_1$ at the output of the periodically operated track-hold circuit 3, and resets integrator 2 through a flip-flop.
4. Integrator 4 compiles the total penalty function; service charges are accumulated simply by integration of the reset pulses.

The total cost $C(t)$ is read out at $t = T$ (corresponding, say, to 1 year), and results of repeated experiments are averaged.   Since one year's inventory policy can be simulated in a fraction of a second, the effects of policy changes may be grasped intuitively, and

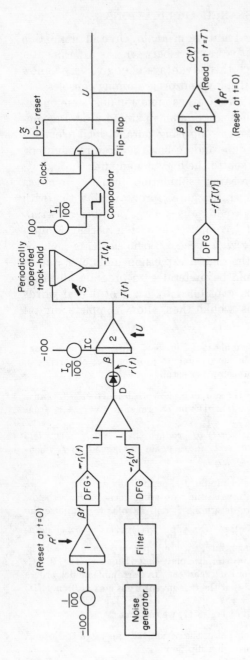

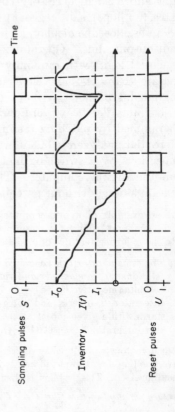

Fig. 8-17. An inventory-control model (a), and time history (b) (see also ref. 48).

rapid manual or automatic optimization is possible. It is clear that the model can be generalized in many ways. The model can also be combined with other models generating demand rate, constraints on the supply, and effects of pricing policies.

Note that in direct Monte-Carlo simulation of a system or operation, the variances of our estimates are often themselves useful results, since they measure fluctuations of system performance.

8-13. Studies of System-parameter Tolerances. Consider a dynamical system described by a set of state equations

$$\frac{dx^i}{dt} = f_i(x_1, x_2, \ldots, x_n; \alpha_1, \alpha_2, \ldots) \qquad (i = 1, 2, \ldots, n) \quad (8\text{-}28)$$

where $\alpha_1, \alpha_2, \ldots$ are system design parameters to be determined so as to minimize a criterion function (functional) $F(\alpha_1, \alpha_2, \ldots)$. Typical examples of such criterion functions are

$$F = x_1(T) \qquad F = \frac{1}{T} \int_0^T x_3{}^2(t)\, dt = \langle x_3{}^2(t) \rangle_T$$

$$F = E\{x_3{}^2(t_1)\} \qquad F = \text{Prob}\,[a < x_2(t_1) \le b]$$

References 49 and 67 describe analog and hybrid/analog digital techniques for performing the required *parameter optimization* (see also Sec. 8-15). Unfortunately, production tolerances in actual systems will not permit us to realize the exact optimal parameter values. Instead, it is reasonable to consider the system parameters $\alpha_1, \alpha_2, \ldots$ as statistically independent Gaussian random variables with mean values $\alpha_{10}, \alpha_{20}, \ldots$ and variances $\sigma_1{}^2, \sigma_2{}^2, \ldots$. The variances as well as the mean values should be regarded as new unknown design parameters, since low parameter variances will tend to improve system performance but increase production costs. It becomes necessary to minimize a new criterion function

$$\begin{aligned} F' &= F'(\alpha_{10}, \alpha_{20}, \ldots; \sigma_1{}^2, \sigma_2{}^2, \ldots) \\ &= E\{F(\alpha_1, \alpha_2, \ldots)\} + C(\alpha_{10}, \alpha_{20}, \ldots; \sigma_1{}^2, \sigma_2{}^2, \ldots) \quad (8\text{-}29) \end{aligned}$$

where C represents the effect of production costs. Note that consideration of parameter-tolerance effects will, in general, lead to new optimum nominal parameter values $\alpha_{10}, \alpha_{20}, \ldots$ which are not exactly optimal for the simpler criterion function $F(\alpha_1, \alpha_2, \ldots)$. Perhaps even more interesting is the fact that different parameter tolerances may interact so that if, say, $\sigma_1{}^2$ is given, $\sigma_2{}^2 = 0$ is no longer the optimal variance. Parameter-tolerance studies of this type could, therefore, uncover the possibility of using relatively large tolerances with impunity, and very large savings might be realized for mass-produced systems. This fact was brought to light by Levine and McGhee in their pioneering Monte-Carlo study of a mass-produced air-to-air missile.[47,49]

Computer optimization of the statistical criterion function (29) requires a random sample of computer runs for each of many combinations of the parameters $\alpha_{10}, \alpha_{20}, \ldots ; \sigma_1{}^2, \sigma_2{}^2, \ldots$. The resulting exceedingly large number of computer runs make this a fruitful area for high-speed digitally controlled analog computers.

SOME SPECIAL MONTE-CARLO TECHNIQUES

8-14. Hybrid-computer Monte-Carlo Solution of Partial Differential Equations. Some of the earliest investigators of the Monte-Carlo method[46,50] have suggested its application to generalized Dirichlet problems requiring the solution of a linear partial differential equation

$$a_1 \frac{\partial^2 u}{\partial x^2} + a_2 \frac{\partial^2 u}{\partial y^2} = K_1(x,y) \frac{\partial u}{\partial x} + K_2(x,y) \frac{\partial u}{\partial y} \qquad (a_1, a_2 \geq 0) \quad (8\text{-}30)$$

for the unknown function $u(x,y)$ inside a simple closed contour C of the xy plane, where $u(x,y)$ is given, bounded, single-valued, and piecewise continuous on the boundary C. A special case is the Dirichlet boundary-value problem for the familiar Laplace equation

$$\frac{\partial^2 u}{\partial x^2} + \frac{\partial^2 u}{\partial y^2} = 0 \qquad [u = u(x,y) \text{ on } C] \qquad (8\text{-}31)$$

In this case, $a_1 = a_2 = 1$, $K_1 \equiv K_2 \equiv 0$ (Fig. 8-18a).

A derivation rather too elaborate for inclusion here [50,53,57] shows that *the random walk generated by the solutions $x(t)$, $y(t)$ of the stochastic equations of motion*

$$\frac{dx}{dt} = -K_1(x,y) + X(t) \qquad \frac{dy}{dt} = -K_2(x,y) + Y(t) \qquad (8\text{-}32)$$

with starting values $x(0) = x_0$, $y(0) = y_0$ and independent white-Gaussian-noise forcing functions $X(t)$, $Y(t)$ with zero mean and power spectral densities respectively proportional to a_1, a_2 will cross the boundary C at random points (x_C, y_C) such that

$$E\{u(x_C, y_C)\} = u(x_0, y_0) \qquad (8\text{-}33)$$

Hence, the sample average $\overline{u(x_C, y_C)}$ over a suitable number n of random walks is an unbiased estimate for the desired solution $u(x_0, y_0)$ at (x_0, y_0). Simple convergence conditions were derived by Petrowsky.[57]

Chuang, Kazda, and Windeknecht[57] were the first to employ this theorem for analog/hybrid-computer solution of partial differential equations. They solved the ordinary differential equations (32) on a conventional "slow" analog computer with tape-recorded random-noise inputs and applied $x(t)$, $y(t)$ to the horizontal and vertical plates of an oscilloscope. To demonstrate the feasibility of the Monte-Carlo method, they restricted themselves to boundary functions $u(x_C, y_C)$ constant and

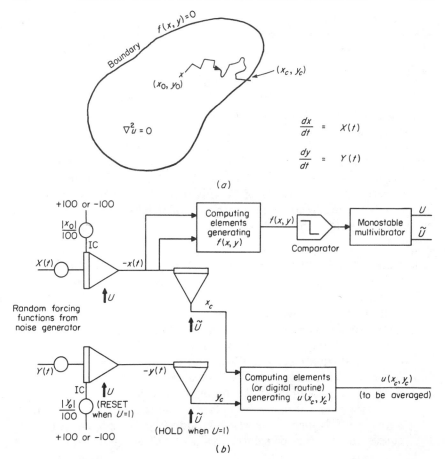

Fig. 8-18. Hybrid-computer solution of the Dirichlet problem for Laplace's differential equation $\partial^2 u/\partial x^2 + \partial^2 u/\partial y^2 = 0$. Integrators 1 and 2 solve the stochastic equations of motion $dx/dt = X(t)$, $dy/dt = Y(t)$ with independent Gaussian white-noise inputs $X(t)$, $Y(t)$. The comparator-actuated flip-flop samples $x(t)$, $y(t)$ and resets the integrators when the point (x,y) crosses the boundary C defined by $f(x,y) \geq 0$. The boundary function $u(x_C, y_C)$ of the track-hold outputs x_C, y_C is computed by analog or digital circuits and is averaged, preferably digitally, to produce the solution estimates $u(x_0, y_0)$. The boundary could also be defined in the form

$$U = 1 \quad \text{if} \quad [y - f_1(x) \geq 0] \quad \text{OR} \quad [y - f_2(x) \leq 0]$$

which would be implemented with two comparators and patched logic.

equal to 100 on a continuous portion C_1 of the boundary C and equal to 0 on the remaining boundary. Boundary crossings of the oscilloscope beam marking the point (x,y) were detected by an arrangement of masks and photocells associated with C and C_1, and $E\{u(x_C, y_C)\}$ could be estimated simply by 100 times the fraction of boundary crossings taking place across C_1, as determined by a decimal counter. Computer and noise source limited computing speed to about one random walk per second; solution errors for samples of 300 to 2,200 runs were of the order of a few per cent and were ascribed mainly to statistical fluctuations.

In modern analog/hybrid computers, accurate and convenient combinations of function generators, analog comparators, and digital logic replace the cumbersome photocell circuits used to detect boundary crossings, and complicated boundary functions can be generated and averaged digitally (Fig. 8-18b). More significantly, ASTRAC II-type iterative differential analyzers can perform the 500 to 2,000 complete random walks required for each solution point within 1 to 3 sec; it is this fact which may make the hybrid-computer Monte-Carlo method competitive with other methods of solving partial differential equations. The Monte-Carlo method, still largely unexplored because of insufficient computing speeds with earlier equipment, offers a number of intriguing possibilities:

1. Unlike other solution methods, the Monte-Carlo method permits us to compute the solution $u(x,y)$ *only at specific desired points* (x,y) *of interest.*

2. Computer setups such as those in Fig. 8-18b are easily generalized to apply to *three-dimensional problems.* Relatively little additional equipment is required, while conventional methods of solving partial differential equations would become radically more complicated.

3. After the solution is computed for a number of points, it is often possible to simplify computation of the solution at a point (x,y) by averaging over solution values $u(x,y)$ computed earlier for surrounding points. In particular, the solution $u(x,y)$ of Laplace's equation equals the average of solution values over any circle centered at x, y.[54]

4. Solution time can be reduced through sequential estimation (Sec. 8-3) and by the variance-reducing techniques of Sec. 8-5. In particular, shift-register noise generators can generate successive negatively correlated random walks for variance reduction. The shift register can, for instance, be reset to produce each pseudo-random-noise sequence twice (Sec. 4-12), and we can invert one sequence of each pair to introduce negative correlation between them.

Finally, the application of Monte-Carlo methods to more general classes of partial differential equations[70,71] and more general random forcing functions presents a fascinating field for future research.

At least in principle, one sample of random walks starting at (x_0,y_0) defines the solution of the partial differential equation (29) at (x_0,y_0) for *all* admissible boundary functions $u(x_C,y_C)$. If we divide the boundary C into small arcs centered at the boundary points (x_1,y_1), (x_2,y_2), . . . , (x_m,x_m) and record the fractions h_k of the total number of crossings falling into the kth arc, then

$$E\{u(x_0,y_0)\} \approx \sum_{k=1}^{m} h_k u(x_k,y_k) \qquad (8\text{-}34)$$

8-15. Random-search Methods for Parameter Optimization. The most commonly used computer methods for determining the parameter values $\alpha_1, \alpha_2, \ldots$ which will optimize (minimize) a differentiable criterion function $F(\alpha_1,\alpha_2, \ldots)$ involve computation or measurement of the gradient components

$$\frac{\partial F}{\partial \alpha_1} \approx \frac{\Delta F}{\Delta \alpha_1} \qquad \frac{\partial F}{\partial \alpha_2} \approx \frac{\Delta F}{\Delta \alpha_2} \qquad \cdots$$

corresponding to each parameter at a trial point $(\alpha_1,\alpha_2, \ldots)$. Each trial parameter value is then incremented by an amount proportional to the corresponding gradient component, so that the parameter point progresses in the direction of steepest descent (Fig. 8-19a); we usually

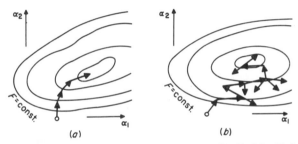

Fig. 8-19. Two-dimensional parameter optimization ("hill climbing") by a gradient method (a), and by sequential random perturbations (b).

decrease the step size as the minimum is approached.[67]   Gradient methods may fail to converge, or converge too slowly, if the criterion-function "hill" has ridges, winding canyons, etc., or if the function $F(\alpha_1,\alpha_2, \ldots)$ is only piecewise differentiable or continuous.   In such situations, one may turn to random-search methods which can, in addition, simplify the computation routines.   A *pure random search* would simply compute the criterion function at a number of randomly chosen points $(\alpha_1,\alpha_2, \ldots)$ in parameter space and select the parameter point yielding the smallest value of $F(\alpha_1,\alpha_2, \ldots)$.   This optimization technique, which does not utilize any known continuity properties of the criterion function, is sometimes employed to find starting values for other optimization methods, but it is essentially impractical by itself.   Assume that we have N parameters $\alpha_1, \alpha_2, \ldots, \alpha_N$, each capable of varying between zero and 100 per cent and that we wish to locate a single minimum with only 10 per cent accuracy.   In this case, the probability of finding the desired minimum in a single trial is 10^{-N}, and the probability of finding the minimum at least once in m independent trials is

$$P = 1 - (1 - 10^{-N})^m \approx 10^{-N}m \tag{8-35}$$

We are truly looking for a needle in an N-dimensional haystack; with the number N of parameters only as large as five or six, any realistic optimization method must utilize known properties of the criterion function $F(\alpha_1, \alpha_2, \ldots, \alpha_N)$, such as continuity and differentiability. *Optimization by sequential random perturbations* (creeping random search) permits multiparameter optimization with a minimum of control logic.[62-66] Referring for simplicity to the two-parameter example of Fig. 8-19b, we start with a trial point $(^0\alpha_1, {}^0\alpha_2)$ and vary α_1, α_2 simultaneously by independent *random* positive or negative increments $\delta\alpha_1$, $\delta\alpha_2$ obtained from a noise generator. If $F(\alpha_1, \alpha_2)$ is not improved, we try new random increments $\delta\alpha_1$, $\delta\alpha_2$ until an improvement is obtained; then we use $(^0\alpha_1 + \delta\alpha_1, {}^0\alpha_2 + \delta\alpha_2)$ as the next trial point $(^1\alpha_1, {}^1\alpha_2)$. With random perturbations distributed about zero with a small standard deviation (small step sizes), the iteration will surely converge whenever the gradient method does. Although convergence is slower, our random-perturbation scheme involves no exploration steps, varies all parameters simultaneously, and is not affected by ugly parameter-space terrain features, such as ridges and canyons.

Since unused perturbations $\delta\alpha_1$, $\delta\alpha_2$ must be stored and subtracted out, it appears best to restrict perturbation values to h, $-h$ or to h, $-h$, and 0, where h is a suitably chosen step size; increment values can then be stored digitally, say in flip-flops.[66] A shift-register noise generator is, once again, an especially convenient source of binary random perturbations.

Random-perturbation optimization is especially suitable for very fast iterative differential analyzers like ASTRAC II (Sec. 8-2), where it is conveniently implemented with hybrid analog-digital coefficient-setting circuits (Fig. 8-19c). The following relatively simple improvements have been shown to speed convergence at the expense of relatively little added digital logic:

1. The hybrid analog-digital parameter-setting circuit of Fig. 8-20 makes it easy to change the step size h as a function of past failures or successes, or as a function of F.[66]
2. We can make, say, every tenth or twentieth step a large one to detect secondary maxima or minima, or saddle points.[63,66]
3. We can *correlate* successive random perturbations; i.e., we can make perturbations in the direction of the last success more likely than perturbations in the directions of past failures.[66]

Rastrigin[65] has shown that, even with randomly directed perturbations in an N-dimensional parameter space, the expected rate of progress *in the gradient direction* exceeds that of a simple gradient method employing N

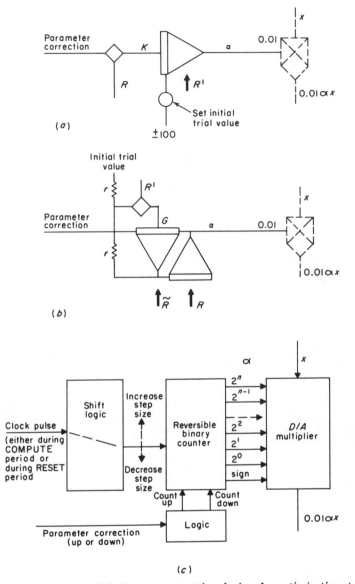

Fig. 8-20. Hybrid analog-digital parameter-setting devices for optimization studies. In (c), a reversible binary counter controls a switched-resistance network (D/A multiplier) to set the parameter α.   A shift register moves the counter input to higher or lower digits to implement digital step-size control.[66,67]

gradient-determining steps followed by a working step, provided that $N \geq 4$. Rastrigin's result is not conclusive, because both gradient/and random-perturbation methods are usually modified by various step-size changing strategies and other maneuvers.[67] His result is, however, suggestive if one considers the relative simplicity of the sequential-perturbation method.

REFERENCES AND BIBLIOGRAPHY

The ASTRAC II System

1. Korn, G. A.: New High-speed Analog and Analog-digital Computing Techniques: The ASTRAC System, *Proc. 3d AICA Conf.*, Opatija, Yugoslavia, 1961; Presses Académiques Européennes, Brussels, 1962.

2. ————: The Impact of Hybrid Analog-digital Techniques on the Analog-computer Art, *Proc. IRE*, May, 1962.

3. ————: ASTRAC Offers New Computing Methods, *Electronic Ind.*, July, 1962.

4. ————: Parameter-perturbation Generator for Analog-computer Error and Optimization Studies, *Ann. AICA*, April, 1963.

5. ————: Performance of Operational Amplifiers with Electronic Mode Switching, *IEEETEC*, June, 1963.

6. ————: Analog/Hybrid Storage and Pulse Modulation, *IEEETEC*, August, 1963.

7. ————: 1962 Progress and ASTRAC II Project, *ACL Memo* 59, University of Arizona, December, 1962.

8. Hampton, R., G. A. Korn, and B. A. Mitchell: Hybrid Analog-digital Noise Generator, *IEEETEC*, August, 1963.

9. Eckes, H. R.: Digital Expansion System for ASTRAC I, *Ann. AICA*, January, 1964.

10. ————: and G. A. Korn: Digital Program Control for Iterative Differential Analyzers (ASTRAC II Control Logic), *Simulation*, February, 1964.

11. Brubaker, T. A.: ASTRAC I Design, Performance, and Accuracy Studies, *Ann. AICA*, April, 1964.

12. Hampton, R. L.: A Hybrid Analog-digital Pseudo-random-noise Generator, *Proc. Southern Joint Computer Conf.*, 1964.

13. Handler, H., and R. H. Mangels: A Delta-sigma Modulation System for Time Delay and Analog Function Storage, *Proc. Spring Joint Computer Conf.*, 1964.

14. Mitchell, B. A.: A Hybrid Analog-digital Parameter Optimizer for ASTRAC II, *Proc. Spring Joint Computer Conf.*, 1964.

15. Korn, G. A.: Fast Analog-hybrid Computation with Digital Control: the ASTRAC II System, *Proc. 4th AICA Conf.*, Brighton, England, 1964; Presses Académiques Européennes, Brussels, 1965.

16. Maybach, R. L.: Hybrid Analog-digital Measurement of Sample Averages and Correlation Functions, *ACL Memo* 85, University of Arizona, 1965.

17. ————: New Techniques for Measuring Probability and Probability Density *ACL, Memo* 97, University of Arizona, 1965.

18. Whigham, R.: A Fast Quarter-square Multiplier, *ACL Memo* 88, University of Arizona, 1964; *Simulation*, August, 1965.

19. ————: A Fast and Accurate Analog Comparator with Digital Output, *ACL Memo* 95, University of Arizona, 1965; *IEEETEC*, August, 1965.

20. Eckes, H. R.: A Fast Mode-control Switch for ASTRAC II. *ACL Memo* 107, University of Arizona, 1965; *IEEETEC*, October, 1965.

Studies of Regression and Prediction

21. Hald, A.: *Statistical Theory with Engineering Applications*, Wiley, New York, 1952.
22. Bates, M. R., et al.: Analog-computer Applications in Predictor Design, *IRETEC*, September, 1957.
23. Rubin, A. I.: Continuous Data Analysis with Analog Computers Using Statistical and Regression Techniques, *PCC Rept.* 160, Electronic Associates, Inc., Princeton, N.J., 1960.
24. ———— et al.: Plotting Results of a Quadratic Regression Analysis, *PCC Rept.* 135, Electronic Associates, Inc., Princeton, N.J., 1956.
25. Chang, S.: *Synthesis of Optimum Control Systems*, McGraw-Hill, New York, 1961.
26. Enochson, L. D.: Prediction of Time Series Using Multiple Regression Techniques, and Seakeeping Applications, *Rept.* 307-01, Measurement Analysis Corp., Los Angeles, Calif., 1963.
27. Melsa, J. L., and M. J. Wozny: Iterative-differential-analyzer Study of Prediction Networks, *Simulation*, August, 1964.
28. Thrall, G. P.: Mean Square Measurements of Nonstationary Random Processes, SAE Paper 925D, presented at the National Aeronautic and Space Engineering Meeting, Los Angeles, Calif., 1964.

Simulation of Communication and Detection Systems

29. Palumbo, O. J., and E. A. Sevian: Analog Study of FM Discriminator, *Memo*. Radio Corporation of America, Moorestown, N.J., 1959.
30. Lambert, J. M., and A. J. Heidrich: Radar System Simulation Techniques, *IRE Natl. Convention Record*, pt. 4, 1959.
31. Frazier, J. P., and J. M. Lambert: Analog Simulation of Radio Guidance and Space Communication Systems, *Rept.* R60D SD15, General Electric Co., Syracuse, N.Y., Oct. 31, 1960.
32. Frazier, J. P., and J. Page: Phase-lock Loop Frequency Acquisition Study, *Rept*. R61 DSD25, General Electric Co., Syracuse, N.Y., 1961.
33. Berger, E. L., and R. M. Taylor: Optimization of Radar in Its Environment by GEESE Techniques, *Proc. Western Joint Computer Conf.*, 1961.
34. Kepcke, J. J.: Computer Simulation of a Complex, Secure Communication System, Eastern Simulation Council Paper, Syracuse, N.Y., July, 1962.
35. Robinson, E. M.: An Analysis of Automatic Frequency and Phase Control Using GEESE Techniques, *IRE East Coast Conf. Aerospace and Navigational Electronics*, Baltimore, Md., October, 1962.
36. Heartz, R. A.: Analog Simulation Techniques, *IEEE Spectrum*, March, 1964.
37. Bibliography of GEESE Reports (Simulation Council Newsletter), *Instruments and Control Systems*, November, 1962.
38. Fischer, L. G., and G. Frenkel: Search-radar Analog Simulator Reproduces Jamming, Scintillation, *Electronics*, Aug. 25, 1961.
39. Kettel, E.: Die Anwendungsmöglichkeiten der Analogrechentechnik in Messtechnik and Nachrichtenverarbeitung, *Telefunken Z.*, **33** (September, 1960).
40. Korn, G. A.: Electronic Analog/Hybrid Computers and Their Use in Systems Engineering, in Machol, R. E., S. N. Alexander, and W. P. Tanner, *System Engineering Handbook*, McGraw-Hill, New York, 1965.
41. Diamantides, N. D.: Artificial Neurons through Simulation, *Proc. 3d AICA Conf.*, Yugoslavia, September, 1961; Presses Académiques Européennes, Brussels, Belgium.
42. Handler, H., and M. J. Wozny: A Monte-Carlo Study of the Phase Distribution

of a Sine Wave plus Narrow-band Noise, *ACL Memo* 106, University of Arizona, 1964.

43. Janac, K., and J. Skrivanek: The Analog Differential Analyzer for Solving Probabilistic Problems, *Info. Processing Machines* (Czechoslovakia), October, 1964.

44. Conant, B. K.: ASTRAC I Study of an Orthogonal-function Multiplex System Using Matched Filters, *Ann. AICA*, July, 1965.

Applications to Operations Research and System Engineering

45. Two Applications of GEDA Computers to Statistical Problems of Operations Research, *Rept.* GER-6729, Goodyear Aircraft Corp., Akron, Ohio, 1955.

46. King, G. W.: Applied Mathematics in Operations Research, in Beckenbach, E. F., *Modern Mathematics for the Engineer*, First Series, McGraw-Hill, New York, 1956.

47. McGhee, R. B., and A. Levine: Determination of Optimum Production Tolerances by Analog Simulation, *Proc. Eastern Joint Computer Conf.*, 1959; reprinted in *Simulation*, November, 1964.

48. Rideout, V. C.: Solution of an Inventory Problem by Computer Methods, *Memo.* Electrical Engineering, University of Wisconsin, 1963.

49. Levine, L.: *Methods for Solving Engineering Problems Using Analog Computers*, McGraw-Hill, New York, 1964.

Special Monte Carlo Techniques (see also refs. 1 to 17 in Chap. 4)

50. Metropolis, N., and S. Ulam: The Monte Carlo Method, *J. Am. Statist. Assoc.*, **44**: 335 (1949).

51. Monte Carlo Method, *NBS Appl. Math. Series*, vol. 12, 1951.

52. Kahn, H., and A. W. Marshall: Methods of Reducing Sample Size in Monte Carlo Computations, *J. Operations Res. Soc. Am.*, **1**: 263 (1953).

53. King, G. W.: Monte Carlo Method for Solving Diffusion Problems, *Ind. Eng. Chem.*, **43**: 2475 (1951).
    Note also the papers by G. W. King, L. H. Thomas, and E. C. Yowell in *Proc. Seminar Sci. Computation*, December, 1949, IBM Corporation, New York, 1951.

54. Brown, G. W.: Monte Carlo Methods, in Beckenbach, E. F., *Modern Mathematics for the Engineer*, First Series, McGraw-Hill, New York, 1956 (note bibliography).

55. Hammersley, J. M., et al., A New Monte Carlo Technique: Antithetic Variates, *Proc. Cambridge Phil. Soc.*, **449, 476** (1956).

56. Hammersley, J. M., and D. C. Handscomb: *Monte Carlo Methods*, Methuen, London, 1964.

57. Chuang, K., et al.: A Stochastic Method for Solving Partial Differential Equations Using an Electronic Analog Computer, *Project Michigan Rept.* 2900-91-T, Willow Run Laboratories, University of Michigan, Ann Arbor, Mich., 1960.

58. Dawson, D. F.: Continuous Measurement and Display of Time Averages, *ACL Memo* 108, University of Arizona, 1965.

Optimization by Random Perturbations

59. Brooks, S. H.: A Discussion of Random Methods for Seeking Maxima, *Operations Research*, March-April, 1958.

60. ——— and M. Ray Mickey: Optimum Estimation of Gradient Directions in Steepest-ascent Experiments, *Biometrics*, March, 1961.

61. Favreau, R. R., and R. Franks: Random Optimization by Analog Techniques, *Proc. 2d AICA Conf.*, Strasbourg, France, 1958; Presses Académiques Européennes, Brussels, 1959.

62. Munson, J. K., and A. I. Rubin: Optimization by Random Search on the Analog Computer, *IRETEC*, June, 1959.
63. Karnopp, D. C.: Search Theory Applied to Parameter-scan Optimization, MIT Ph.D. Thesis, 1963.
64. Rastrigin, L. A.: Extremal Control by the Random Search Method, *Automatika i Telemekhanika*, September, 1960.
65. ———: The Convergence of the Random Search Method, *Automatika i Telemekhanika*, November, 1963.
66. Mitchell, B. A., Hybrid Analog-digital Parameter Optimizer for ASTRAC II, University of Arizona M.S. Thesis, 1964; *Proc. Spring Joint Computer Conf.*, 1964.

Miscellaneous

67. Korn, G. A., and T. M. Korn: *Electronic Analog and Hybrid Computers*, McGraw-Hill, New York, 1964.
68. Streets, R. B.: A Note on Arbitrary Non-mean-square Error Criteria, *ACL Memo 55*, University of Arizona; *IRE Trans. PGAC*, October, 1963.
69. Low, H.: First-passage-time Properties of Bandpass-Limited Gaussian Noise, *Proc. 3d AICA Conf.*, Opatija, Yugoslavia, 1961; Presses Académiques Européennes, Brussels, 1962.
70. Curtiss, J. H.: Sampling Methods Applied to Differential and Difference Equations, *Proc. Seminar Sci. Computation*, IBM Corp., New York, November, 1949.
71. Donsker, M., and M. Kac: The Monte-Carlo Method and Its Applications, *Proc. Seminar Conf. Computation*, IBM Corp., New York, December, 1949.

APPENDIX: STATISTICAL TABLES

Table A-1. Normal-curve Ordinates*

Ordinates (heights) of the unit normal curve. The height (y) at any number of standard deviations $\dfrac{k}{\sigma}$ from the mean is

$$y = 0.3989e^{-\frac{1}{2}\left(\frac{k}{\sigma}\right)^2}$$

To obtain answers in units of particular problems, multiply these ordinated by $\dfrac{N\Delta x}{\sigma}$ where N is the number of cases, Δx the class interval, and σ the standard deviation. Each figure in the body of the table is preceded by a decimal point.

k/σ	0.00	0.01	0.02	0.03	0.04	0.05	0.06	0.07	0.08	0.09
0.0	39894	39892	39886	39876	39862	39844	39822	39797	39767	39733
0.1	39695	39654	39608	39559	39505	39448	39387	39322	39253	39181
0.2	39104	39024	38940	38853	38762	38667	38568	38466	38361	38251
0.3	38139	38023	37903	37780	37654	37524	37391	37255	37115	36973
0.4	36827	36678	36526	36371	36213	36053	35889	35723	35553	35381
0.5	35207	35029	34849	34667	34482	34294	34105	33912	33718	33521
0.6	33322	33121	32918	32713	32506	32297	32086	31874	31659	31443
0.7	31225	31006	30785	30563	30339	30114	29887	29658	29430	29200
0.8	28969	28737	28504	28269	28034	27798	27562	27324	27086	26848
0.9	26609	26369	26129	25888	25647	25406	25164	24923	24681	24439
1.0	24197	23955	23713	23471	23230	22988	22747	22506	22265	22025
1.1	21785	21546	21307	21069	20831	20594	20357	20121	19886	19652
1.2	19419	19186	18954	18724	18494	18265	18037	17810	17585	17360
1.3	17137	16915	16694	16474	16256	16038	15822	15608	15395	15183
1.4	14973	14764	14556	14350	14146	13943	13742	13542	13344	13147
1.5	12952	12758	12566	12376	12188	12001	11816	11632	11450	11270
1.6	11092	10915	10741	10567	10396	10226	10059	09893	09728	09566
1.7	09405	09246	09089	08933	08780	08628	08478	08329	08183	08038
1.8	07895	07754	07614	07477	07341	07206	07074	06943	06814	06687
1.9	06562	06438	06316	06195	06077	05959	05844	05730	05618	05508
2.0	05399	05292	05186	05082	04980	04879	04780	04682	04586	04491
2.1	04398	04307	04217	04128	04041	03955	03871	03788	03706	03626
2.2	03547	03470	03394	03319	03246	03174	03103	03034	02965	02898
2.3	02833	02768	02705	02643	02582	02522	02463	02406	02349	02294
2.4	02239	02186	02134	02083	02033	01984	01936	01888	01842	01797
2.5	01753	01709	01667	01625	01585	01545	01506	01468	01431	01394
2.6	01358	01323	01289	01256	01223	01191	01160	01130	01100	01071
2.7	01042	01014	00987	00961	00935	00909	00885	00861	00837	00814
2.8	00792	00770	00748	00727	00707	00687	00668	00649	00631	00613
2.9	00595	00578	00562	00545	00530	00514	00499	00485	00470	00457
3.0	00443									
3.5	0008727									
4.0	0001338									
4.5	0000160									
5.0	000001487									

* This table was adapted, by permission, from F. C. Kent, *Elements of Statistics*, McGraw-Hill, New York, 1924.

APPENDIX

Table A-2. Normal-distribution Areas*

Fractional parts of the total area (1.000) under the normal curve between the mean and a perpendicular erected at various numbers of standard deviations (k/σ) from the mean. To illustrate the use of the table, 39.065 per cent of the total area under the curve will lie between the mean and a perpendicular erected at a distance of 1.23σ from the mean.

Each figure in the body of the table is preceded by a decimal point.

k/σ	0.00	0.01	0.02	0.03	0.04	0.05	0.06	0.07	0.08	0.09
0.0	00000	00399	00798	01197	01595	01994	02392	02790	03188	03586
0.1	03983	04380	04776	05172	05567	05962	06356	06749	07142	07535
0.2	07926	08317	08706	09095	09483	09871	10257	10642	11026	11409
0.3	11791	12172	12552	12930	13307	13683	14058	14431	14803	15173
0.4	15554	15910	16276	16640	17003	17364	17724	18082	18439	18793
0.5	19146	19497	19847	20194	20450	20884	21226	21566	21904	22240
0.6	22575	22907	23237	23565	23891	24215	24537	24857	25175	25490
0.7	25804	26115	26424	26730	27035	27337	27637	27935	28230	28524
0.8	28814	29103	29389	29673	29955	30234	30511	30785	31057	31327
0.9	31594	31859	32121	32381	32639	32894	33147	33398	33646	33891
1.0	34134	34375	34614	34850	35083	35313	35543	35769	35993	36214
1.1	36433	36650	36864	37076	37286	37493	37698	37900	38100	38298
1.2	38493	38686	38877	39065	39251	39435	39617	39796	39973	40147
1.3	40320	40490	40658	40824	40988	41149	41308	41466	41621	41774
1.4	41924	42073	42220	42364	42507	42647	42786	42922	43056	43189
1.5	43319	43448	43574	43699	43822	43943	44062	44179	44295	44408
1.6	44520	44630	44738	44845	44950	45053	45154	45254	45352	45449
1.7	45543	45637	45728	45818	45907	45994	46080	46164	46246	46327
1.8	46407	46485	46562	46638	46712	46784	46856	46926	46995	47062
1.9	47128	47193	47257	47320	47381	47441	47500	47558	47615	47670
2.0	47725	47778	47831	47882	47932	47982	48030	48077	48124	48169
2.1	48214	48257	48300	48341	48382	48422	48461	48500	48537	48574
2.2	48610	48645	48679	48713	48745	48778	48809	48840	48870	48899
2.3	48928	48956	48983	49010	49036	49061	49086	49111	49134	49158
2.4	49180	49202	49224	49245	49266	49286	49305	49324	49343	49361
2.5	49379	49396	49413	49430	49446	49461	49477	49492	49506	49520
2.6	49534	49547	49560	49573	49585	49598	49609	49621	49632	49643
2.7	49653	49664	49674	49683	49693	49702	49711	49720	49728	49736
2.8	49744	49752	49760	49767	49774	49781	49788	49795	49801	49807
2.9	49813	49819	49825	49831	49836	49841	49846	49851	49856	49861
3.0	49865									
3.5	4997674									
4.0	4999683									
4.5	4999966									
5.0	4999997133									

* This table was adapted, by permission, from F. C. Kent, *Elements of Statistics*, McGraw-Hill, New York, 1924.

Table A-3. Distribution of χ^2 *

Values of χ^2 corresponding to certain selected probabilities (*i.e.*, tail areas under the curve). To illustrate: the probability is 0.05 that a sample with 20 degrees of freedom, taken from a normal distribution, would have $\chi^2 = 31.410$ or larger.

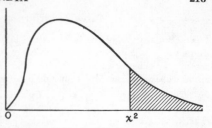

DF	Probability										
	0.99	0.98	0.95	0.90	0.80	0.20	0.10	0.05	0.02	0.01	0.001
1	0.0³157	0.0³628	0.00393	0.0158	0.0642	1.642	2.706	3.841	5.412	6.635	10.827
2	0.0201	0.0404	0.103	0.211	0.446	3.219	4.605	5.991	7.824	9.210	13.815
3	0.115	0.185	0.352	0.584	1.005	4.642	6.251	7.815	9.837	11.341	16.268
4	0.297	0.429	0.711	1.064	1.649	5.989	7.779	9.488	11.668	13.277	18.465
5	0.554	0.752	1.145	1.610	2.343	7.289	9.236	11.070	13.388	15.086	20.517
6	0.872	1.134	1.635	2.204	3.070	8.558	10.645	12.592	15.033	16.812	22.457
7	1.239	1.564	2.167	2.833	3.822	9.803	12.017	14.067	16.622	18.475	24.322
8	1.646	2.032	2.733	3.490	4.594	11.030	13.362	15.507	18.168	20.090	26.125
9	2.088	2.532	3.325	4.168	5.380	12.242	14.684	16.919	19.679	21.666	27.877
10	2.558	3.059	3.940	4.865	6.179	13.442	15.987	18.307	21.161	23.209	29.588
11	3.053	3.609	4.575	5.578	6.989	14.631	17.275	19.675	22.618	24.725	31.264
12	3.571	4.178	5.226	6.304	7.807	15.812	18.549	21.026	24.054	26.217	32.909
13	4.107	4.765	5.892	7.042	8.634	16.985	19.812	22.362	25.472	27.688	34.528
14	4.660	5.368	6.571	7.790	9.467	18.151	21.064	23.685	26.873	29.141	36.123
15	5.229	5.985	7.261	8.547	10.307	19.311	22.307	24.996	28.259	30.578	37.697
16	5.812	6.614	7.962	9.312	11.152	20.465	23.542	26.296	29.633	32.000	39.252
17	6.408	7.255	8.672	10.085	12.002	21.615	24.769	27.587	30.995	33.409	40.790
18	7.015	7.906	9.390	10.865	12.857	22.760	25.989	28.869	32.346	34.805	42.312
19	7.633	8.567	10.117	11.651	13.716	23.900	27.204	30.144	33.687	36.191	43.820
20	8.260	9.237	10.851	12.443	14.578	25.038	28.412	31.410	35.020	37.566	45.315
21	8.897	9.915	11.591	13.240	15.445	26.171	29.615	32.671	36.343	38.932	46.797
22	9.542	10.600	12.338	14.041	16.314	27.301	30.813	33.924	37.659	40.289	48.268
23	10.196	11.293	13.091	14.848	17.187	28.429	32.007	35.172	38.968	41.638	49.728
24	10.856	11.992	13.848	15.659	18.062	29.553	33.196	36.415	40.270	42.980	51.179
25	11.524	12.697	14.611	16.473	18.940	30.675	34.382	37.652	41.566	44.314	52.620
26	12.198	13.409	15.379	17.292	19.820	31.795	35.563	38.885	42.856	45.642	54.052
27	12.879	14.125	16.151	18.114	20.703	32.912	36.741	40.113	44.140	46.963	55.476
28	13.565	14.847	16.928	18.939	21.588	34.027	37.916	41.337	45.419	48.278	56.893
29	14.256	15.574	17.708	19.768	22.475	35.139	39.087	42.557	46.693	49.588	58.302
30	14.953	16.306	18.493	20.599	23.364	36.250	40.256	43.773	47.962	50.892	59.703

* This table is reproduced in abridged form from Table IV of Fisher and Yates, *Statistical Tables for Biological, Agricultural, and Medical Research,* published by Oliver & Boyd, Ltd., Edinburgh, by permission of the authors and publishers.

APPENDIX

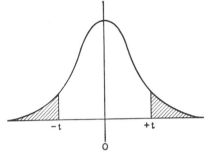

Table A-4. Distribution of t^*

Values of t corresponding to certain selected probabilities (*i.e.*, tail areas under the curve). To illustrate: the probability is 0.05 that a sample with 20 degrees of freedom would have $t = 2.086$ or larger.

DF	Probability							
	0.80	0.40	0.20	0.10	0.05	0.02	0.01	0.001
1	0.325	1.376	3.078	6.314	12.706	31.821	63.657	636.619
2	0.289	1.061	1.886	2.920	4.303	6.965	9.925	31.598
3	0.277	0.978	1.638	2.353	3.182	4.541	5.841	12.941
4	0.271	0.941	1.533	2.132	2.776	3.747	4.604	8.610
5	0.267	0.920	1.476	2.015	2.571	3.365	4.032	6.859
6	0.265	0.906	1.440	1.943	2.447	3.143	3.707	5.959
7	0.263	0.896	1.415	1.895	2.365	2.998	3.499	5.405
8	0.262	0.889	1.397	1.860	2.306	2.896	3.355	5.041
9	0.261	0.883	1.383	1.833	2.262	2.821	3.250	4.781
10	0.260	0.879	1.372	1.812	2.228	2.764	3.169	4.587
11	0.260	0.876	1.363	1.796	2.201	2.718	3.106	4.437
12	0.259	0.873	1.356	1.782	2.179	2.681	3.055	4.318
13	0.259	0.870	1.350	1.771	2.160	2.650	3.012	4.221
14	0.258	0.868	1.345	1.761	2.145	2.624	2.977	4.140
15	0.258	0.866	1.341	1.753	2.131	2.602	2.947	4.073
16	0.258	0.865	1.337	1.746	2.120	2.583	2.921	4.015
17	0.257	0.863	1.333	1.740	2.110	2.567	2.898	3.965
18	0.257	0.862	1.330	1.734	2.101	2.552	2.878	3.922
19	0.257	0.861	1.328	1.729	2.093	2.539	2.861	3.883
20	0.257	0.860	1.325	1.725	2.086	2.528	2.845	3.850
21	0.257	0.859	1.323	1.721	2.080	2.518	2.831	3.819
22	0.256	0.858	1.321	1.717	2.074	2.508	2.819	3.792
23	0.256	0.858	1.319	1.714	2.069	2.500	2.807	3.767
24	0.256	0.857	1.318	1.711	2.064	2.492	2.797	3.745
25	0.256	0.856	1.316	1.708	2.060	2.485	2.787	3.725
26	0.256	0.856	1.315	1.706	2.056	2.479	2.779	3.707
27	0.256	0.855	1.314	1.703	2.052	2.473	2.771	3.690
28	0.256	0.855	1.313	1.701	2.048	2.467	2.763	3.674
29	0.256	0.854	1.311	1.699	2.045	2.462	2.756	3.659
30	0.256	0.854	1.310	1.697	2.042	2.457	2.750	3.646
40	0.255	0.851	1.303	1.684	2.021	2.423	2.704	3.551
60	0.254	0.848	1.296	1.671	2.000	2.390	2.660	3.460
120	0.254	0.845	1.289	1.658	1.980	2.358	2.617	3.373
∞	0.253	0.842	1.282	1.645	1.960	2.326	2.576	3.291

* This table is reproduced in abridged form from Table III of Fisher and Yates, *Statistical Tables for Biological, Agricultural, and Medical Research*, published by Oliver & Boyd, Ltd., Edinburgh, by permission of the authors and publishers.

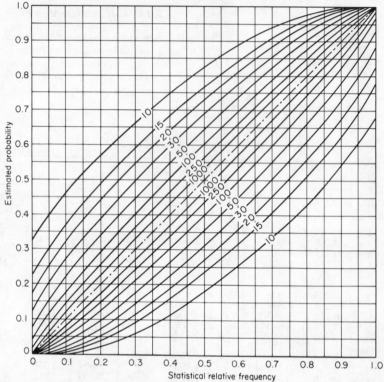

Fɪɢ. A-1. Confidence limits for estimation of probabilities from statistical relative frequencies $z = \bar{f}$ obtained in repeated independent trials. (*Secs. 5-12 and 5-14c; data from W. Dixon and F. Massey, Introduction to Statistical Analysis, 2d ed., McGraw-Hill, New York, 1957; reprinted from C. J. Clopper and E. S. Pearson, The Use of Confidence or Fiducial Limits Illustrated in the Case of the Binomial, Biometrica, vol.* **26,** *p.* 404 (1934).)

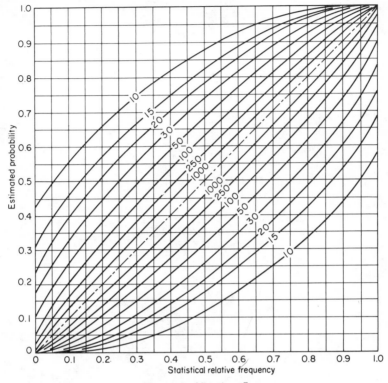

Fɪɢ. A-1. (*Continued*)

GLOSSARY OF SYMBOLS

Prob $[a < x \le b]$

probability of the event $a < x \le b$

$p(x)$, $p(x,y)$, $p_2[x(t_1), y(t_2)]$

probability densities, 1-3

$E\{f(x)\} = \int_{-\infty}^{\infty} f(x)p(x)\,dx$

expected value or ensemble average of $f(x)$, 1-3

$\text{Var}\,\{x\} = E\{[x - E\{x\}]^2\}$

(ensemble) variance of x, 1-3

$\text{Cov}\,\{x,y\} = E\{[x - E\{x\}][y - E\{y\}]\}$

(ensemble) covariance of x and y

$\chi_x(q) = E\{e^{jqx}\}$

(ensemble) characteristic function of x, 6-2

$R_{xx}(t_1,t_2)$, $R_{xx}(\tau)$

ensemble autocorrelation function, 1-3

$R_{xy}(t_1,t_2)$, $R_{xy}(\tau)$

ensemble cross-correlation function, 1-3

$\Phi_{xx}(\omega) = \int_{-\infty}^{\infty} R_{xx}(\tau)e^{-j\omega\tau}\,d\tau$

(ensemble) power spectral density, 1-7; note

$$\int_{-\infty}^{\infty} \Phi_{xx}(\omega)\,\frac{d\omega}{2\pi} = E\{x^2\}$$

$\Phi_{xy}(\omega) = \int_{-\infty}^{\infty} R_{xy}(\tau)e^{-j\omega\tau}\,d\tau$

(ensemble) cross-spectral density, 1-7

$\langle x(t_1) \rangle = \lim_{T \to \infty} \frac{1}{T} \int_{-T/2}^{T/2} x(t_1 + \lambda)\,d\lambda$

time average of x, 1-4

$\langle x(t_1)x(t_2) \rangle$, $\langle x(t_1)y(t_2) \rangle$ $(t_2 - t_1 = \tau)$

time correlation functions, 1-4

$\langle x(t) \rangle_T = \frac{1}{T} \int_0^T x(t)\,dt$

finite-time average of x, 1-4

$\langle x(t) \rangle_{\text{EWP}} = \frac{1}{T_0} \int_{-\infty}^{t} e^{-\frac{t-\lambda}{T_0}} x(\lambda)\,d\lambda$

exponentially-weighted-past (EWP) average of $x(t)$ with time constant T_0, 5-1

$[x(t)]_n = \frac{1}{n} \sum_{k=1}^{n} x(k\Delta t)$

sampled-data finite-time average of $x(t)$

223

$$\bar{x}(t_1) = \frac{1}{n} \sum_{k=1}^{n} {}^k x(t_1)$$

sample average of $x(t_1)$ (over repeated independent experiments), **1**-5

$\delta(t)$

symmetrical (Dirac) unit impulse, **1**-6

$\delta_+(t)$

asymmetrical unit impulse, **2**-10

$$\text{sign } x = \begin{cases} 1 & (x > 0) \\ -1 & (x < 0) \end{cases}$$

sign function, **6**-5

$$\text{sinc } x = \frac{\sin \pi x}{\pi x}$$

sampling function, **7**-1

$$\text{rect } x = \begin{cases} 1 & (|x| < \frac{1}{2}) \\ 0 & (|x| > \frac{1}{2}) \end{cases}$$

window function, **6**-8

$$j = \sqrt{-1}$$

AUTHOR INDEX

The author index refers by page number to the entries in the *References and Bibliography* sections arranged by subject matter at the end of each individual chapter. To obtain references by subject matter, consult the subject index and refer to the *References and Bibliography* sections for the appropriate chapters.

SUBJECT INDEX

References in the subject index are to section numbers, not page numbers. Note that section numbers are displayed at the top of each page for convenient reference.

SOCIAL SCIENCE LIBRARY

Manor Road Building
Manor Road
Oxford OX1 3UQ
Tel: (2)71093 (enquiries and renewals)
http://www.ssl.ox.ac.uk

This is a NORMAL LOAN item.

We will email you a reminder before this item is due.

Please see http://www.ssl.ox.ac.uk/lending.html
for details on:

- loan policies; these are also displayed on the notice boards and in our library guide.

- how to check when your books are due back.

- how to renew your books, including information on the maximum number of renewals.
  Items may be renewed if not reserved by another reader. Items must be renewed before the library closes on the due date.

- level of fines; fines are charged on overdue books.

Please note that this item may be recalled during Term.